Burgess

LIFE SCIENCE SERIES

BIOCHEMISTRY - MICROBIOLOGY

Consulting Editors
ROBERT H. BURRIS and HERMAN C. LICHSTEIN

PRINCIPLES OF RADIOISOTOPE METHODOLOGY . . Chase

ELEMENTARY BIOCHEMISTRY . . . . Mertz

BEHAVIOR OF ENZYME SYSTEMS . . . . Reiner

METABOLIC MAPS, Volume II . . . . Umbreit

MANOMETRIC TECHNIQUES . . . . Umbreit-Burris-Stauffer

SYMPOSIUM: LATENCY AND
MASKING IN VIRAL AND
RICKETTSIAL INFECTIONS . . . . . Walker-Hanson-Evans

METABOLIC MAPS

VOLUME II

by

W. W. UMBREIT

Department of Bacteriology

Rutgers, The State University

New Brunswick, N. J.

Illustrated by
Virginia Force

with a chapter by
J. A. Johnston

BURGESS PUBLISHING COMPANY
426 South 6th Street — Minneapolis 15, Minnesota

Library of Congress Catalog Card No. 52-4038

Printed in the United States of America

REPRODUCTION PERMISSION

Because of the widespread use of METABOLIC MAPS, the

author and publisher hereby grant permission to repro-

duce up to 10 pages of these maps for scientific purposes

or publications. We would be happy, indeed, if the maps

were found unique and useful enough for such reproduction.

ACKNOWLEDGMENTS

The following assisted in the literature search necessary
for the construction of certain maps, and we herewith convey
our thanks.

G. W. Campbell	N. S. Mhatre
W. S. Ceglowski	H. Nathan
T. M. Cook	D. Polhemus
B. Djordjevic	C. Pootjes
G. E. Doscher III	M. Reich
V. C. Dunkel	F. A. Rosenberg
G. Greenspan	T. J. Russell
P. Hill	R. S. Safferman
H. R. Kells	E. Schuldt
R. Kessel	W. J. Taylor
A. Merola	C. West

ON THE NATURE AND USE OF MAPS IN BIOCHEMISTRY

A tremendous number of chemical reactions occur in living tissue; so many, indeed, that one becomes confused by the vast amount of data and information. This situation is quite comparable to that of a survey of terrain, where masses of data in the form of measurements, elevations, directions and composition are obtained. In the latter case the problem is solved by cartography; by the construction of a map in which an abundance of field data is correlated into a form which is readily grasped and used. Such a correlation, such a map, can be used to summarize a variety of related but uncorrelated information in biochemistry, and frequently from such "mapping," one may discern relationships that are otherwise obscure.

A certain amount of sense and selection must go into any map construction; too much detail defeats the purpose and some kinds of information are simply not mappable. There is, in map construction, a certain arbitrariness and maps constructed of a city for the tourist to follow, for the city engineer to use, for the voters to know which election or school district they are in, will all be somewhat different. Certainly the purpose for which the map is made will determine its content and form. It is the same with metabolic maps. But no one denies that they are useful - even if not precisely constructed for our own purpose - and we can always redraw a map, shape it closer to the heart's desire when we wish. Certainly no one is preventing you from keeping your maps up to date.

NOTE ON THE USE OF THIS BOOK

Readers familiar with Volume I will note that in II we have eliminated the detailed reference to the literature. In 1950, it was perhaps possible to use maps as a key to the literature; in 1960, it is not. In our experience, one should first look up a given compound, in which one is interested, in the index of this book, which has been rather elaborately prepared for this purpose. This will give one the various reactions and interrelations known (to the author) at the time of publication. After examining these, one looks for the same compound in the index of the appropriate journal or review (Annual Review of Biochemistry, for example), which will put one in touch with the recent literature on the subject. In this fashion one lets this book serve as refresher background, and one lets the reviewers and the indexing publications "keep up" with the literature, not, of course, without some trouble, but certainly with less trouble than if one tried to keep up all by one's self.

TABLE OF CONTENTS

Page No.

Chapter 1. THE MEYERHOF-EMBDEN SYSTEM 1

Map 1. Diagram of the Meyerhof-Embden Pathway 3
Map 2. Sectors of the Meyerhof-Embden Pathway. 4
Map 3. Sector A. Glucose to fructose-1,6-diphosphate
(drawn in open chain form). 5
Map 4. Sector A. Glucose to fructose-1,6-diphosphate
(drawn in closed chain form). 6
Map 5. Sector A. Glucose to fructose-1,6-diphosphate
(drawn in perspective) 7
Map 6. Sector B. Fructose-1,6-diphosphate to triose phosphates 8
Map 7. Phosphate ester aldolase 9
Map 8. Sector C. "Mechanism" of oxidation of glyceraldehyde-3-
phosphate 10
Map 9. Sector C. Phosphoglyceric acid to pyruvate 11
Map 10. Methyl glyoxal 12
Map 11. "Mechanism" of phosphoglyceric acid mutase. 13
Map 12. Glycerol and glycero phosphates - optical isomerism 14
Map 12. (continued). Results of dismutation of hexose-diphosphate....... 15
Map 13. Metabolism of glycerol. 17
Map 14. Glucose-6-phosphate to glucose-1-phosphate 19
Map 15. Reactions of glucose-1,6-diphosphate 20
Map 16. Starch and glycogen 21
Map 17. Structure and formation of UDPG 22
Map 18. Sucrose 23
Map 19. The formation of lactose 24
Map 20. General reactions of the sugar-1-phosphates 25
Map 21. Uronic acid metabolism 26
Map 22. Amino sugar metabolism 27

Chapter 2. THE "MONOPHOSPHATE PATHWAYS" 29

Map 23. The monophosphate pathways 31
Map 24. Sector map - Monophosphate pathways 32
Map 25. Sector A. Glucose-6-phosphate to phosphogluconic acid 33
Map 26. Sector B. Phosphogluconic acid to ribulose-5-phosphate 34
Map 27. Sector C. Ribulose-5-phosphate to heptulose phosphate 35
Map 28. Reactions of transketolase 36
Map 29. Further reactions of transketolase 37
Map 30. Reactions of transaldolase 38
Map 31. Sector D. Reactions of heptulose 39
Map 32. Distribution of isotopes 40
Map 33. Sector E. Ribulose to phosphoglyceric acid
(a pathway of photosynthesis) 41
Map 34. A second pathway of phosphogluconic acid. 43
Map 35. Other paths of sugar metabolism (frequently not
involving phosphorylation) 45

Map 36.   Ascorbic acid synthesis   47
Map 37.   Sugar alcohol oxidation   48
Map 38.   Inositol metabolism   49

Chapter 3. THE PATHWAYS TO OXYGEN 51

Map 39.   Mechanism of oxygen metabolism.   53
Map 40.   Pathway to oxygen (Slater)   54
Map 41.   Pathway to oxygen (Hartree).   55
Map 42.   Structure of pyridine coenzymes   56
Map 43.   Mechanism of hydrogen transport by pyridine coenzymes   57
Map 44.   Structure of flavin coenzymes.   58
Map 45.   Hydrogen transport by flavin coenzymes   59
Map 46.   Structure and action of lipoic acid   60
Map 47.   Attachment of lipoic acid to enzymes   61
Map 48.   The vitamin E - vitamin K series.   62
Map 49.   Action of quinone coenzymes   63

Chapter 4. PHOSPHORYLATION 65

Map 50.   Formation and transfer of "energy rich" phosphate bonds   67
Map 51.   Phosphorylation in oxidative pathways   68
Map 52.   Possible mechanism of oxidative phosphorylation   69
Map 53.   Basic mechanisms of oxidative phosphorylation   70
Map 54.   Postulated details of phosphorylation by carriers   71
Map 55.   Phosphorus compounds in biosynthesis   72
Map 55.   (Continued)   73
Map 55.   (Continued)   74

Chapter 5. THE CITRIC ACID CYCLE 77

Map 56.   The citric acid cycle   79
Map 57.   Sector A.   Condensation to citric acid.   80
Map 58.   Sector B.   Citric to oxalosuccinic acids   81
Map 59.   Sector C.   Oxalosuccinic to succinic acids   82
Map 60.   Sector D.   Succinic to pyruvic acids   83

Chapter 6. THE METABOLISM OF PYRUVIC ACID 85

Map 61.   Pyruvic acid metabolism   87
Map 62.   Sector A.   To lactic acid and alanine   88
Map 63.   Sector B.   To acetaldehyde and ethanol   89
Map 64.   Reactions of the acyloins   90
Map 65.   Sector C.   Acyloin formation   91
Map 66.   Sector D.   Hydrogen, formic acid, and acetyl phosphate   92
Map 67.   Sector E.   Acetone, butanol, and isopropyl formation   93
Map 68.   Malonic acid metabolism   94
Map 69.   Propionic acid metabolism   95
Map 70.   Other routes to alpha-ketoglutaric acid.   96
Map 71.   Acetyl CoA to succinic acid   97

Map 72.   Glyoxalic acid and glycolic acid metabolism   99
Map 73.   Tartaric acid metabolism   101
Map 74.   Synthesis of pantothenic acid   102
Map 75.   Metabolism of coenzyme A   103

Chapter 7. THE INTRODUCTION OF NITROGEN 105

Map 76.   Inorganic nitrogen metabolism   107
Map 77.   Nitrogen fixation   108
Map 78.   Nitrification   109
Map 79.   Nitrate reduction to nitrite   110
Map 80.   Postulated path of nitrate assimilation   111
Map 81.   Denitrification   112
Map 82.   Conversion of ammonia to amino groups   113
Map 83.   Aspartic acid metabolism   114
Map 84.   Glutamic acid metabolism   115
Map 85.   General reactions of amino acids   116
Map 86.   The vitamin B_6 group   117
Map 87.   Amino acid activation; protein synthesis   119

Chapter 8. SHORT-CHAIN AMINO ACIDS 121

Map 88.   Metabolism of glycine and serine   123
Map 89.   Synthesis of leucine   124
Map 90.   Breakdown of leucine   125
Map 91.   Synthesis of isoleucine   126
Map 92.   Breakdown of isoleucine   127
Map 93.   Synthesis of valine   128
Map 94.   Breakdown of valine   129
Map 95.   Example of feedback mechanism   130
Map 96.   Synthesis and breakdown of threonine   131

Chapter 9. THE METABOLISM OF SULFUR 133

Map 97.   Sulfate activation   134
Map 98.   Metabolism of sulfur amino acids   135
Map 99.   Relations between cysteine and homocysteine   136
Map 100. Synthesis of homoserine   137
Map 101. Relations to the choline cycle   139

Chapter 10. PROLINE AND ARGININE 141

Map 102. The citric acid and urea cycles   142
Map 103. The proline, urea, and citric acid cycles   143
Map 104. Metabolism of hydroxyproline   144
Map 105. The proline cycle   145
Map 106. The proline and urea cycles   147
Map 107. Synthesis of ornithine   148
Map 108. Synthesis of citrulline   149
Map 109. Synthesis of arginine   150

Map 110. Metabolism of arginine 151
Map 111. Metabolism of canavanine 153

Chapter 11. LYSINE AND HISTIDINE 155

Map 112. Metabolism of lysine 157
Map 113. Synthesis of histidine 158
Map 114. Main paths of histidine breakdown 159
Map 115. Minor urocanic acid path 160
Map 116. Major urocanic acid path 161
Map 117. Transamination path 162
Map 118. Histamine path 163

Chapter 12. AROMATIC RING STRUCTURES 165

Map 119. Synthesis of aromatic rings 167
Map 120. Catechol path of aromatic breakdown 168
Map 121. Protocatechuic path of aromatic breakdown 169
Map 122. Path to keto-adipic acid 170
Map 123. Homogentisic acid 171
Map 124. Analogous oxidations 172
Map 125. Naphthalene breakdown 173
Map 126. Phenylpyruvic acid metabolism 174
Map 127. Related structures arranged in order of possible origin 175
Map 128. Synthesis of kojic acid 177

Chapter 13. AROMATIC AMINO ACIDS 179

Map 129. Synthesis of tyrosine and phenylalanine. 181
Map 130. Main routes of tyrosine metabolism 182
Map 131. Paths through dihydroxyphenylalanine 183
Map 132. Paths through adrenaline 184
Map 133. Paths through thyroxine 185
Map 134. Paths through phenylpyruvic acid 186
Map 135. Comparison between tyrosine and phenols 187
Map 136. Phenylalanine metabolism (other than to tyrosine) 188
Map 137. Main routes of tryptophan metabolism 189
Map 138. Tryptophan activation 190
Map 139. Tryptophan synthesis 191
Map 140. Path through indole 192
Map 141. Path to indole acetic acid 193
Map 142. Path to kynurenine and hydroxyanthranilic acid 194
Map 143. Serotonin path 195
Map 144. Kynurenine metabolism 196
Map 145. Hydroxyanthranilic acid metabolism 197
Map 146. Nicotinic acid metabolism 199

Chapter 14. PURINES, PYRIMIDINES, NUCLEIC ACID 201

Map 147.   Purine synthesis: Amination of ribose phosphates (to "PRA"). ...   203
Map 148.   Purine synthesis: To imidazole ribotide (to "AIR")   204
Map 149.   Purine synthesis: To inosinic acid.   205
Map 150.   Purine synthesis: Interconversion of ribotides   207
Map 151.   Purine breakdown: To uric acid   208
Map 152.   Purine breakdown: Uric acid metabolism   209
Map 153.   Pyrimidine synthesis: Origins of carbamyl phosphate   210
Map 154.   Pyrimidine synthesis: Uridine synthesis   211
Map 155.   Pyrimidine synthesis: Cytidine series   212
Map 156.   Pyrimidine synthesis: Thymine.   213
Map 157.   Pyrimidine breakdown: Uracil   214
Map 158.   Pyrimidine breakdown: Thymine   215
Map 159.   Pyrimidine interconversion: Ribotides to deoxyribotides   217
Map 160.   Synthesis of ribose nucleic acids.   219
Map 161.   Synthesis of deoxyribose nucleic acids.   220
Map 162.   Replication of deoxyribose nucleic acids.   221
Map 163.   Replication of separate strands yields initial structure   222
Map 164.   Second stage replication of a single strand   223

Chapter 15. FATTY ACID AND STEROID METABOLISM...... 225

Map 165.   Synthesis and degradation of fatty acids   227
Map 166.   Fate of propanyl-CoA.   228
Map 167.   Fate of acetoacetyl CoA: Mevalonic acid synthesis   229
Map 168.   Biosynthesis of squalene (to farnesyl pyrophosphate)   230
Map 169.   Biosynthesis of squalene (to squalene)   231
Map 170.   Cyclization of squalene   233
Map 171.   Conformation and configuration of steroids   234
Map 171.   (Continued)   235
Map 171.   (Continued)   236
Map 171.   (Continued)   237
Map 172.   Nomenclature of steroids   238
Map 172.   (Continued)   239
Map 172.   (Continued)   240
Map 172.   (Continued)   241
Map 173.   Carotenoids   243
Map 174.   Synthesis of triglycerides and phosphatides   244
Map 175.   Synthesis of complex lipids.   245

Chapter 16. OTHER REACTIONS 247

Map 176.   The choline cycle   249
Map 177.   Creatine synthesis   250
Map 178.   "Active" methionine and methyl transfer   251
Map 179.   Formic acid metabolism   253
Map 180.   Formaldehyde metabolism   255
Map 181.   Folic acid metabolism   256
Map 182.   Folic acid coenzymes   257
Map 183.   Riboflavin metabolism   259

Page No.

Map 184.   Biotin   261
Map 185.   Vitamin B_{12}   262
Map 186.   Porphyrin synthesis   263
Map 187.   Synthesis of penicillin   264
Map 188.   Action of penicillin   265

INDEX   267

Chapter I
THE MEYERHOF-EMBDEN SYSTEM

TABLE OF CONTENTS

Map No.	Title	Page No.
1	The Main Pathway	3
2	Sectors of the Pathway	4
3	Sector A - Open Chain Form - Glucose to Hexose Diphosphate	5
4	Sector A - Closed Ring Form " " " "	6
5	Sector A - Perspective " " " "	7
6	Sector B - To Triose Phosphate	8
7	Phosphate Ester Aldolases	9
8	Mechanism of Glyceraldehyde-3-Phosphate Oxidation	10
9	Sector C - Phosphoglyceric Acid to Pyruvate	11
10	Methylglyoxal	12
11	Mechanism of Phosphoglyceric Acid Mutase	13
12	Optical Isomerism of Glycerol Phosphates	14
12 (cont.)	Dismutation of Fructose-1,6-Diphosphate	15
13	Metabolism of Glycerol	17
14	Glucose-6-phosphate to Glucose-1-phosphate	19
15	Reactions of Glucose-1,6-diphosphate	20
16	Starch and Glycogen	21
17	Formation of UDPG	22
18	Sucrose	23
19	Formation of Lactose	24
20	General Reactions of Sugar-1-phosphates	25
21	Uronic Acid Metabolism	26
22	Amino Sugar Metabolism	27

MAP 1. DIAGRAM OF THE MEYERHOF-EMBDEN PATHWAY

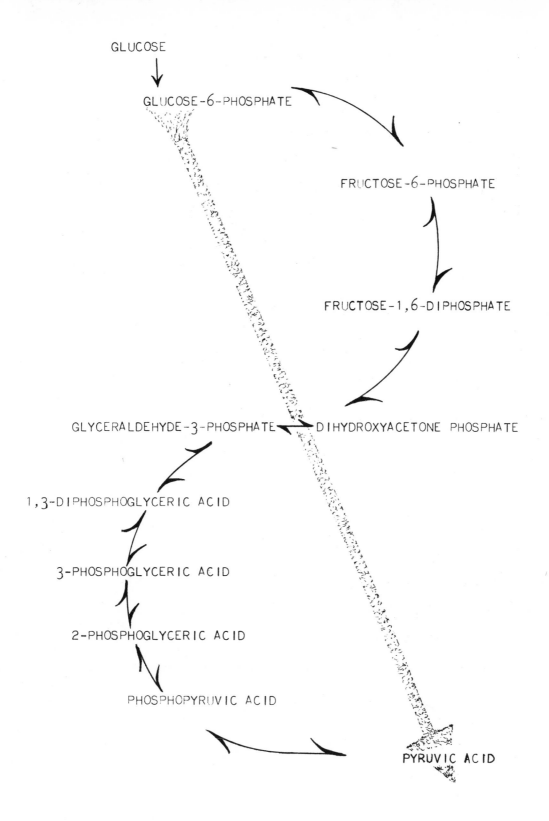

GLUCOSE

GLUCOSE-6-PHOSPHATE

FRUCTOSE-6-PHOSPHATE

FRUCTOSE-1,6-DIPHOSPHATE

GLYCERALDEHYDE-3-PHOSPHATE   DIHYDROXYACETONE PHOSPHATE

1,3-DIPHOSPHOGLYCERIC ACID

3-PHOSPHOGLYCERIC ACID

2-PHOSPHOGLYCERIC ACID

PHOSPHOPYRUVIC ACID

PYRUVIC ACID

4

MAP 2. SECTORS OF THE MEYERHOF-EMBDEN PATHWAY

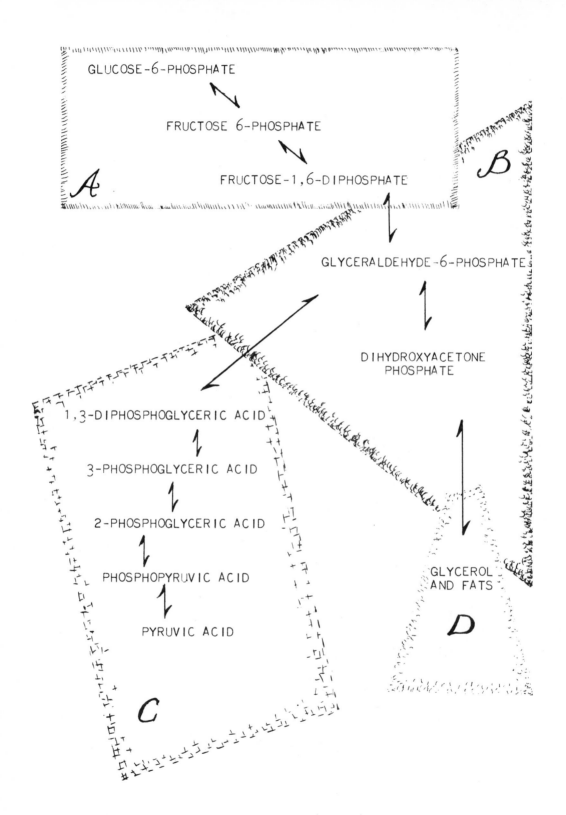

MAP 3. SECTOR A. GLUCOSE TO FRUCTOSE-1,6-DIPHOSPHATE
(DRAWN IN OPEN CHAIN FORM)

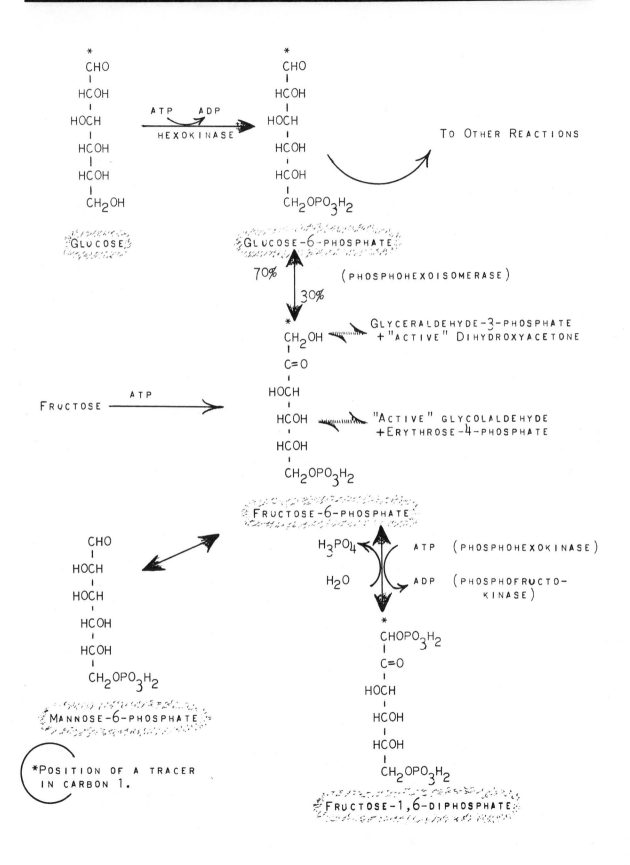

MAP 4. SECTOR A. GLUCOSE TO FRUCTOSE-1,6-DIPHOSPHATE
(DRAWN IN CLOSED CHAIN FORM)

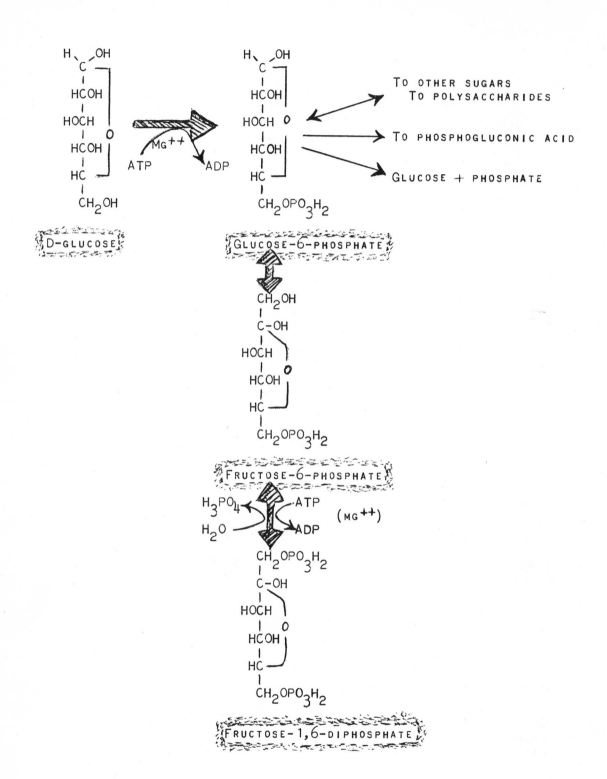

MAP 5. SECTOR A. GLUCOSE TO FRUCTOSE-1,6-DIPHOSPHATE (DRAWN IN PERSPECTIVE)

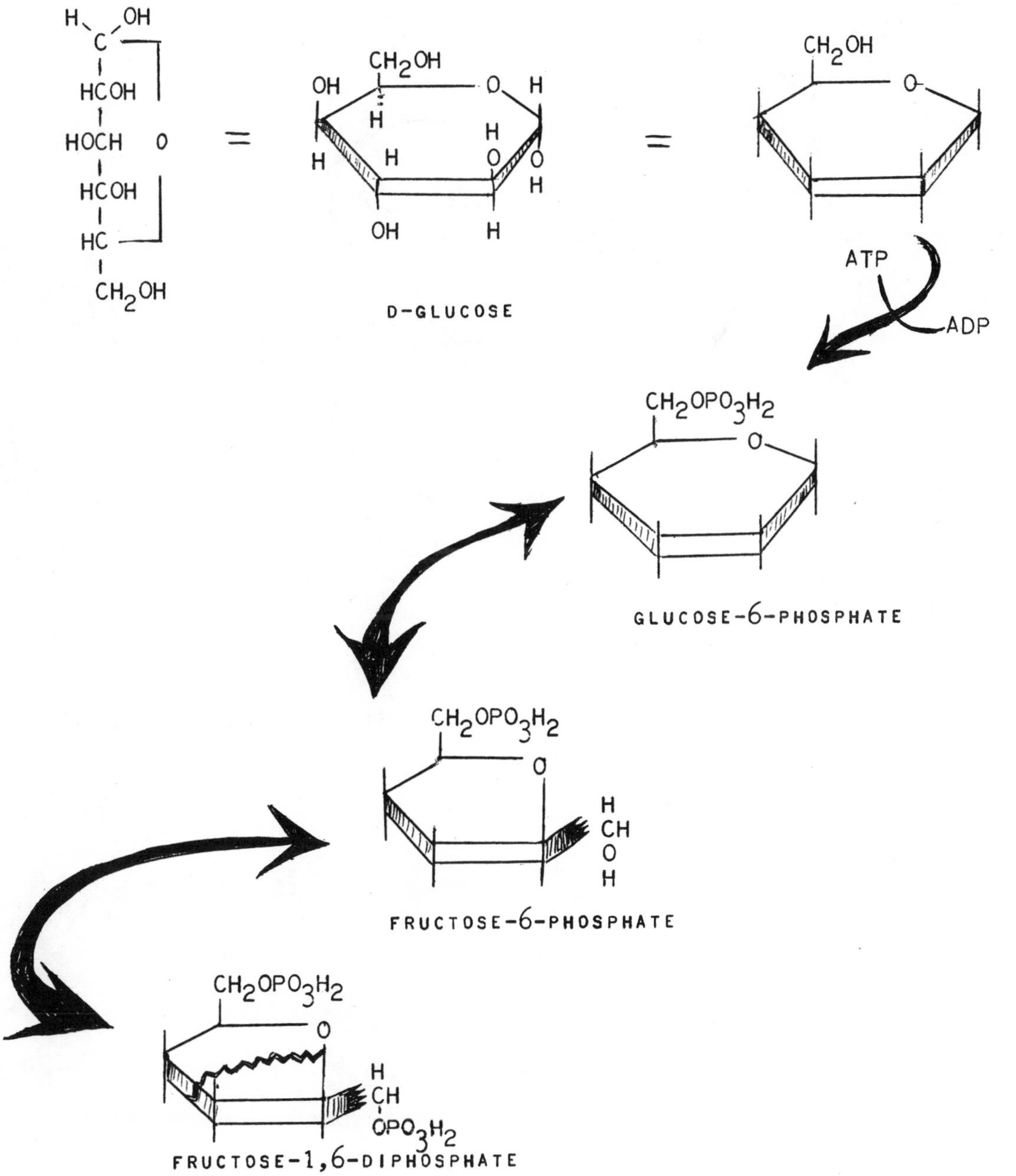

8

**MAP 6.   SECTOR B. FRUCTOSE-1,6-DIPHOSPHATE
TO TRIOSE PHOSPHATES**

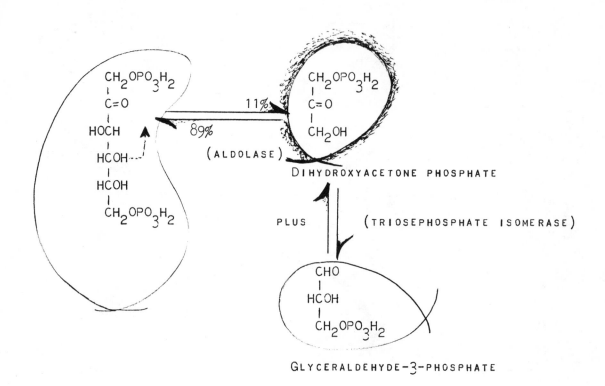

DIHYDROXYACETONE PHOSPHATE

GLYCERALDEHYDE-3-PHOSPHATE

ENTIRE COMPLEX OF ALDOLASE AND
TRIOSEPHOSPHATE ISOMERASE CALLED
"ZYMOHEXASE."

MAP 7. PHOSPHATE ESTER ALDOLASE

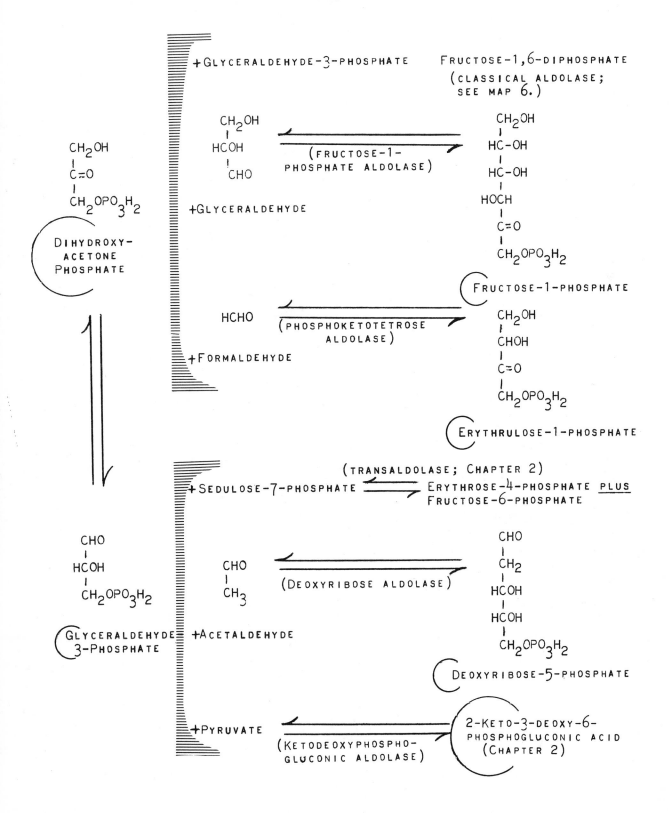

+GLYCERALDEHYDE-3-PHOSPHATE   FRUCTOSE-1,6-DIPHOSPHATE
                                (CLASSICAL ALDOLASE;
                                  SEE MAP 6.)

CH₂OH
|
C=O
|
CH₂OPO₃H₂

DIHYDROXY-
ACETONE
PHOSPHATE

CH₂OH   CH₂OH
| |
HCOH   (FRUCTOSE-1-   HC-OH
| PHOSPHATE ALDOLASE) |
CHO   HC-OH
                                          |
+GLYCERALDEHYDE   HOCH
                                          |
                                          C=O
                                          |
                                          CH₂OPO₃H₂

                                    FRUCTOSE-1-PHOSPHATE

HCHO   CH₂OH
          (PHOSPHOKETOTETROSE |
            ALDOLASE)   CHOH
+FORMALDEHYDE |
                                          C=O
                                          |
                                          CH₂OPO₃H₂

                                    ERYTHRULOSE-1-PHOSPHATE

                  (TRANSALDOLASE; CHAPTER 2)
+SEDULOSE-7-PHOSPHATE   ERYTHROSE-4-PHOSPHATE PLUS
                            FRUCTOSE-6-PHOSPHATE

CHO   CHO
| |
HCOH   CHO   CH₂
| | (DEOXYRIBOSE ALDOLASE) |
CH₂OPO₃H₂   CH₃   HCOH
                                          |
                                          HCOH
GLYCERALDEHYDE +ACETALDEHYDE |
3-PHOSPHATE   CH₂OPO₃H₂

                                    DEOXYRIBOSE-5-PHOSPHATE

+PYRUVATE   2-KETO-3-DEOXY-6-
          (KETODEOXYPHOSPHO-   PHOSPHOGLUCONIC ACID
            GLUCONIC ALDOLASE)   (CHAPTER 2)

MAP 8.   SECTOR C.   "MECHANISM" OF OXIDATION OF GLYCERALDEHYDE-3-PHOSPHATE

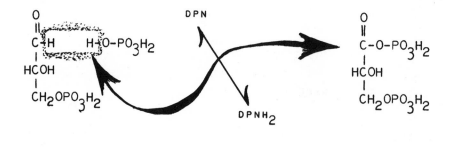

MAP 9. SECTOR C. PHOSPHOGLYCERIC ACID TO PYRUVATE

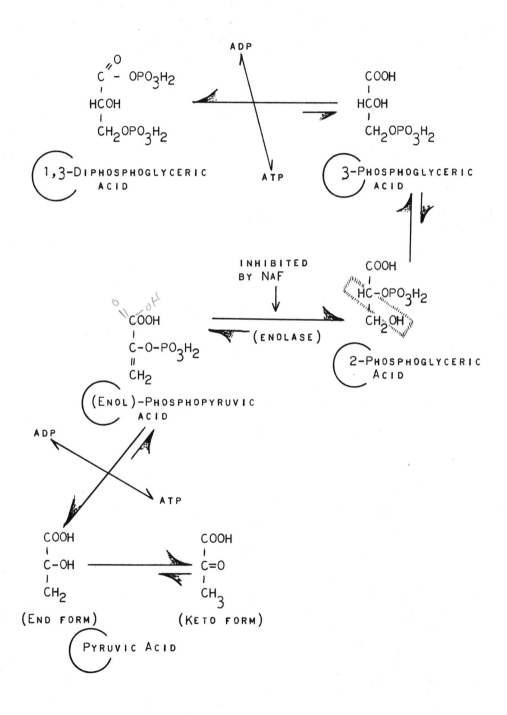

1,3-DIPHOSPHOGLYCERIC ACID

3-PHOSPHOGLYCERIC ACID

INHIBITED BY NaF

(ENOLASE)

2-PHOSPHOGLYCERIC ACID

(ENOL)-PHOSPHOPYRUVIC ACID

(END FORM)   (KETO FORM)

PYRUVIC ACID

MAP 10. METHYL GLYOXAL

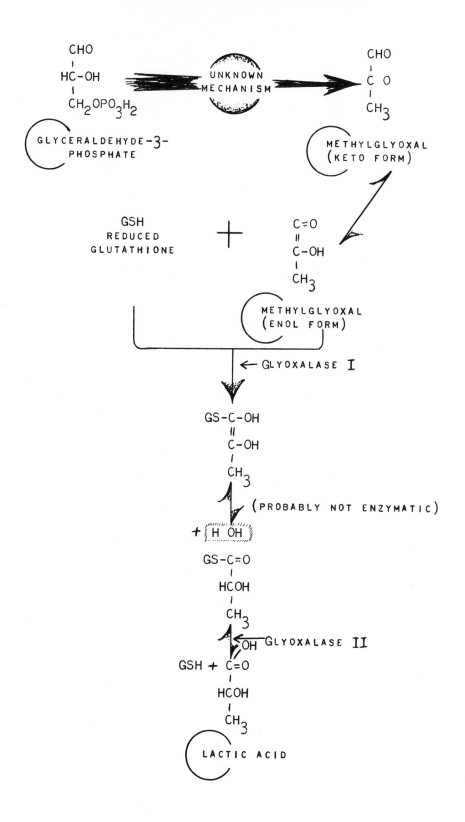

MAP 11. "MECHANISM" OF PHOSPHOGLYCERIC ACID MUTASE

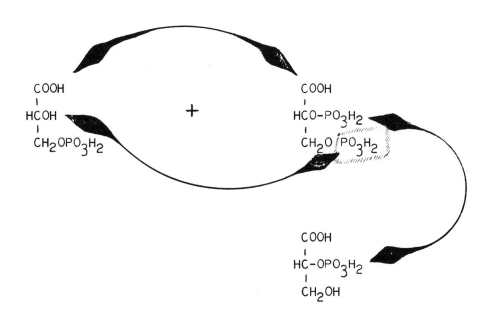

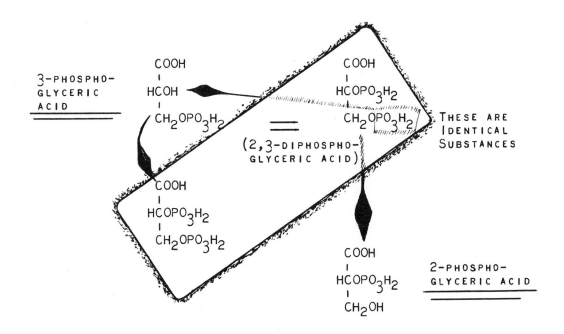

MAP 12. GLYCEROL AND GLYCERO PHOSPHATES OPTICAL ISOMERISM

NOT OPTICALLY ACTIVE -- NO ASYMMETRIC CARBONS

$$CH_2OH$$
$$|$$
$$HCOH$$
$$|$$
$$CH_2OH$$

$=$

$$CH_2OH$$
$$|$$
$$HOCH$$
$$|$$
$$CH_2OH$$

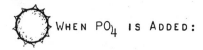 WHEN PO_4 IS ADDED:

MAY GO TO CARBON 2:

β-GLYCEROL PHOSPHATE

$$CH_2OH$$
$$|$$
$$HC-OPO_3H_2$$
$$|$$
$$CH_2OH$$

$=$

$$CH_2OH$$
$$|$$
$$H_2O_3POCH$$
$$|$$
$$CH_2OH$$

MAY GO TO CARBONS 1 OR 3:

α-GLYCEROL PHOSPHATE

$$CH_2OH$$
$$|$$
$$HCOH$$
$$|$$
$$CH_2OPO_3H_2$$

D-GLYCEROL
PHOSPHATE

$$CH_2OH$$
$$|$$
$$HOCH$$
$$|$$
$$CH_2OPO_3H_2$$

L-GLYCEROL
PHOSPHATE

BIOLOGICALLY
ACTIVE FORM

15

MAP 12 (CONTINUED).   RESULTS OF DISMUTATION
OF HEXOSE-DIPHOSPHATE

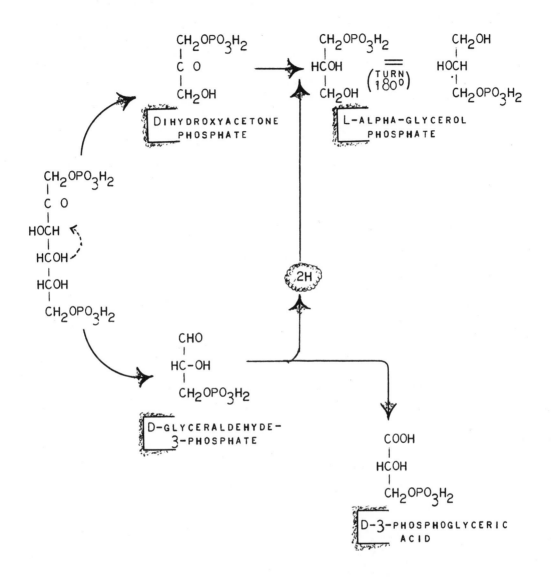

WHEN FRUCTOSE-1,6-DIPHOSPHATE IS DISMUTATED,
ITS PRODUCTS BELONG TO DIFFERENT OPTICAL SERIES.

NOTES

MAP 13. METABOLISM OF GLYCEROL

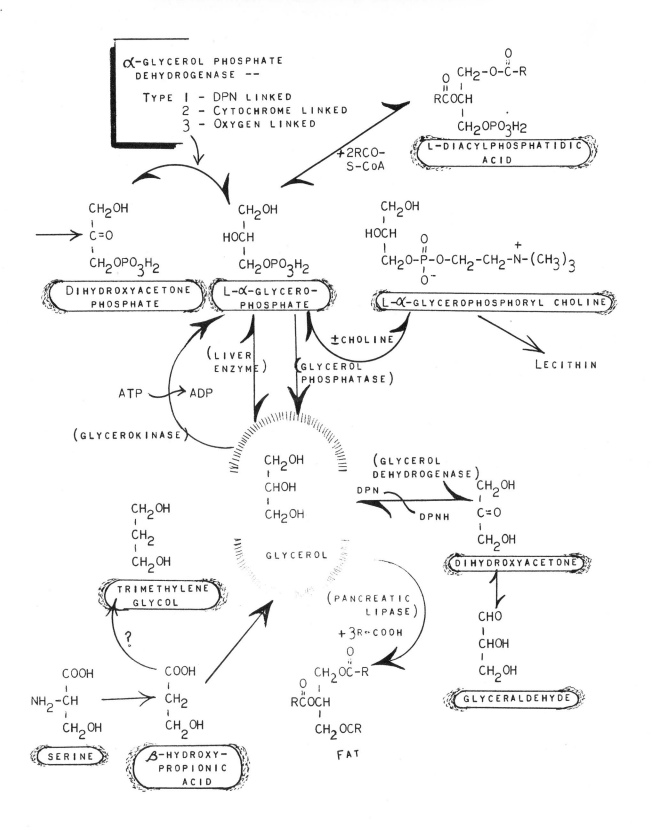

NOTES

MAP 14.   GLUCOSE-6-PHOSPHATE TO GLUCOSE-1-PHOSPHATE

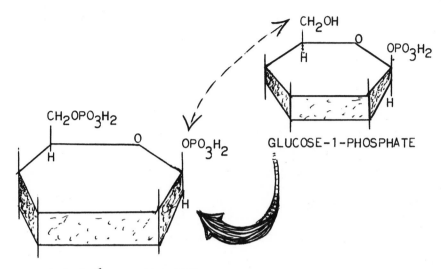

GLUCOSE-1-PHOSPHATE

GLUCOSE-1,6-DIPHOSPHATE

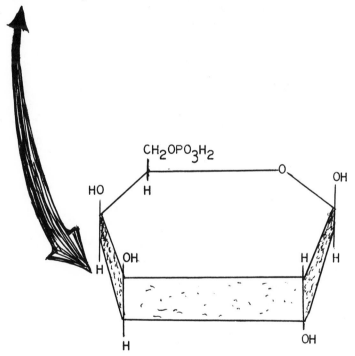

GLUCOSE-6-PHOSPHATE

MAP 15. REACTIONS OF GLUCOSE-1,6-DIPHOSPHATE

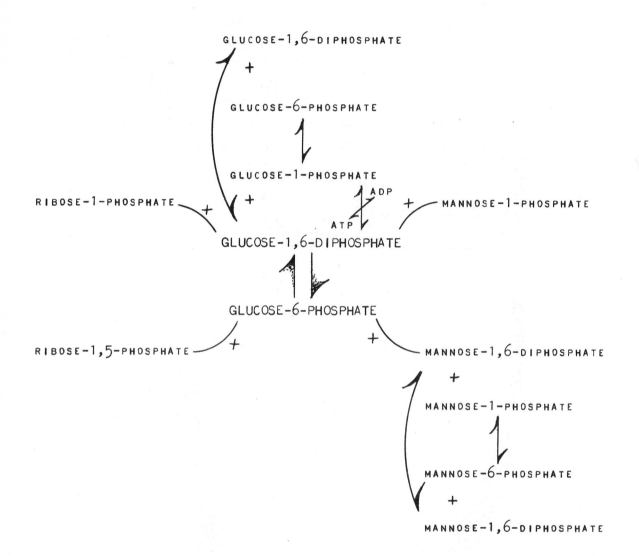

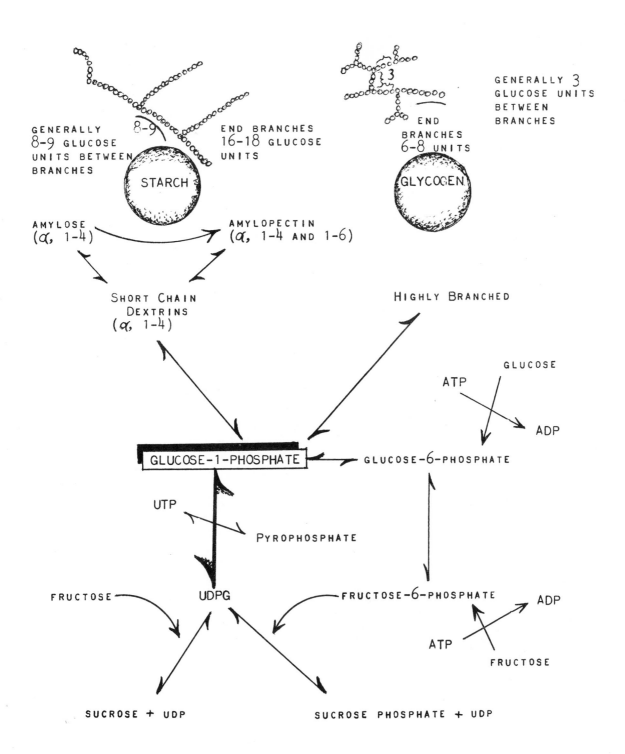

MAP 16.   STARCH AND GLYCOGEN

GENERALLY 8-9 GLUCOSE UNITS BETWEEN BRANCHES

8-9

END BRANCHES 16-18 GLUCOSE UNITS

STARCH

GENERALLY 3 GLUCOSE UNITS BETWEEN BRANCHES

3

END BRANCHES 6-8 UNITS

GLYCOGEN

AMYLOSE (α, 1-4)

AMYLOPECTIN (α, 1-4 AND 1-6)

SHORT CHAIN DEXTRINS (α, 1-4)

HIGHLY BRANCHED

GLUCOSE

ATP

ADP

GLUCOSE-1-PHOSPHATE

GLUCOSE-6-PHOSPHATE

UTP

PYROPHOSPHATE

UDPG

FRUCTOSE

FRUCTOSE-6-PHOSPHATE

ADP

ATP

FRUCTOSE

SUCROSE + UDP

SUCROSE PHOSPHATE + UDP

MAP 17. STRUCTURE AND FORMATION OF UDPG

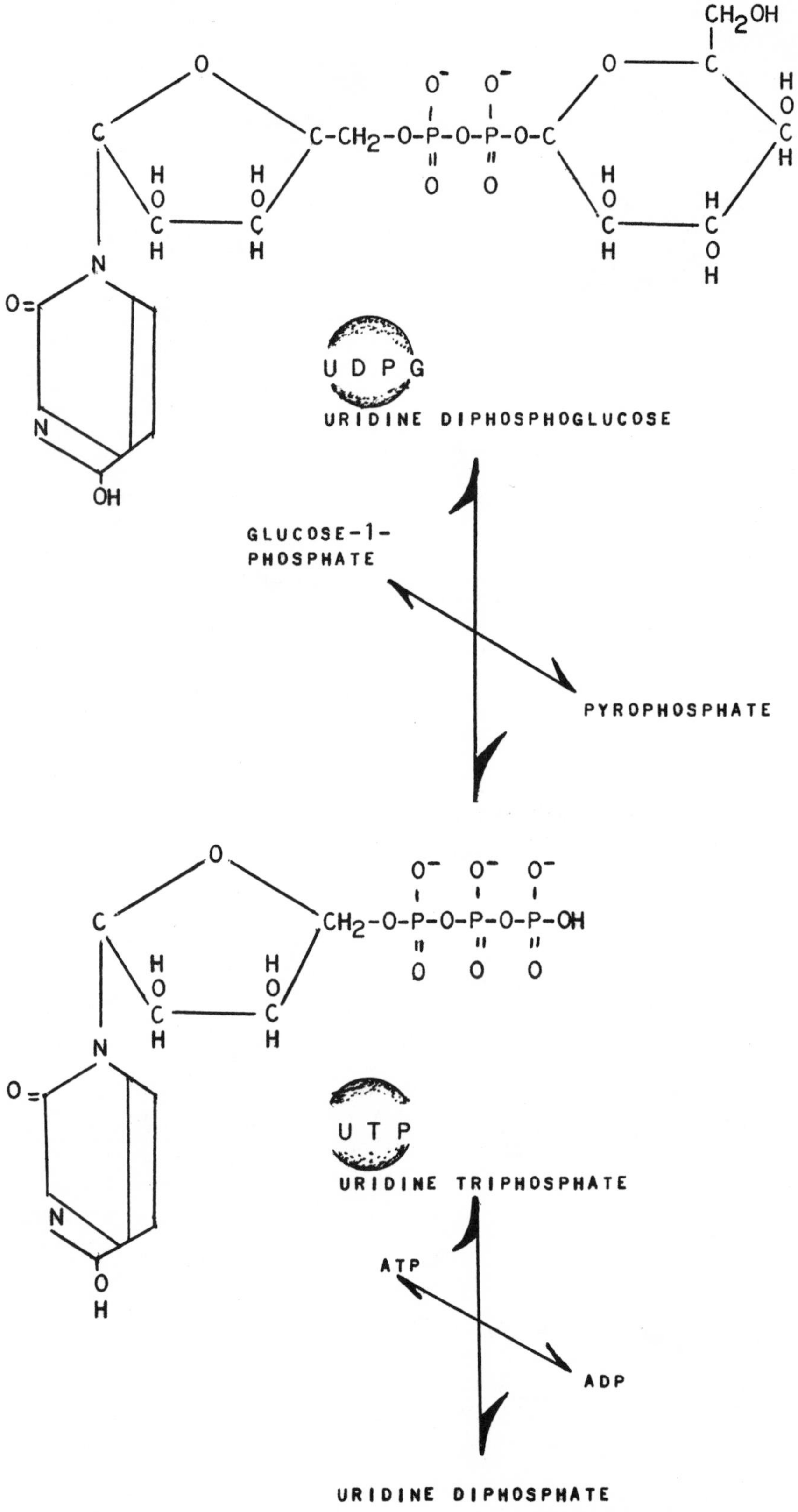

UDPG
URIDINE DIPHOSPHOGLUCOSE

GLUCOSE-1-
PHOSPHATE

PYROPHOSPHATE

UTP
URIDINE TRIPHOSPHATE

ATP

ADP

URIDINE DIPHOSPHATE

MAP 18. SUCROSE

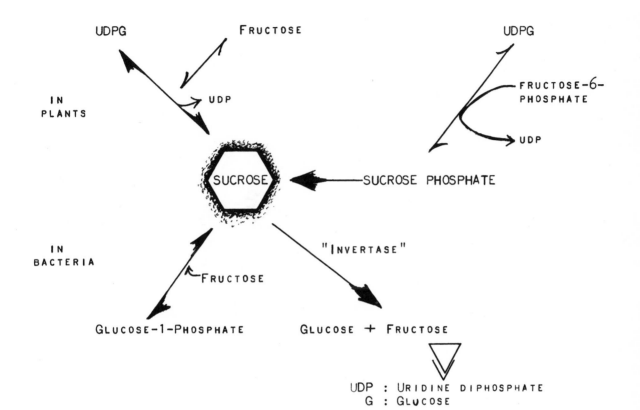

UDPG   FRUCTOSE   UDPG

IN
PLANTS

FRUCTOSE-6-
PHOSPHATE

UDP

UDP

SUCROSE   SUCROSE PHOSPHATE

IN
BACTERIA

"INVERTASE"

FRUCTOSE

GLUCOSE-1-PHOSPHATE   GLUCOSE + FRUCTOSE

UDP : URIDINE DIPHOSPHATE
G : GLUCOSE

MAP 19. THE FORMATION OF LACTOSE

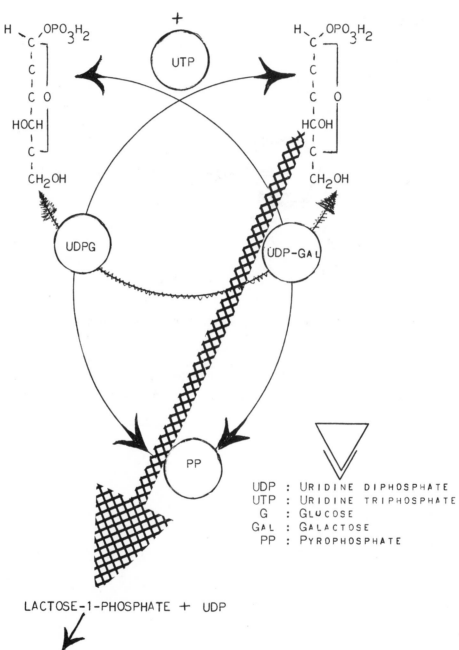

GALACTOSE-1-PHOSPHATE

GLUCOSE-1-PHOSPHATE

UDP : URIDINE DIPHOSPHATE
UTP : URIDINE TRIPHOSPHATE
G : GLUCOSE
GAL : GALACTOSE
PP : PYROPHOSPHATE

LACTOSE-1-PHOSPHATE + UDP

LACTOSE

MAP 20.   GENERAL REACTIONS OF THE SUGAR-1-PHOSPHATES

GENERAL   REACTIONS

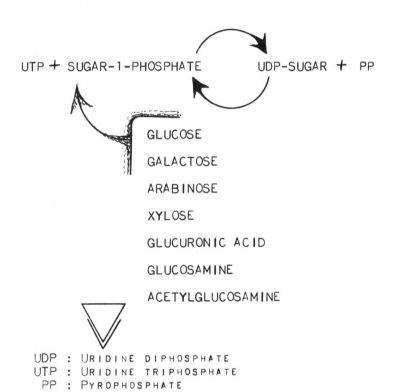

UTP + SUGAR-1-PHOSPHATE   UDP-SUGAR + PP

GLUCOSE

GALACTOSE

ARABINOSE

XYLOSE

GLUCURONIC ACID

GLUCOSAMINE

ACETYLGLUCOSAMINE

UDP : URIDINE DIPHOSPHATE
UTP : URIDINE TRIPHOSPHATE
 PP : PYROPHOSPHATE

MAP 21.   URONIC ACID METABOLISM

After Deuel and Stutz, Adv. Enz. <u>20</u>, 341, (1958)

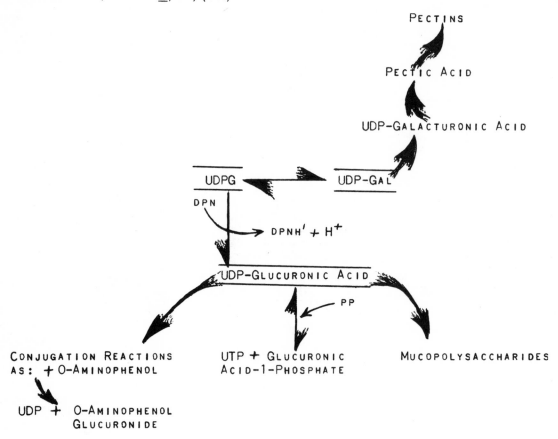

PECTINS

PECTIC ACID

UDP-GALACTURONIC ACID

UDPG   UDP-GAL

DPN

DPNH' + H$^+$

UDP-GLUCURONIC ACID

CONJUGATION REACTIONS
AS: + O-AMINOPHENOL

UTP + GLUCURONIC
ACID-1-PHOSPHATE

PP

MUCOPOLYSACCHARIDES

UDP + O-AMINOPHENOL
GLUCURONIDE

: ANILINE

UDP + ANILINE GLUCURONIDE

UDP : URIDINE DIPHOSPHATE
UTP : URIDINE TRIPHOSPHATE
G   : GLUCOSE
GAL : GALACTOSE

MAP 22. AMINO SUGAR METABOLISM

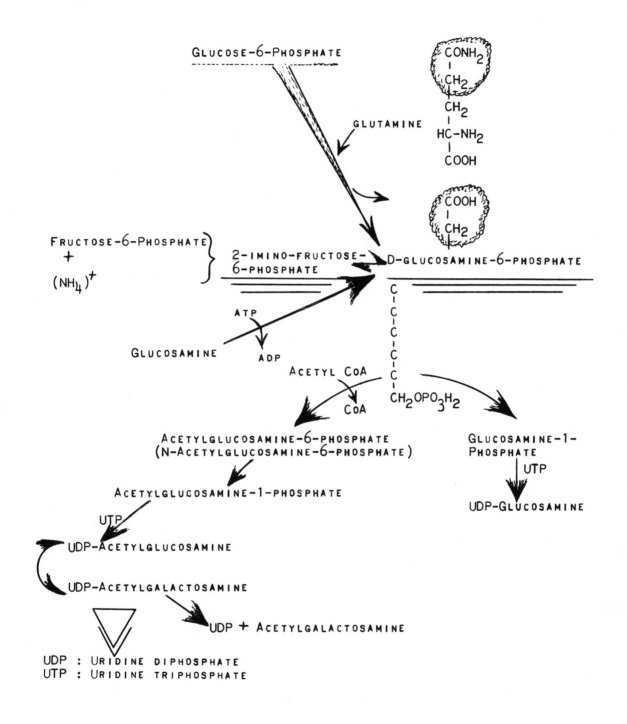

GLUCOSE-6-PHOSPHATE

CONH₂
|
CH₂
|
CH₂
|
HC–NH₂
|
COOH

GLUTAMINE

COOH
|
CH₂

FRUCTOSE-6-PHOSPHATE
+
(NH₄)⁺

2-IMINO-FRUCTOSE-6-PHOSPHATE

D-GLUCOSAMINE-6-PHOSPHATE

ATP

GLUCOSAMINE   ADP

ACETYL CoA

CoA

CH₂OPO₃H₂

ACETYLGLUCOSAMINE-6-PHOSPHATE
(N-ACETYLGLUCOSAMINE-6-PHOSPHATE)

GLUCOSAMINE-1-PHOSPHATE

UTP

UDP-GLUCOSAMINE

ACETYLGLUCOSAMINE-1-PHOSPHATE

UTP

UDP-ACETYLGLUCOSAMINE

UDP-ACETYLGALACTOSAMINE

UDP + ACETYLGALACTOSAMINE

UDP : URIDINE DIPHOSPHATE
UTP : URIDINE TRIPHOSPHATE

NOTES

Chapter 2
THE "MONOPHOSPHATE PATHWAYS"

TABLE OF CONTENTS

Map No.	Title	Page No.
23	The Monophosphate Pathways	31
24	Sector Map	32
25	Sector A - Glucose-6-phosphate to Phosphogluconic Acid	33
26	Sector B - Phosphogluconic Acid to Ribulose-5-phosphate	34
27	Sector C - Ribulose-5-phosphate to Heptulose-phosphate	35
28	Reactions of Transketolase	36
29	Further Reactions of Transketolase	37
30	Reactions of Transaldolase	38
31	Sector D - Reactions of Heptulose	39
32	Distribution of Isotopes	40
33	Sector E - Ribulose to Phosphoglyceric Acid	41
34	Second Pathway of Phosphogluconic Acid	43
35	Other Pathways	45
36	Ascorbic Acid Synthesis	47
37	Sugar Alcohol Oxidation	48
38	Inositol Metabolism	49

MAP 23. THE MONOPHOSPHATE PATHWAYS

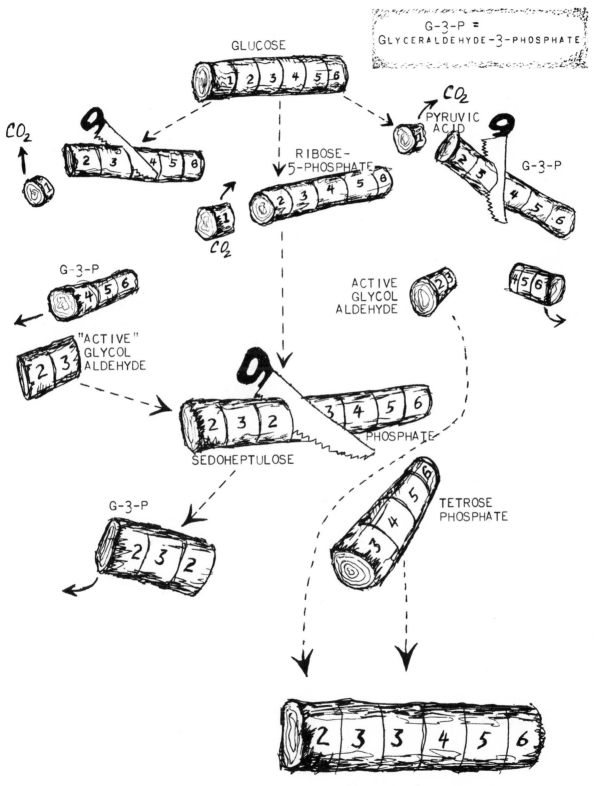

G-3-P = GLYCERALDEHYDE-3-PHOSPHATE

FRUCTOSE-6-PHOSPHATE

MAP 24. SECTOR MAP – MONOPHOSPHATE PATHWAYS

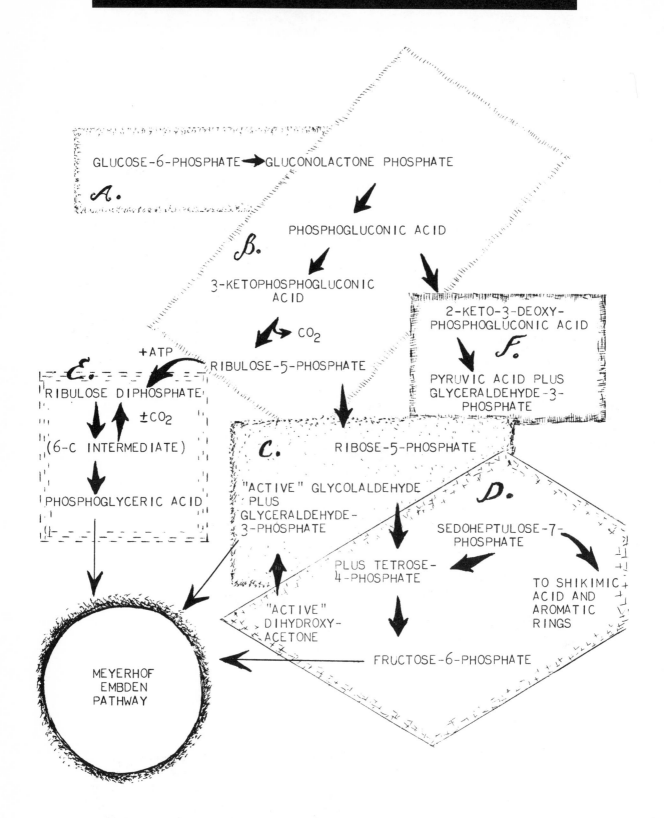

GLUCOSE-6-PHOSPHATE ⟶ GLUCONOLACTONE PHOSPHATE

A.

PHOSPHOGLUCONIC ACID

B.

3-KETOPHOSPHOGLUCONIC ACID

CO_2

2-KETO-3-DEOXY-PHOSPHOGLUCONIC ACID

F.

RIBULOSE-5-PHOSPHATE

PYRUVIC ACID PLUS GLYCERALDEHYDE-3-PHOSPHATE

+ATP

E.

RIBULOSE DIPHOSPHATE

$\pm CO_2$

(6-C INTERMEDIATE)

C.

RIBOSE-5-PHOSPHATE

"ACTIVE" GLYCOLALDEHYDE PLUS GLYCERALDEHYDE-3-PHOSPHATE

D.

SEDOHEPTULOSE-7-PHOSPHATE

PHOSPHOGLYCERIC ACID

PLUS TETROSE-4-PHOSPHATE

TO SHIKIMIC ACID AND AROMATIC RINGS

"ACTIVE" DIHYDROXY-ACETONE

MEYERHOF EMBDEN PATHWAY

FRUCTOSE-6-PHOSPHATE

MAP 25. SECTOR A. GLUCOSE-6-PHOSPHATE TO PHOSPHOGLUCONIC ACID

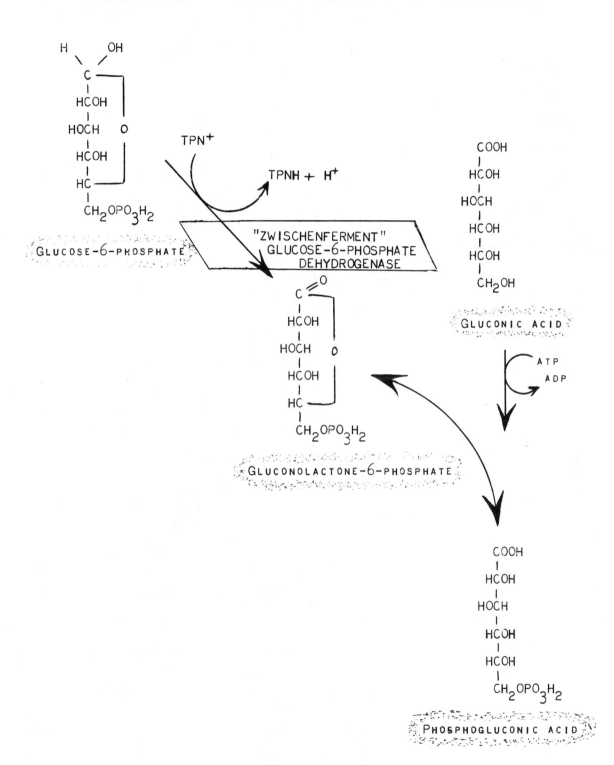

MAP 26. SECTOR B. PHOSPHOGLUCONIC ACID TO RIBULOSE-5-PHOSPHATE

```
      COOH
       |
      HCOH
       |
  HOCH
       |
      HCOH
       |
      HCOH
       |
      CH₂OPO₃H₂
```

PHOSPHOGLUCONIC ACID

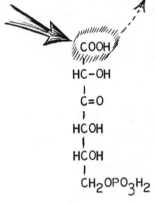

```
      COOH
       |
     HC-OH
       |
      C=O
       |
     HCOH
       |
     HCOH
       |
     CH₂OPO₃H₂
```

3-KETOPHOSPHOGLUCONIC ACID

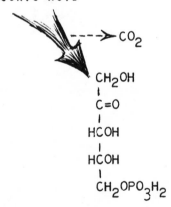

- - ->CO₂

```
     CH₂OH
      |
      C=O
      |
     HCOH
      |
     HCOH
      |
     CH₂OPO₃H₂
```

RIBULOSE-5-PHOSPHATE

MAP 27.   SECTOR C.   RIBULOSE-5-PHOSPHATE TO HEPTULOSE PHOSPHATE

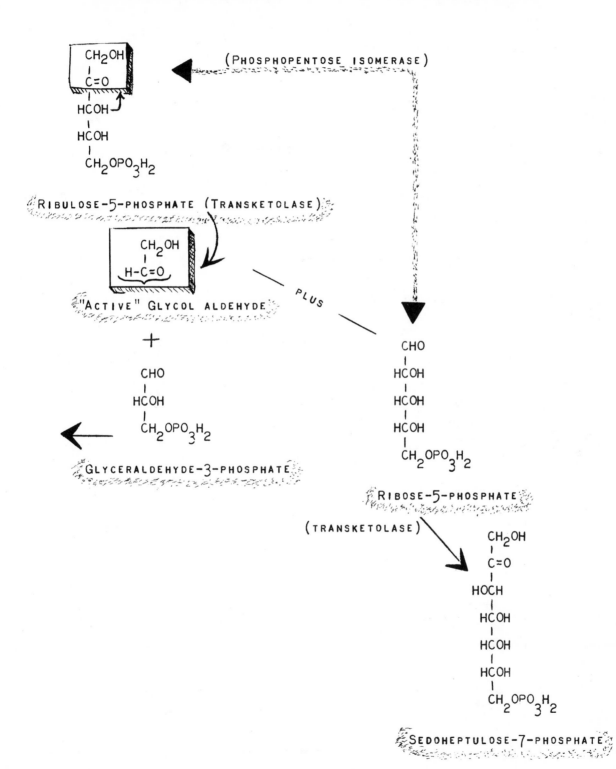

(PHOSPHOPENTOSE ISOMERASE)

CH_2OH
$C=O$
$HCOH$
$HCOH$
$CH_2OPO_3H_2$

RIBULOSE-5-PHOSPHATE (TRANSKETOLASE)

CH_2OH
$H-C=O$

"ACTIVE" GLYCOL ALDEHYDE

PLUS

$+$

CHO
$HCOH$
$CH_2OPO_3H_2$

GLYCERALDEHYDE-3-PHOSPHATE

CHO
$HCOH$
$HCOH$
$HCOH$
$CH_2OPO_3H_2$

RIBOSE-5-PHOSPHATE

(TRANSKETOLASE)

CH_2OH
$C=O$
$HOCH$
$HCOH$
$HCOH$
$HCOH$
$CH_2OPO_3H_2$

SEDOHEPTULOSE-7-PHOSPHATE

MAP 28. REACTIONS OF TRANSKETOLASE

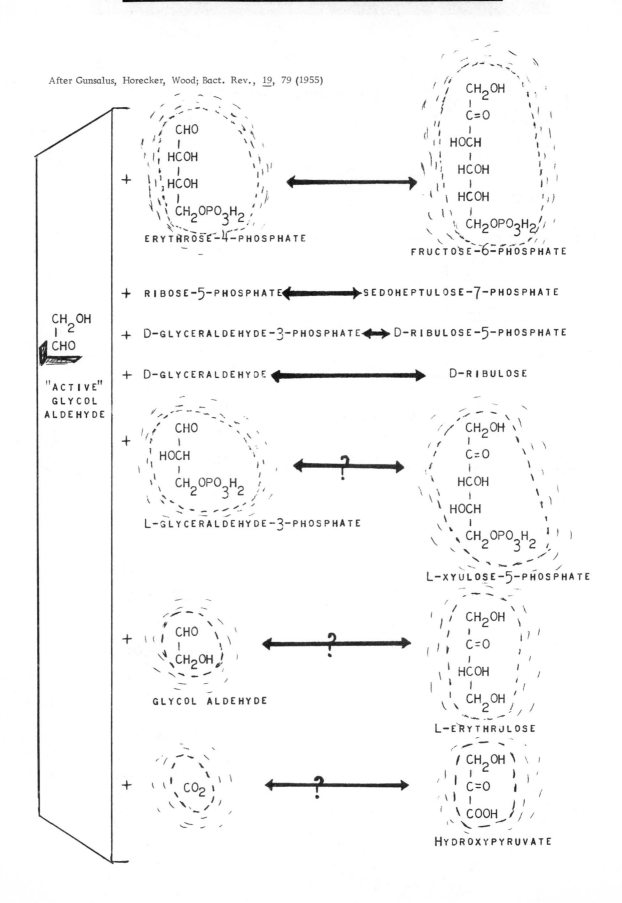

After Gunsalus, Horecker, Wood; Bact. Rev., 19, 79 (1955)

MAP 29. FURTHER REACTIONS OF TRANSKETOLASE

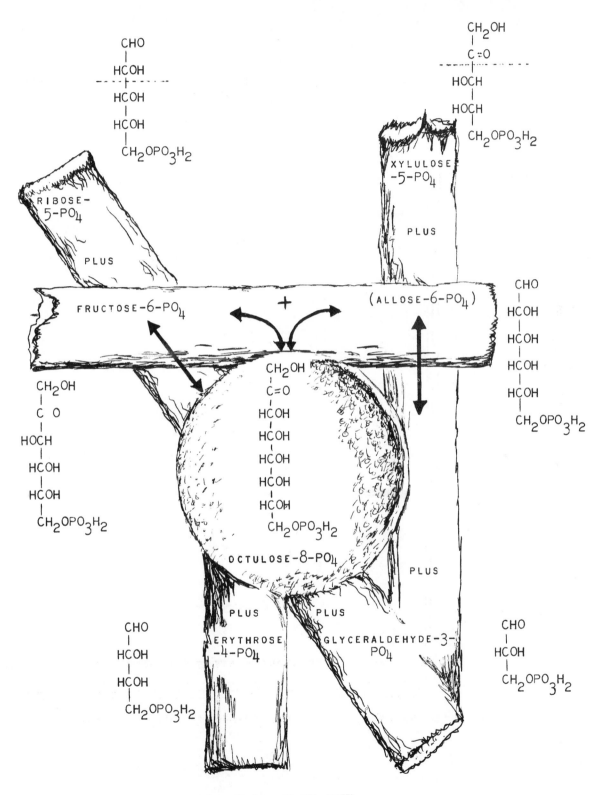

After Racker and Schroeder, Arch. Biochem. Biophys., 66, 241, (1957)

38

MAP 30. REACTIONS OF TRANSALDOLASE

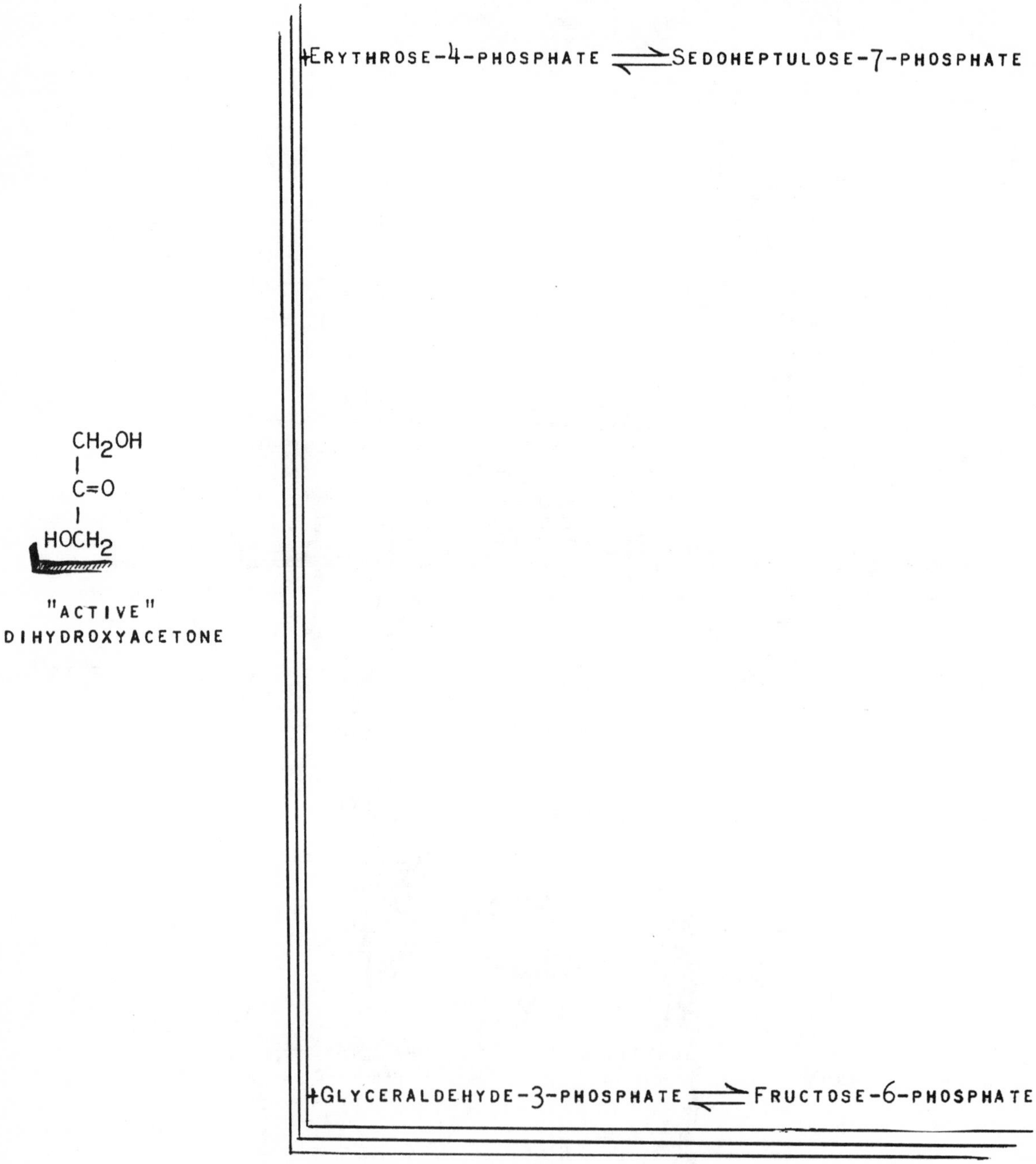

ERYTHROSE-4-PHOSPHATE $\rightleftharpoons$ SEDOHEPTULOSE-7-PHOSPHATE

$$\begin{array}{c} CH_2OH \\ | \\ C=O \\ | \\ HOCH_2 \end{array}$$

"ACTIVE"
DIHYDROXYACETONE

GLYCERALDEHYDE-3-PHOSPHATE $\rightleftharpoons$ FRUCTOSE-6-PHOSPHATE

(OTHER REACTIONS YET UNKNOWN; SPACE LEFT FOR THEIR INSERTION WHEN DISCOVERED.)

MAP 31. SECTOR D. REACTIONS OF HEPTULOSE

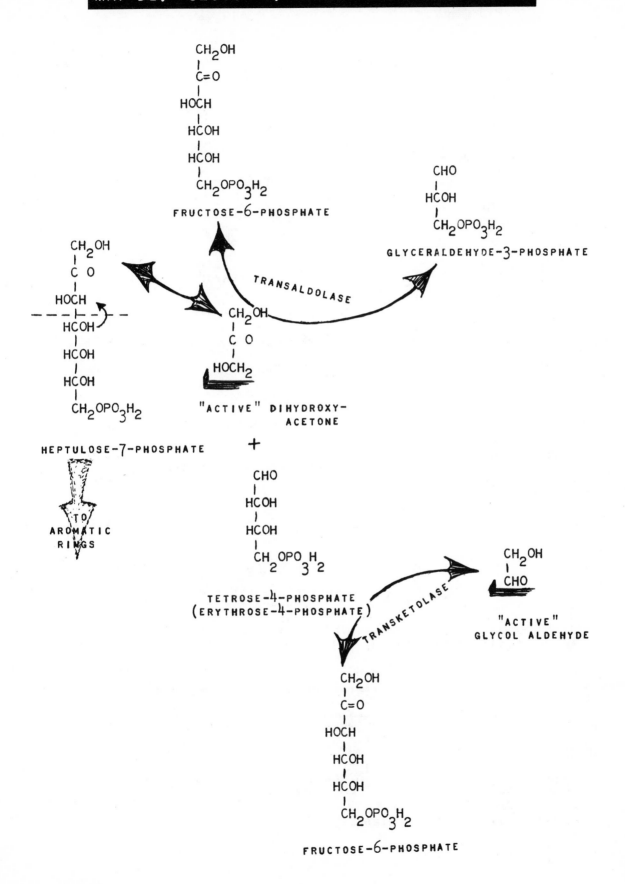

FRUCTOSE-6-PHOSPHATE

GLYCERALDEHYDE-3-PHOSPHATE

TRANSALDOLASE

"ACTIVE" DIHYDROXY-ACETONE

HEPTULOSE-7-PHOSPHATE

TO AROMATIC RINGS

+

TETROSE-4-PHOSPHATE
(ERYTHROSE-4-PHOSPHATE)

TRANSKETOLASE

"ACTIVE" GLYCOL ALDEHYDE

FRUCTOSE-6-PHOSPHATE

MAP 32. DISTRIBUTION OF ISOTOPES

After Vishniac, Horecker, and Ochoa; Adv. Enzym., _19_, 1 (1957)

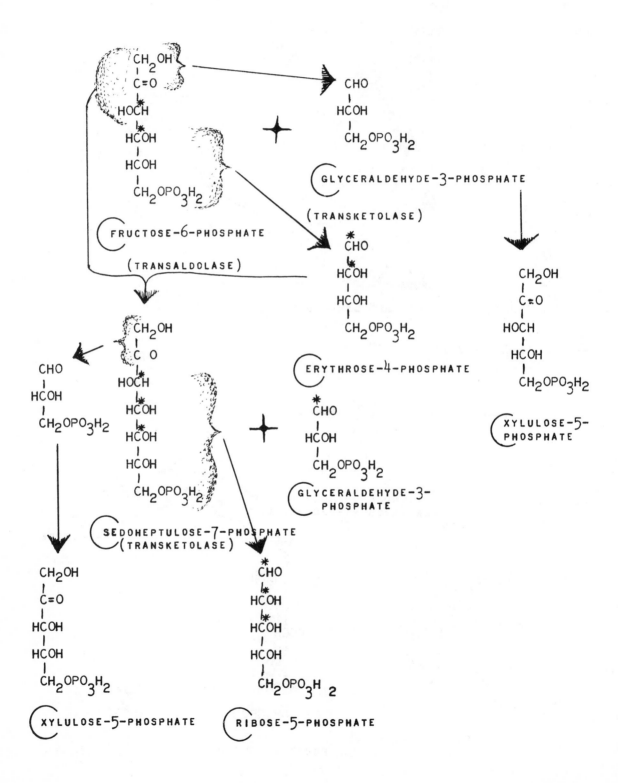

MAP 33. SECTOR E. RIBULOSE TO PHOSPHOGLYCERIC ACID
(A PATHWAY OF PHOTOSYNTHESIS)

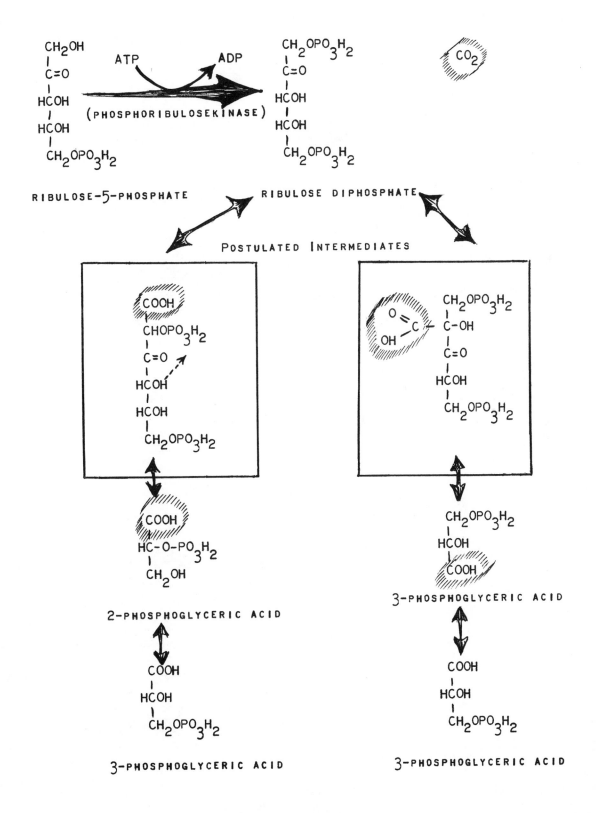

NOTES

MAP 34. A SECOND PATHWAY OF PHOSPHOGLUCONIC ACID

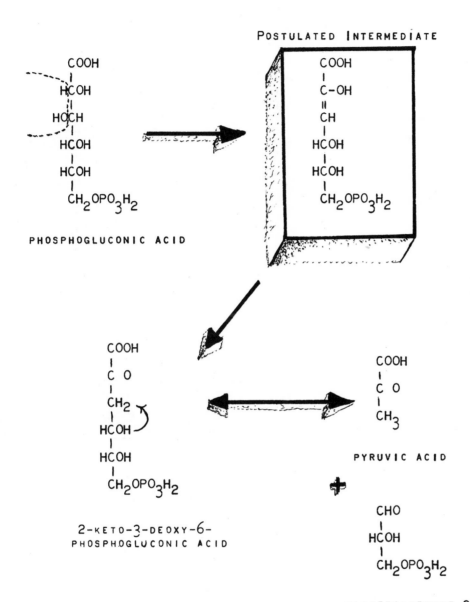

POSTULATED INTERMEDIATE

PHOSPHOGLUCONIC ACID

2-KETO-3-DEOXY-6-
PHOSPHOGLUCONIC ACID

PYRUVIC ACID

GLYCERALDEHYDE-3-PHOSPHATE

44

NOTES

MAP 35.   OTHER PATHS OF SUGAR METABOLISM (FREQUENTLY NOT INVOLVING PHOSPHORYLATION)

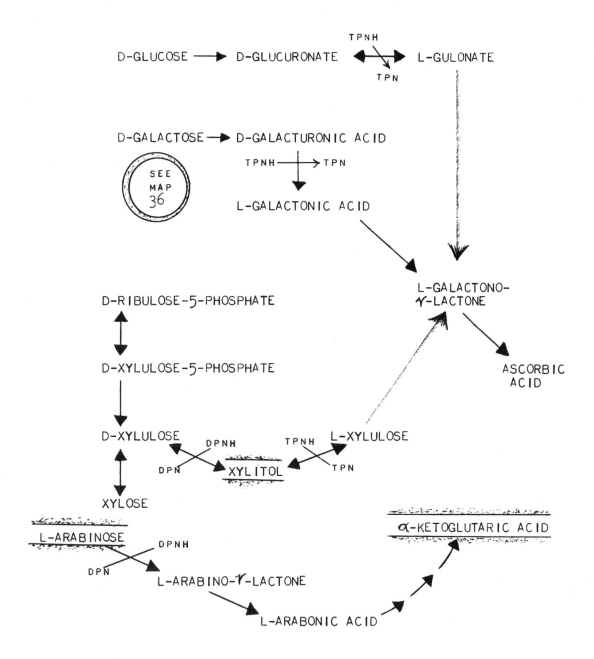

NOTES

MAP 36.   ASCORBIC ACID SYNTHESIS

After Mapson, Vol. XI of 4th Inter. Congress Biochem., Vienna, 1958

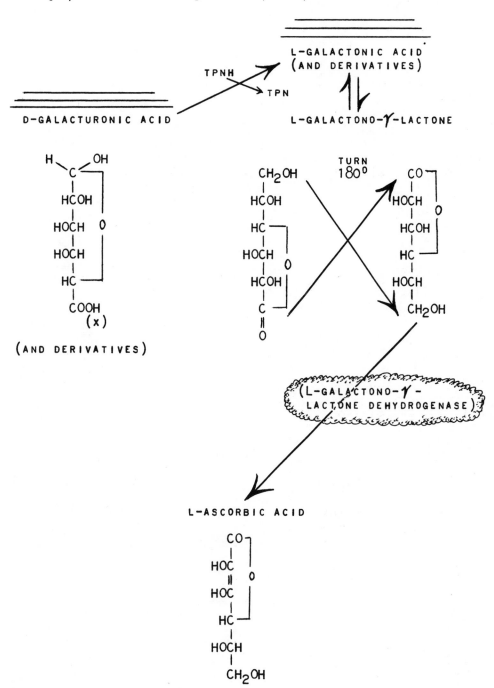

MAP 37. SUGAR ALCOHOL OXIDATION

After Hollmann and Touster, J. Biol. Chem. <u>225</u>, 87 (1957)

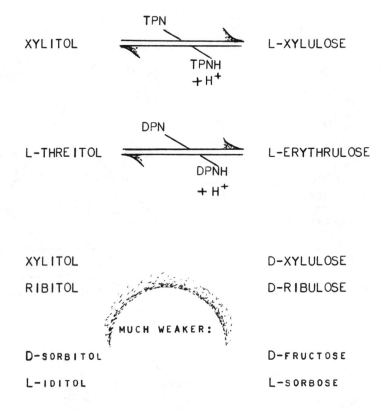

XYLITOL   TPN / TPNH $+ H^+$ L-XYLULOSE

L-THREITOL   DPN / DPNH $+ H^+$ L-ERYTHRULOSE

XYLITOL   D-XYLULOSE

RIBITOL   D-RIBULOSE

MUCH WEAKER:

D-SORBITOL   D-FRUCTOSE

L-IDITOL   L-SORBOSE

MAP 38. INOSITOL METABOLISM

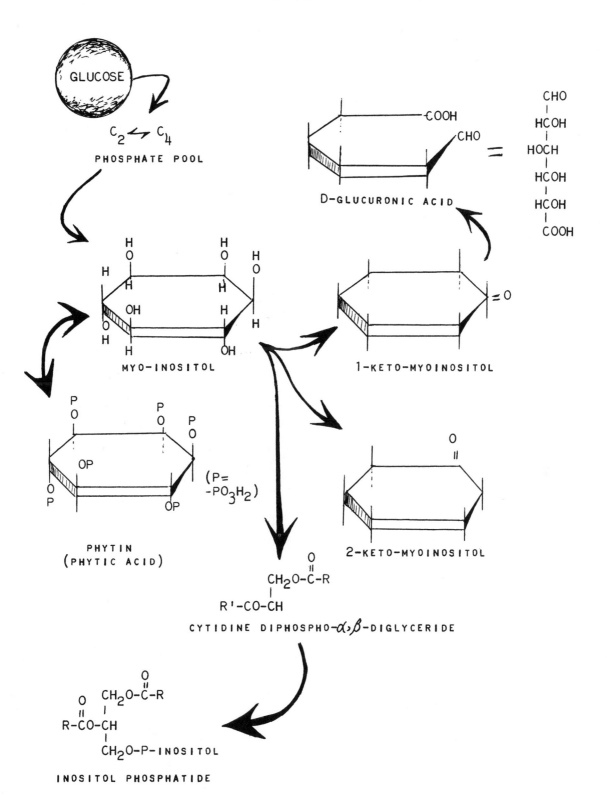

GLUCOSE

$C_2 \rightleftarrows C_4$

PHOSPHATE POOL

—COOH

CHO

$$\begin{array}{c} CHO \\ | \\ HCOH \\ | \\ HOCH \\ | \\ HCOH \\ | \\ HCOH \\ | \\ COOH \end{array}$$

D-GLUCURONIC ACID

MYO-INOSITOL

1-KETO-MYOINOSITOL

$= O$

PHYTIN
(PHYTIC ACID)

$(P = -PO_3H_2)$

2-KETO-MYOINOSITOL

$$\begin{array}{c} O \\ || \\ CH_2O-C-R \\ | \\ R'-CO-CH \end{array}$$

CYTIDINE DIPHOSPHO-α,β-DIGLYCERIDE

$$\begin{array}{c} O \\ || \\ CH_2O-C-R \\ | \\ R-CO-CH \\ || \quad | \\ O \quad CH_2O-P-INOSITOL \end{array}$$

INOSITOL PHOSPHATIDE

NOTES

Chapter 3
THE PATHWAYS TO OXYGEN

TABLE OF CONTENTS

Map No.	Title	Page No.
39	Mechanisms of Oxygen Metabolism	53
40	Pathway to Oxygen (Slater)	54
41	Pathway to Oxygen (Hartree)	55

CARRIERS IN OXYGEN UPTAKE CHAINS

Map No.	Title	Page No.
42	Structure of Pyridine Coenzymes	56
43	Mechanism of Hydrogen Transport by Pyridine Coenzymes	57
44	Structure of Flavin Coenzymes	58
45	Hydrogen Transport by Flavin Coenzymes	59
46	Structure and Action of Lipoic Acid	60
47	Attachment of Lipoic Acid to Enzymes	61
48	The Vitamin E – Vitamin K Series	62
49	Action of Quinone Coenzymes	63

MAP 39. MECHANISM OF OXYGEN METABOLISM

After Mason: Advances in Enzymology, 19, 79 (1957)

I SUBSTRATE + O_2 → SUBSTRATE-O_2

"OXYGEN TRANSFERASES"

PYROCATECHASE   (PEROXIDE OXIDASES)
HOMOGENTISATE OXIDASE   DIHYDROXYFUMARATE OXIDASE
3-HYDROXYANTHRANILIC OXIDASE   PEROXIDASE
PROTOCATECHUIC OXIDASE   INDOLE OXIDASE
TRYPTOPHAN OXIDASE   CATALASE
LIPOXIDASE   INDOLE ACETIC ACID OXIDASE

II SUBSTRATE + O_2 + 2E → SUBSTRATE-OH + O^{--}

"MIXED FUNCTION TRANSFERASES"

PHENOLASE COMPLEX   PHENYLALANINE OXIDASE
VARIOUS HYDROXYLATION SYSTEMS   IMIDAZOLE ACETIC ACID OXIDASE
  (MOSTLY PHENOLS)   P-OH-PHENYL PYRUVIC ACID OXIDASE
STEROID: 11-β-HYDROXYLATION   KYNURENINE-3-HYDROXYLASE
         21 HYDROXYLATION   LUCIFERASE
         SQUALINE OXIDOCYCLASE   BILE PIGMENTS; HEME CATALYZED
                                                       OXIDATION

III SUBSTRATE $\xrightarrow{-2H}$ DEHYDROGENATED PRODUCT
            $(H^+ + E)$ ——————————→ $O_2 \searrow H_2O_2$; H_2O

"ELECTRON TRANSFER OXIDASES"

A. TWO ELECTRON TRANSFER   B. FOUR ELECTRON TRANSFER
   (H_2O_2 IS ONE PRODUCT)   (H_2O IS ONE PRODUCT)
   URICASE (OXYGEN OBLIGATORY)   LACCASE
   XANTHINE OXIDASE   CATECHOLASE
   ALDEHYDE OXIDASE   ASCORBIC OXIDASE
   GLUCOSE OXIDASE   CYTOCHROME OXIDASE
   ARABINOSE OXIDASE
   PYRUVIC OXIDASE (BACTERIAL)
   GLYCOLIC OXIDASE
   LACTIC OXIDASE (BACTERIAL)
   MONAMINE OXIDASE
   DIAMINE OXIDASE
   AMINO ACID OXIDASE
   PYRIMIDINE OXIDASE
   DPNH OXIDASE
   TPNH OXIDASE

54

MAP 40.   PATHWAY TO OXYGEN (SLATER)

After Slater: Advances in Enzymology, 20, 147 (1958)

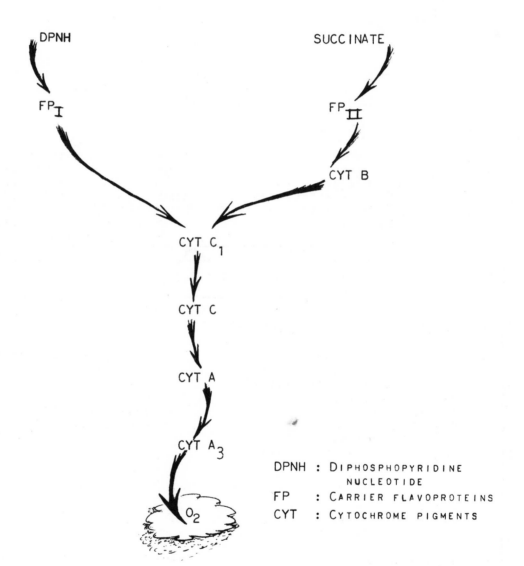

DPNH : DIPHOSPHOPYRIDINE
               NUCLEOTIDE
FP   : CARRIER FLAVOPROTEINS
CYT : CYTOCHROME PIGMENTS

MAP 41.   PATHWAY TO OXYGEN (HARTREE)

After Hartree: Advances in Enzymology, 18, 1 (1957)

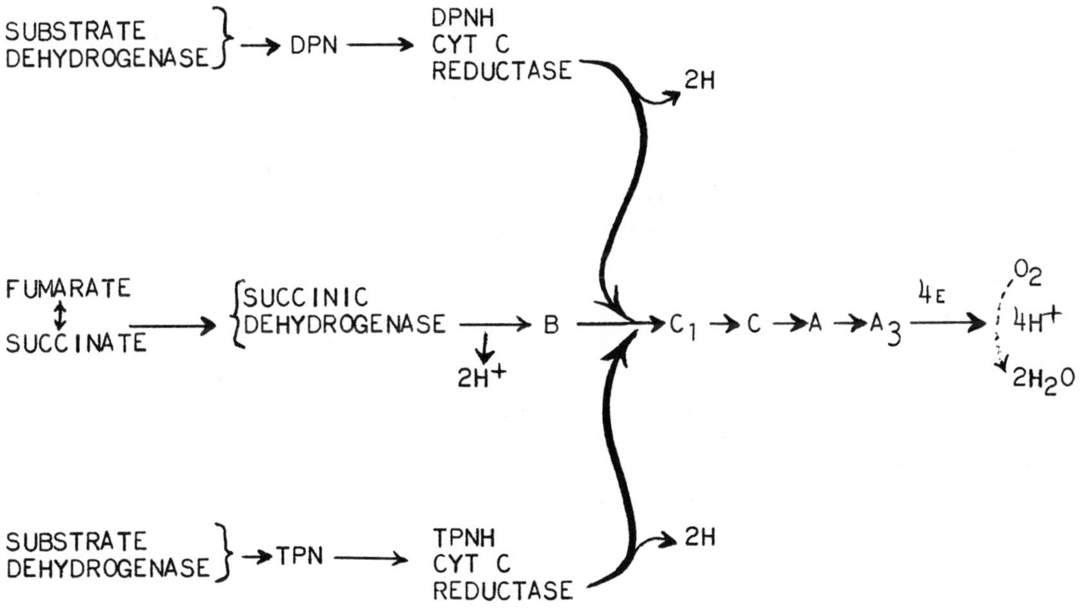

MAP 42. STRUCTURE OF PYRIDINE COENZYMES

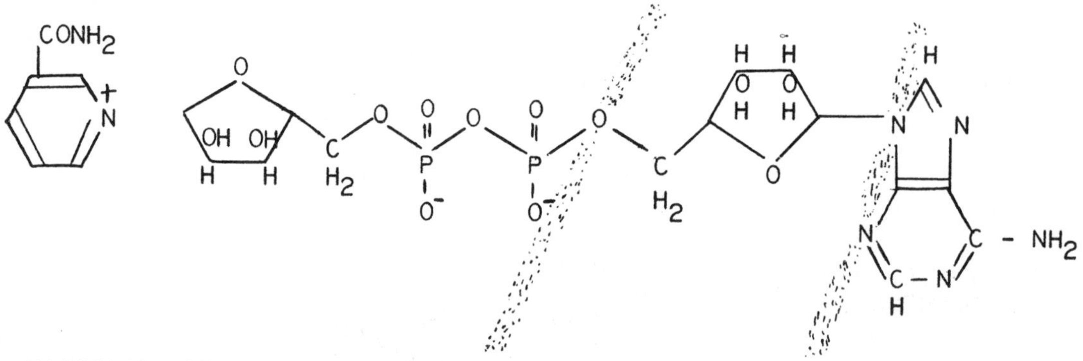

NICOTINAMIDE — RIBOSE — PHOSPHATE — PHOSPHATE — RIBOSE — ADENINE

STRUCTURE OF DPN

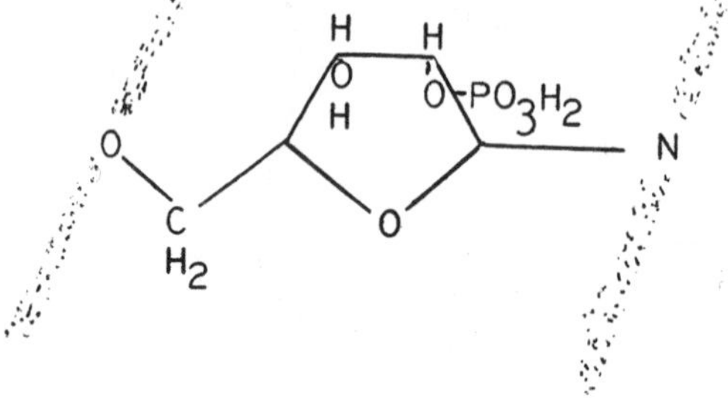

NICOTINAMIDE — RIBOSE — PHOSPHATE — PHOSPHATE — RIBOSE — ADENINE — PHOSPHATE

STRUCTURE OF TPN

MAP 43. MECHANISM OF HYDROGEN TRANSPORT BY PYRIDINE COENZYMES

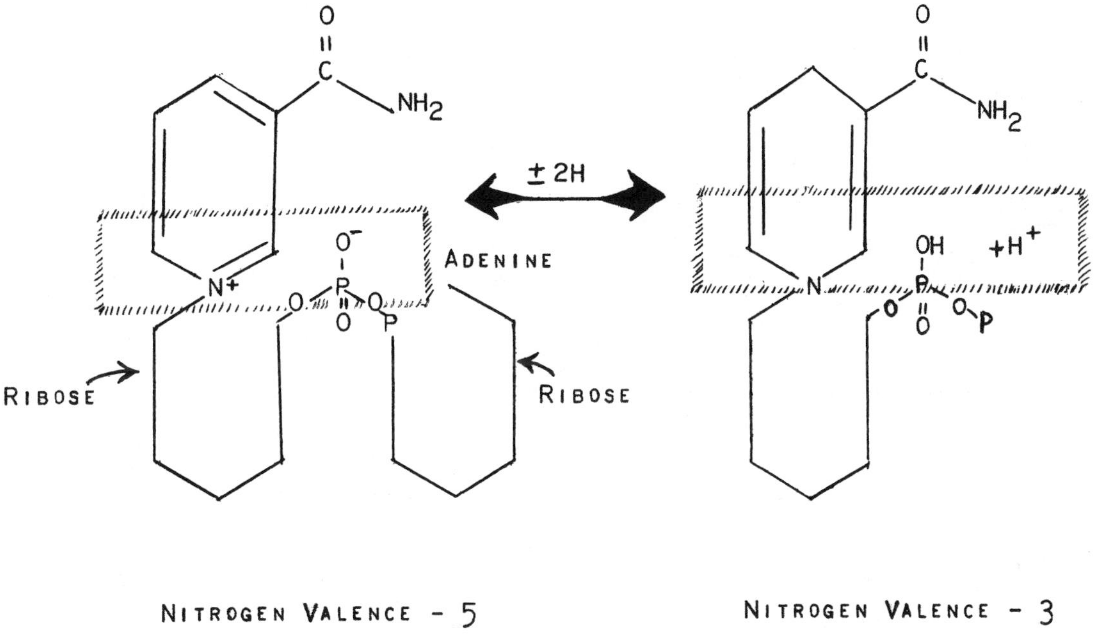

58

MAP 44. STRUCTURE OF FLAVIN COENZYMES

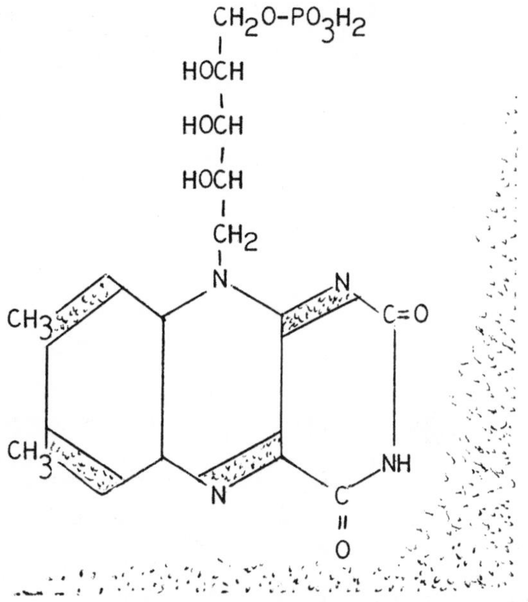

RIBOFLAVIN PHOSPHATE

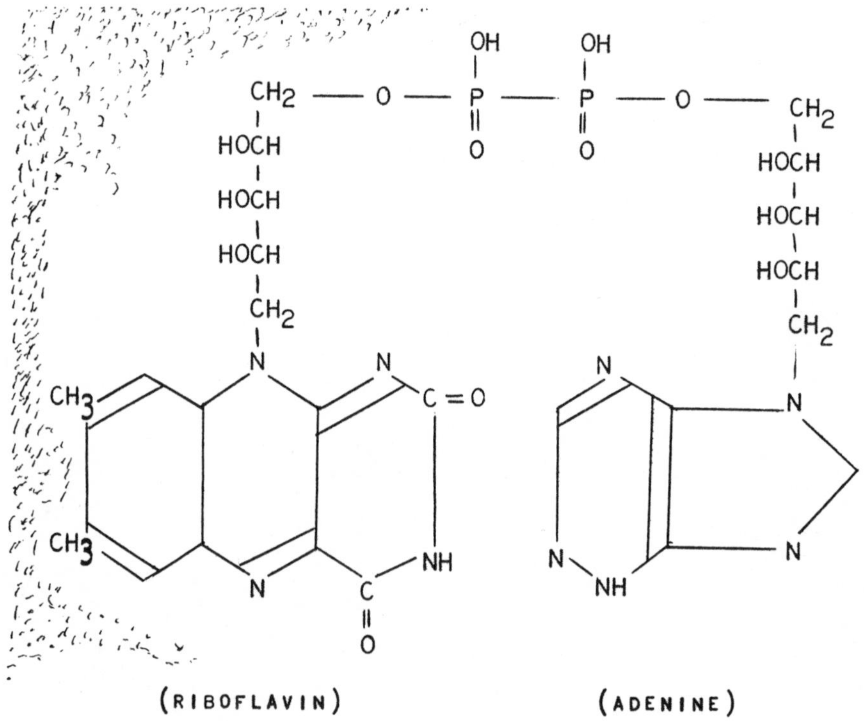

(RIBOFLAVIN)   (ADENINE)

FLAVIN ADENINE DINUCLEOTIDE (FAD)

MAP 45. HYDROGEN TRANSPORT BY FLAVIN COENZYMES

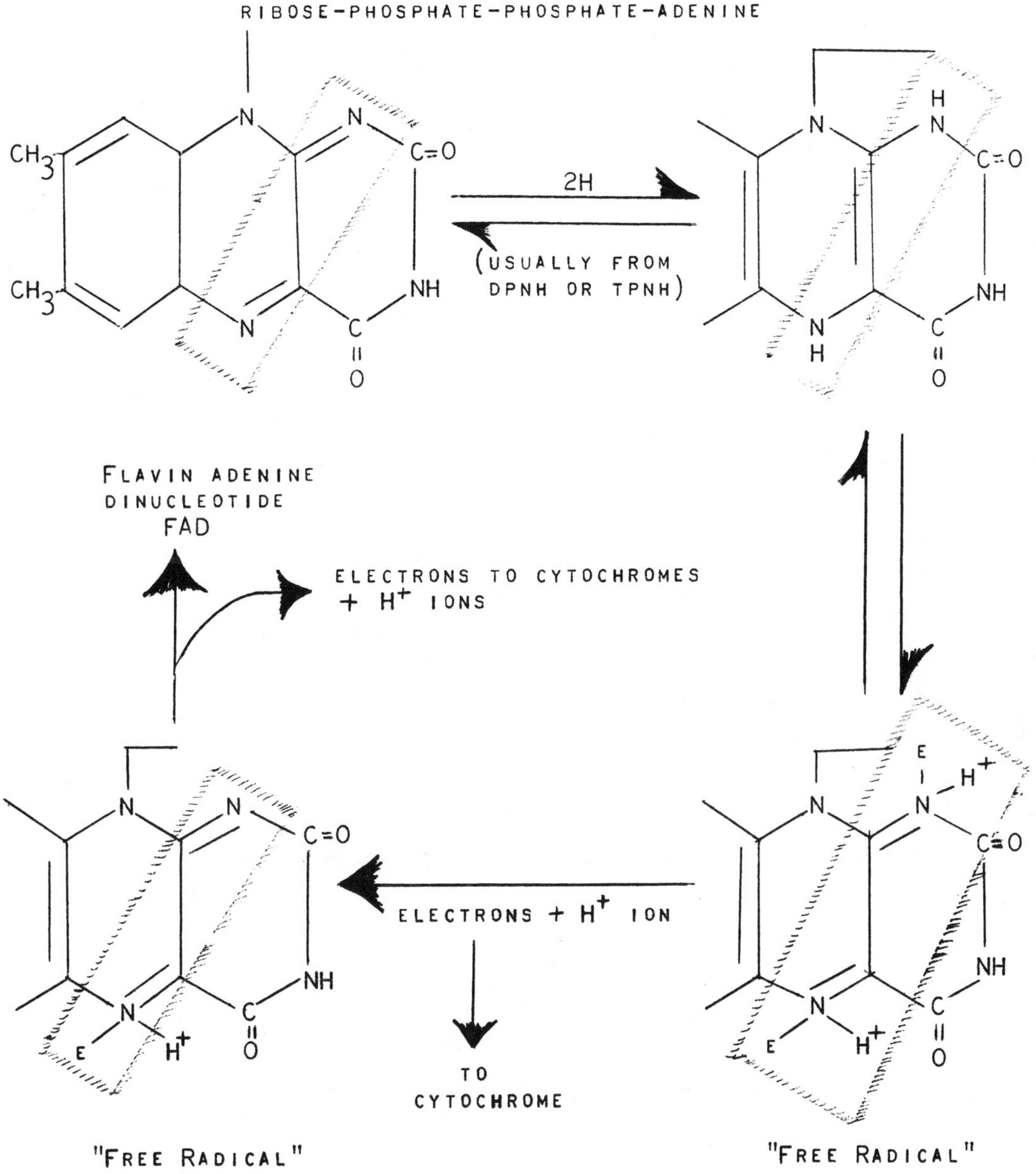

RIBOSE-PHOSPHATE-PHOSPHATE-ADENINE

2H →
← (USUALLY FROM DPNH OR TPNH)

FLAVIN ADENINE DINUCLEOTIDE FAD

ELECTRONS TO CYTOCHROMES + H⁺ IONS

ELECTRONS + H⁺ ION

TO CYTOCHROME

"FREE RADICAL"

"FREE RADICAL"

MAP 46. STRUCTURE AND ACTION OF LIPOIC ACID

CH₂
CH₂   CH-CH₂-CH₂-CH₂-COOH
               "5-THIOCTIC ACID"
CH₂   S
    S

CH₂ — CH₂
CH₂   CH-CH₂-CH₂-COOH
               "4-THIOCTIC ACID"
CH₂   S
    S

.... HAVE BIOLOGICAL ACTIVITY, BUT ...

CH₂
CH₂   CH-CH₂-CH₂-CH₂-CH₂-COOH
               "6-THIOCTIC ACID"
S   S   (+)-α-LIPOIC ACID

.... HAS MUCH MORE ACTIVITY AND IS IDENTICAL WITH
     THE NATURAL COMPOUND.

MECHANISM OF ACTION -- POSTULATED:

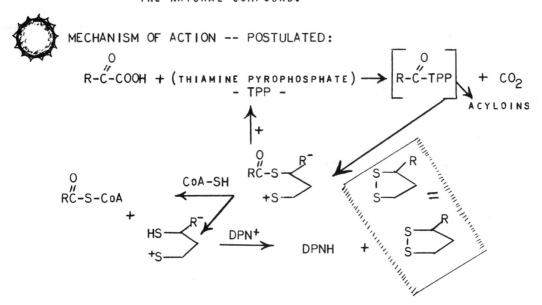

MAP 47. ATTACHMENT OF LIPOIC ACID TO ENZYMES

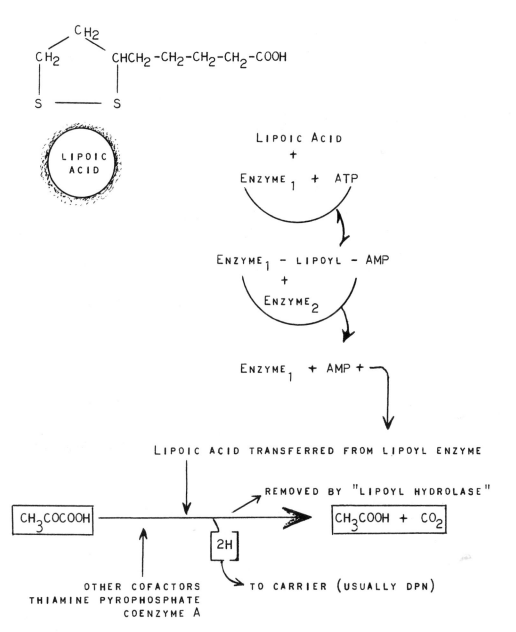

LIPOIC ACID
+
ENZYME$_1$ + ATP

ENZYME$_1$ - LIPOYL - AMP
+
ENZYME$_2$

ENZYME$_1$ + AMP +

LIPOIC ACID TRANSFERRED FROM LIPOYL ENZYME

REMOVED BY "LIPOYL HYDROLASE"

CH$_3$COCOOH   →   2H   →   CH$_3$COOH + CO$_2$

OTHER COFACTORS
THIAMINE PYROPHOSPHATE
COENZYME A

TO CARRIER (USUALLY DPN)

MAP 48.   THE VITAMIN E - VITAMIN K SERIES

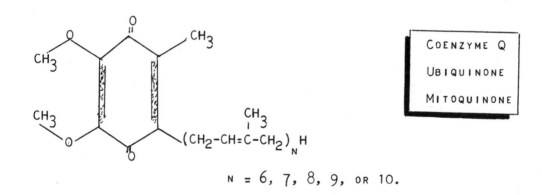

TOCOL

VITAMIN E FAMILY:

α-Tocopherol	–	5,7,8-Trimethyl tocol
β- "	–	5,8-Dimethyl tocol
γ- "	–	7,8-Dimethyl tocol
δ- "	–	8-Methyl tocol
ε- "	–	5-Methyl tocol
ζ- "	–	5,7-Dimethyl tocol
η- "	–	7-Methyl tocol

$(CH_2-CH=C-CH_2)_N\ H$

COENZYME Q

UBIQUINONE

MITOQUINONE

N = 6, 7, 8, 9, OR 10.

VITAMIN K_1

MAP 49.   ACTION OF QUINONE COENZYMES

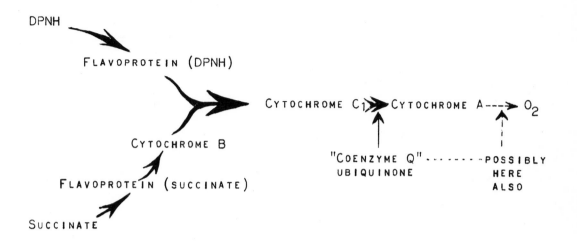

DPNH

FLAVOPROTEIN (DPNH)

CYTOCHROME B

FLAVOPROTEIN (SUCCINATE)

SUCCINATE

CYTOCHROME C_1 ⟶ CYTOCHROME A ---⟶ O_2

"COENZYME Q" - - - - - - POSSIBLY
UBIQUINONE   HERE
                             ALSO

$N = 6, 7, 8, 9,$ OR $10.$

POSSIBLE ACTION:

$\pm E$

$HO-PO_3H_2$

$O-PO_3H_2$

ADP

ATP

NOTES

Chapter 4
PHOSPHORYLATION

TABLE OF CONTENTS

Map No.	Title	Page No.
50	Formation and Transfer of "Energy-Rich" Phosphate Bonds	67
51	Phosphorylation in Oxidative Pathways	68
52	Possible Mechanism of Oxidative Phosphorylation	69
53	Basic Mechanisms of Oxidative Phosphorylation	70
54	Postulated Details of Phosphorylation by Carriers	71
55	Phosphorus Compounds in Biosynthesis	72

MAP 50. FORMATION AND TRANSFER OF "ENERGY RICH" PHOSPHATE BONDS

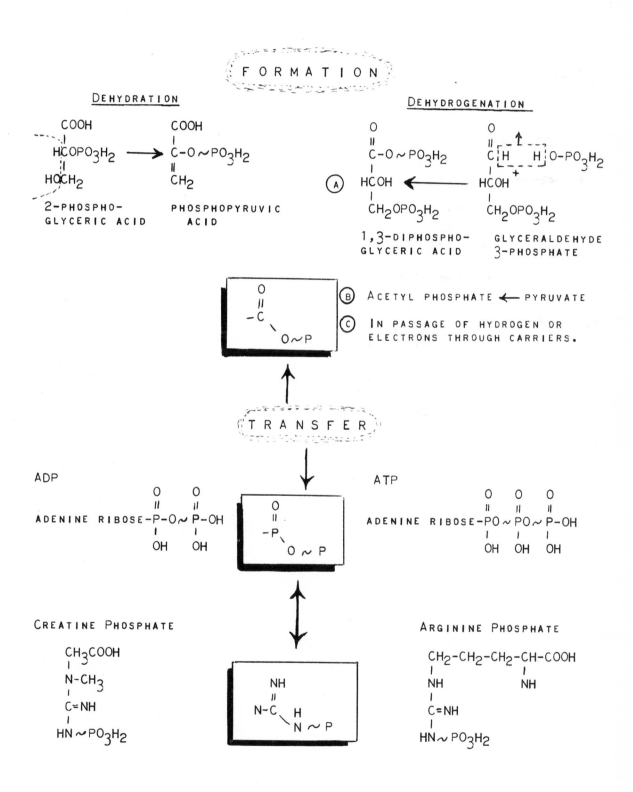

FORMATION

DEHYDRATION

2-PHOSPHO-GLYCERIC ACID → PHOSPHOPYRUVIC ACID

DEHYDROGENATION

Ⓐ 1,3-DIPHOSPHO-GLYCERIC ACID ← GLYCERALDEHYDE 3-PHOSPHATE

Ⓑ ACETYL PHOSPHATE ← PYRUVATE

Ⓒ IN PASSAGE OF HYDROGEN OR ELECTRONS THROUGH CARRIERS.

TRANSFER

ADP

ATP

CREATINE PHOSPHATE

ARGININE PHOSPHATE

68

MAP 51.   PHOSPHORYLATION IN OXIDATIVE PATHWAYS

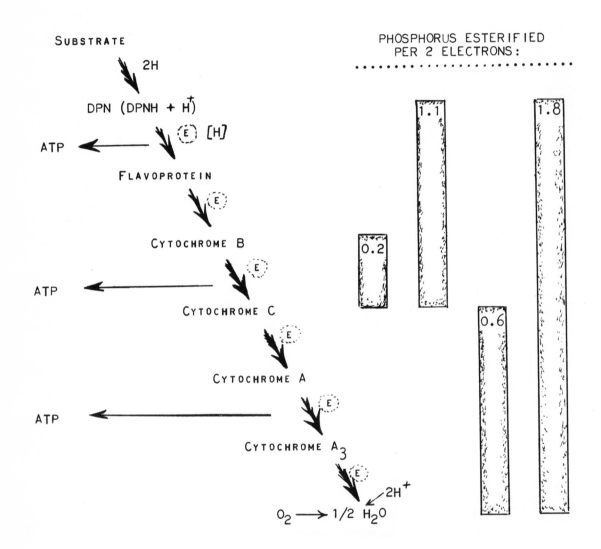

After Lehninger, <u>et al</u>. Science, <u>128</u>, 450 (1958)

MAP 52.   POSSIBLE MECHANISM OF OXIDATIVE PHOSPHORYLATION

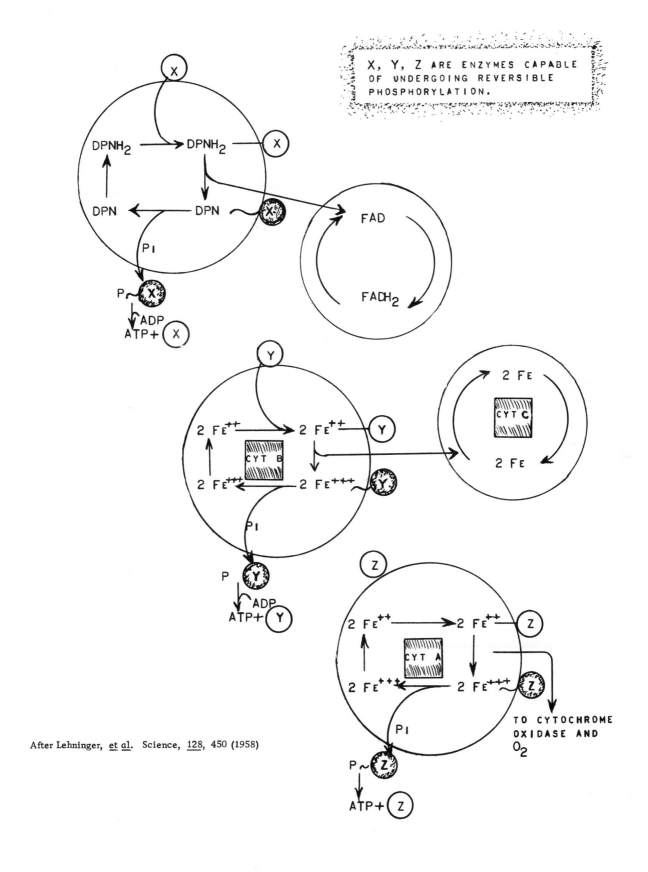

X, Y, Z ARE ENZYMES CAPABLE OF UNDERGOING REVERSIBLE PHOSPHORYLATION.

After Lehninger, et al. Science, 128, 450 (1958)

70

MAP 53.   BASIC MECHANISMS OF OXIDATIVE PHOSPHORYLATION

(PRELIMINARY CO-VALENT BOND FORMATION)

MECHANISM 1:

P ENTERS CO-VALENT BOND

P_i + [CARRIER] → [CARRIER] -P

[CARRIER] -P + ADP → ATP + [CARRIER]

MECHANISM 2:

ADP ENTERS CO-VALENT BOND

ADP + [CARRIER] → [CARRIER] ADP

[CARRIER] ADP + P_i → ATP

IT IS KNOWN THAT: IF ADP

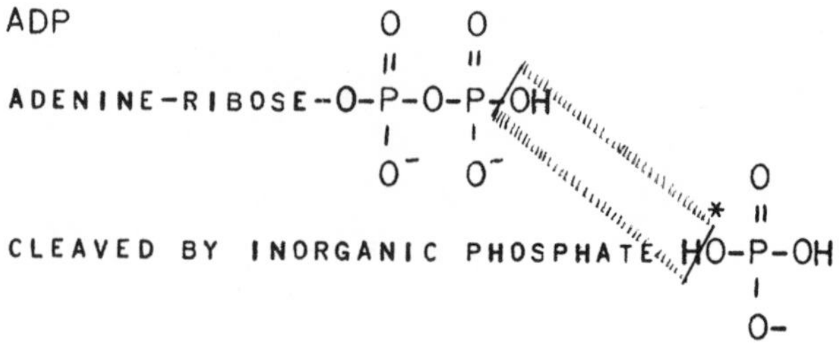

$$\text{ADENINE-RIBOSE-O-}\overset{\overset{O}{\|}}{\underset{\underset{O^-}{|}}{P}}\text{-O-}\overset{\overset{O}{\|}}{\underset{\underset{O^-}{|}}{P}}\text{-OH}$$

IS CLEAVED BY INORGANIC PHOSPHATE

$$\text{HO-}\overset{\overset{*}{\overset{O}{\|}}}{\underset{\underset{O-}{}}{P}}\text{-OH}$$

THE "BRIDGE OXYGEN" IS SUPPLIED BY
INORGANIC PHOSPHATE.

$$\text{ADENINE-RIBOSE-O-}\overset{\overset{O}{\|}}{\underset{\underset{O^-}{|}}{P}}\text{-O-}\overset{\overset{O}{\|}}{\underset{\underset{O^-}{|}}{P}}\text{-O-}\overset{\overset{O}{\|}}{\underset{\underset{O-}{|}}{P}}\text{-OH}$$

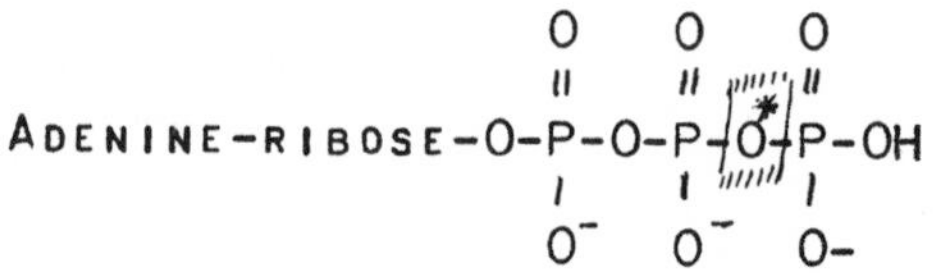

IF MECHANISM 1,

THEN "BRIDGE OXYGEN" FROM ADP.

BRIDGE OXYGEN FOUND NOT
TO COME FROM P_i, ∴ THIS
IS PROBABLY MECHANISM.

IF MECHANISM 2,

THEN "BRIDGE OXYGEN"
FROM P_i

After Boyer, Proc. Inter. Symp. Enzyme Chem., Tokyo, 1957

MAP 54. POSTULATED DETAILS OF PHOSPHORYLATION BY CARRIERS

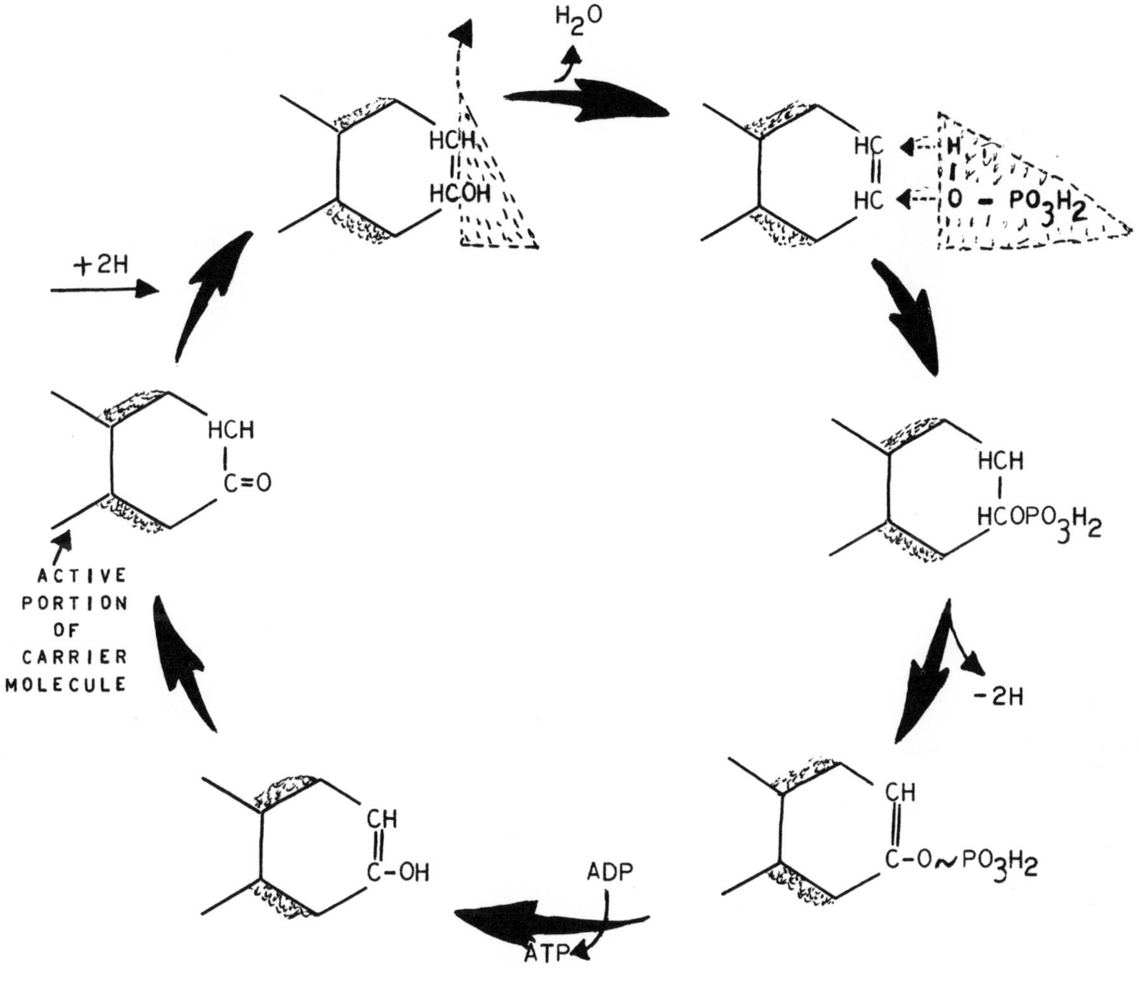

MAP 55. PHOSPHORUS COMPOUNDS IN BIOSYNTHESIS

After Kornberg, Advances in Enzymology, 18, 191, 1957

A. GROUP TRANSFER SYSTEMS

1. NUCLEOSIDE TRIPHOSPHATES

AS P DONORS

ATP + GLUCOSE
⇅
ADP + GLUCOSE-6-PHOSPHATE
(MANY "KINASES" KNOWN)

AS PYROPHOSPHATE DONORS

ATP + RIBOSE-5-PHOSPHATE
⇅
AMP + PHOSPHORIBOSYL PYROPHOSPHATE

OR

ATP + THIAMINE
⇅
AMP + THIAMINE PYROPHOSPHATE
(ONLY A FEW KNOWN

2. NUCLEOSIDE DIPHOSPHATES

AS P DONORS

ADP + ADP
⇅
AMP* + ATP
(MYOKINASE)

(ONLY A FEW KNOWN)

*AMP = ADENOSINE-5'-MONOPHOSPHATE.

AS PYROPHOSPHATE DONORS

(NONE KNOWN)

3. NON-NUCLEOTIDES AS PHOSPHATE TRANSFERS

PHENYLPHOSPHATE + ALCOHOL (ETC.)
↓ PHOSPHATASES
PHENOL + ALCOHOL PHOSPHATE

(AN ALCOHOLYSIS OF THE PHOSPHATE RATHER
THAN HYDROLYSIS OF IT)

4. OTHER GROUP TRANSFERS

A. GLYCOSIDE BOND FORMATION WITH INORGANIC PHOSPHATE LIBERATION:
   As: GLUCOSE-1-PHOSPHATE ⇌ STARCH (OR GLYCOGEN) + INORGANIC PHOSPHATE
   OR RIBOSE-1-PHOSPHATE + GUANINE ⇌ GUANINE RIBOSIDE + " "
   (PYROPHOSPHATE SYSTEMS EMPLOY NUCLEOTIDE CARRIERS.)

B. GLYCOSIDE BOND TRANSFER WITHOUT PHOSPHATE:
   As: SUCROSE ⟶ LEVAN + FRUCTOSE

C. REACTIONS WITH OR WITHOUT PHOSPHATE:
   As: SUCROSE ⇌ GLUCOSYL ENZYME + FRUCTOSE
   ± ARABINOSE   ± INORGANIC PHOSPHATE
   GLUCOSE-1-ARABINOSIDE + ENZYME   GLUCOSE-1-PHOSPHATE + ENZYME

MAP 55 - CONTINUED

B. PYROPHOSPHORYLASES

1. <u>NUCLEOTIDE ANHYDRIDE SYNTHESIS</u>

Nucleoside-P-PP + HO-X $\rightleftharpoons$ Nucleoside-P-O-X + PP
$\quad\quad\quad$ ‖ $\quad\quad\quad\quad\quad\quad\quad\quad\quad\quad\quad$ ‖
$\quad\quad\quad$ O $\quad\quad\quad\quad\quad\quad\quad\quad\quad\quad\quad$ O

<u>As</u>: ATP + riboflavin phosphate $\rightleftharpoons$ Flavin adenine dinucleotide + PP

or: UTP + glucose-1-P $\rightleftharpoons$ UDPG + PP

<u>With ATP</u>   <u>With UTP</u>

DPN   UDPG
CoA   UDP Galactose
FAD   UDP Acetylglucosamine, etc.
Adenyl acetate, butyrate,
    and other fatty acids
Adenyl methionine, leucine, etc.
Adenosyl methionine   <u>With GTP</u>
Adenyl sulfate
"Active" arginine   GDP Mannose
"Active" luciferin

```
A = ADENINE
U = URACIL
G = GUANINE
C = CYTOSINE
```

<u>With CTP</u>

CDP Choline

2. <u>SYNTHESIS OF DNA POLYNUCLEOTIDES</u>

Thymidine triphosphate - TPPP ⎫ Mg^{++}
Desoxycytidine   "   - CPPP ⎬ + $\longrightarrow$ DNA Polynucleotide
Desoxyguanosine   "   - GPPP ⎪ DNA   +
Desoxyadenosine   " "   - APPP ⎭   (4M) PP

(All four must be present.)

3. <u>SYNTHESIS OF N GLYOSIDES</u>

Orotic acid + phosphoribosyl pyrophosphate $\longrightarrow$ Orotidine-5-phosphate
$\quad\quad\quad\quad\quad\quad\quad\quad\quad\quad\quad\quad\quad\quad\quad\quad\quad\quad$ + PP

Anthranilic acid + $\quad\quad$ " $\quad\quad$ " $\longrightarrow$ Indole glycerol phosphate
$\quad\quad\quad\quad\quad\quad\quad\quad\quad\quad\quad\quad\quad\quad\quad\quad\quad\quad$ + PP

MAP 55 - CONTINUED

C. OTHERS

1. GLYCOSIDE SYNTHESIS

GLUCOSE-1-PHOSPHATE $\longrightarrow$ GLYCOGEN, ETC. + P_i
RIBOSE-1-PHOSPHATE + URACIL $\longrightarrow$ URIDINE + P_i
DESOXYRIBOSE-1-PHOSPHATE + GUANINE $\longrightarrow$ DESOXYGUANOSINE + P_i

2. THIOESTER SYNTHESIS

ACETYL CoA + H_3PO_4 $\rightleftharpoons$ ACETYL PHOSPHATE + CoA-SH

3. UREIDE SYNTHESIS

ORNITHINE + CARBAMYL PHOSPHATE $\rightleftharpoons$ CITRULLINE + P_i
ASPARTIC ACID + CARBAMYL PHOSPHATE $\rightleftharpoons$ UREIDOSUCCINIC + P_i

4. SYNTHESIS OF RNA POLYNUCLEOTIDES

$\left.\begin{array}{ll} \text{ADP} & \text{CDP} \\ \text{GDP} & \text{UDP} \end{array}\right\}$ $\longrightarrow$ POLY AGCU + P_i

(ANY COMBINATION)

5. UNKNOWN MECHANISMS

(REQUIRING ATP; GENERALLY FORMING ADP, P_i)

SUCCINIC ACID + CoA $\longrightarrow$ SUCCINYL CoA
PROPANYL CoA + CO_2 $\longrightarrow$ METHYLMALONYL CoA
UTP + NH_3 $\longrightarrow$ CTP
X(5)P + NH_3 $\longrightarrow$ G(5)P
X(5)P + GLUTAMINE $\longrightarrow$ G(5)P + GLUTAMIC ACID
I(5)P + ASPARTIC ACID $\longrightarrow$ A(5)P + FUMARIC ACID
ACETATE + NH_3 $\longrightarrow$ GLYCINE
GLUTAMIC ACID + NH_3 $\longrightarrow$ GLUTAMINE
FORMIC ACID + THF $\longrightarrow$ N^{10} FORMYL THF
GLUTAMIC ACID + CYSTEINE $\longrightarrow$ γ-GLUTAMYL CYSTEINE
γ-GLUTAMYL CYSTEINE + GLYCINE $\longrightarrow$ GLUTATHIONE

NOTES

NOTES

Chapter 5
THE CITRIC ACID CYCLE

TABLE OF CONTENTS

Map No.	Title	Page No.
56	The Citric Acid Cycle	79
57	Sector A - Condensation to Citric Acid	80
58	Sector B - Citric to Oxalosuccinic Acids	81
59	Sector C - Oxalosuccinic to Succinic Acids	82
60	Sector D - Succinic to Pyruvic Acids	83

MAP 56. THE CITRIC ACID CYCLE

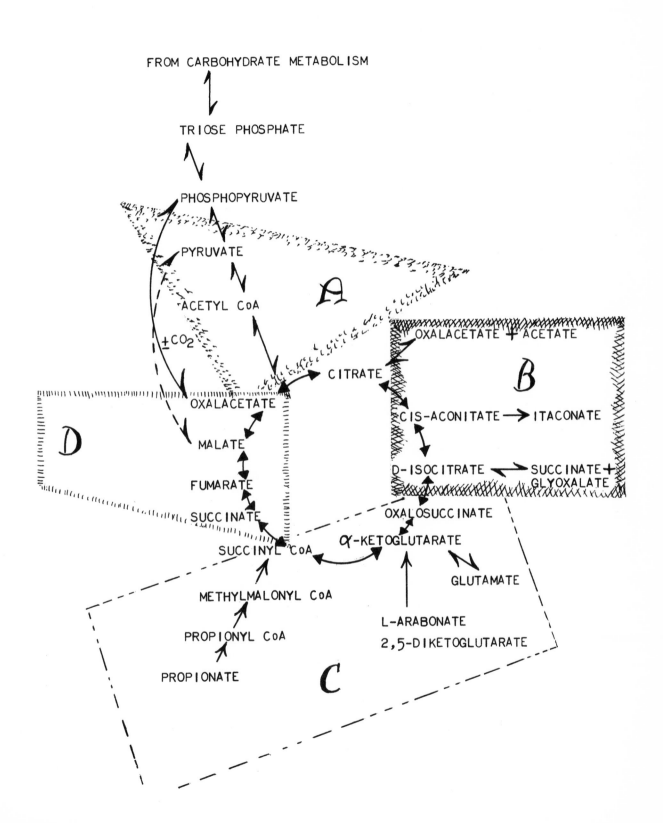

FROM CARBOHYDRATE METABOLISM

TRIOSE PHOSPHATE

PHOSPHOPYRUVATE

PYRUVATE

ACETYL CoA

$\pm CO_2$

A

OXALACETATE + ACETATE

CITRATE

B

CIS-ACONITATE → ITACONATE

OXALACETATE

D

MALATE

D-ISOCITRATE → SUCCINATE + GLYOXALATE

FUMARATE

SUCCINATE

OXALOSUCCINATE

SUCCINYL CoA

α-KETOGLUTARATE

GLUTAMATE

METHYLMALONYL CoA

PROPIONYL CoA

L-ARABONATE

2,5-DIKETOGLUTARATE

PROPIONATE

C

MAP 57.   SECTOR A - CONDENSATION TO CITRIC ACID

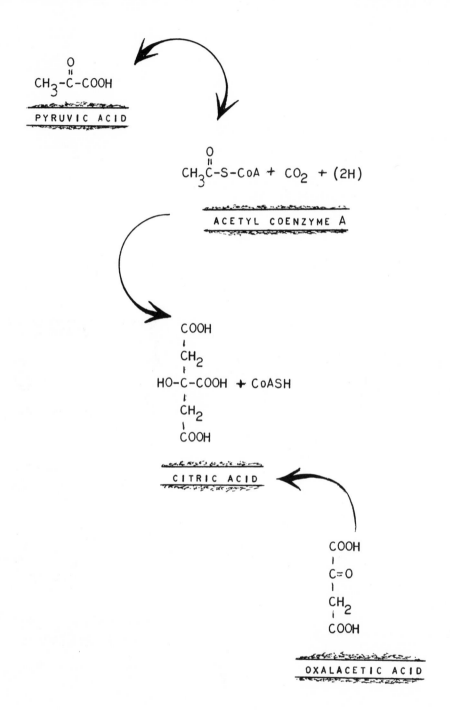

MAP 58. SECTOR B - CITRIC TO OXALOSUCCINIC ACIDS

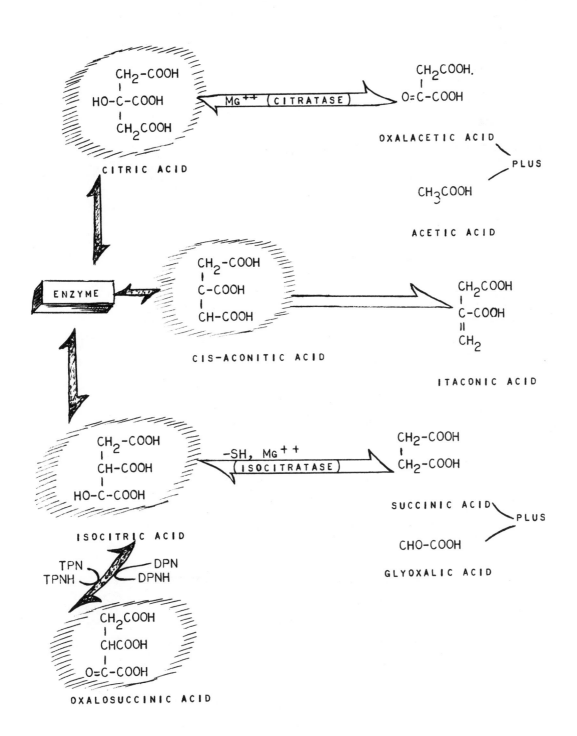

CITRIC ACID

OXALACETIC ACID

PLUS

ACETIC ACID

CIS-ACONITIC ACID

ITACONIC ACID

ENZYME

ISOCITRIC ACID

SUCCINIC ACID

PLUS

GLYOXALIC ACID

TPN   DPN
TPNH   DPNH

OXALOSUCCINIC ACID

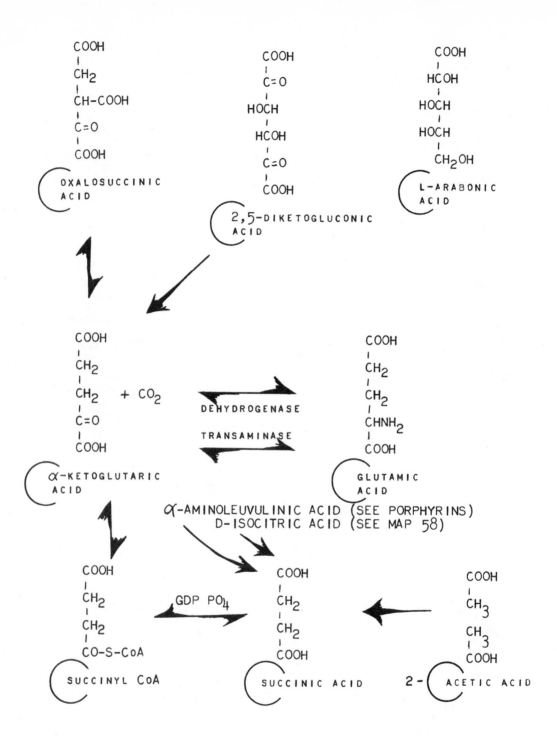

MAP 60.   SECTOR D - SUCCINIC TO PYRUVIC ACIDS

See J. Biol. Chem. 207, 803, 1954

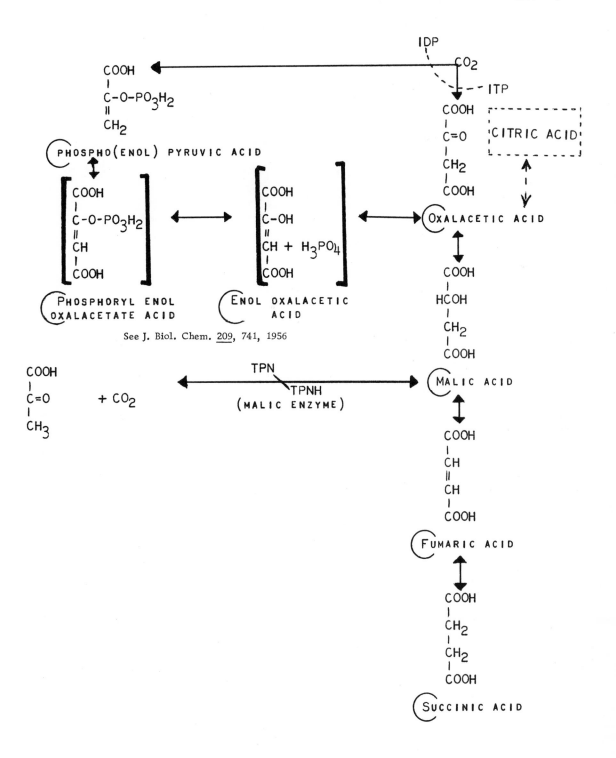

See J. Biol. Chem. 209, 741, 1956

NOTES

Chapter 6
THE METABOLISM OF PYRUVIC ACID

TABLE OF CONTENTS

Map No.	Title	Page No.
61	Pyruvic Acid Metabolism	87
62	Sector A - To Lactic Acid and Alanine	88
63	Sector B - To Acetaldehyde and Ethanol	89
64	Reactions of the Acyloins	90
65	Sector C - Acyloin Formation	91
66	Sector D - Hydrogen, Formic Acid and Acetyl Phosphate	92
67	Sector E - Acetone, Butanol, and Isopropyl Fermentations	93
68	Malonic Acid Metabolism	94
69	Propionic Acid Metabolism	95
70	Other Routes to Alpha-Ketoglutaric Acid	96
71	Acetyl CoA to Succinic Acid	97
72	Glyoxalic Acid and Glycolic Acid Metabolism	99
73	Tartaric Acid Metabolism	101
74	Synthesis of Pantothenic Acid	102
75	Metabolism of Coenzyme A	103

MAP 61. PYRUVIC ACID METABOLISM

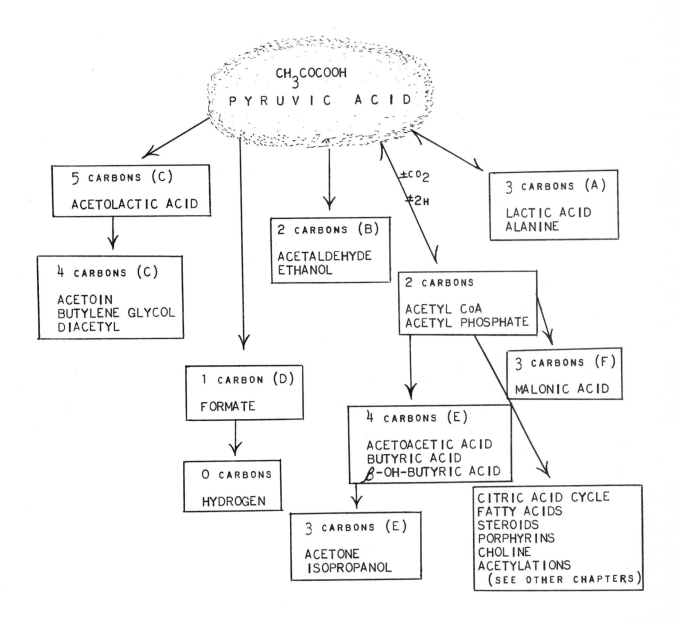

88

MAP 62. SECTOR A - TO LACTIC ACID AND ALANINE

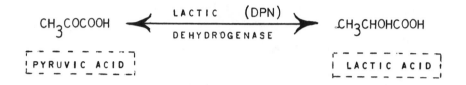

CH$_3$COCOOH ⟵ LACTIC (DPN) ⟶ CH$_3$CHOHCOOH
DEHYDROGENASE

[PYRUVIC ACID]   [LACTIC ACID]

YEAST ENZYME –
LINKED DIRECTLY TO CYTOCHROMES

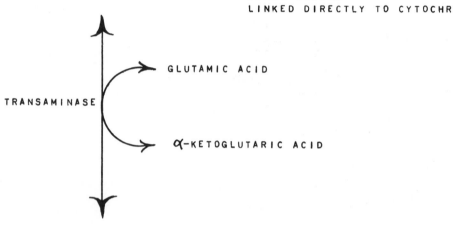

TRANSAMINASE

GLUTAMIC ACID

α-KETOGLUTARIC ACID

CH$_3$CH-COOH
|
NH$_2$

[ALANINE]

MAP 63.   SECTOR B - TO ACETALDEHYDE AND ETHANOL

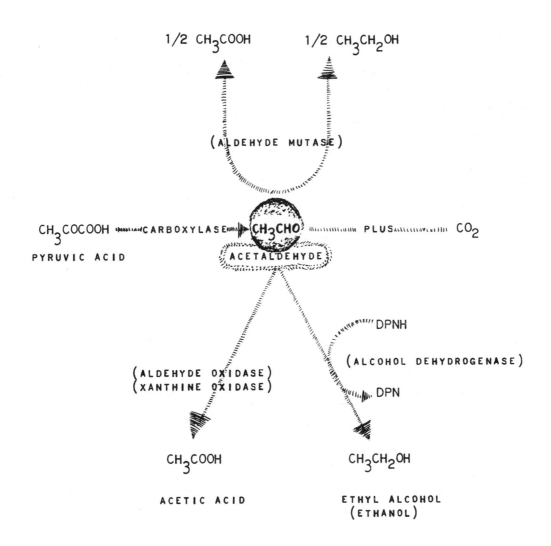

MAP 64. REACTIONS OF THE ACYLOINS

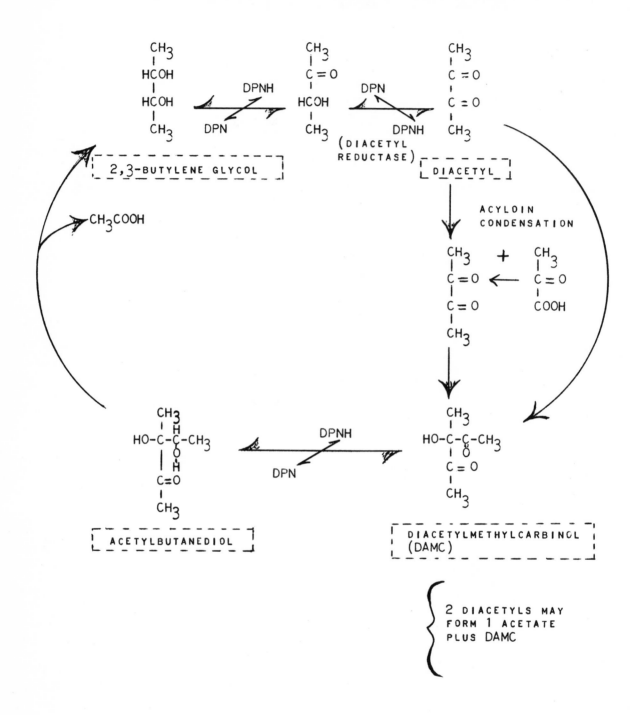

MAP 65.   SECTOR C - ACYLOIN FORMATION

TWO   REACTION   TYPES

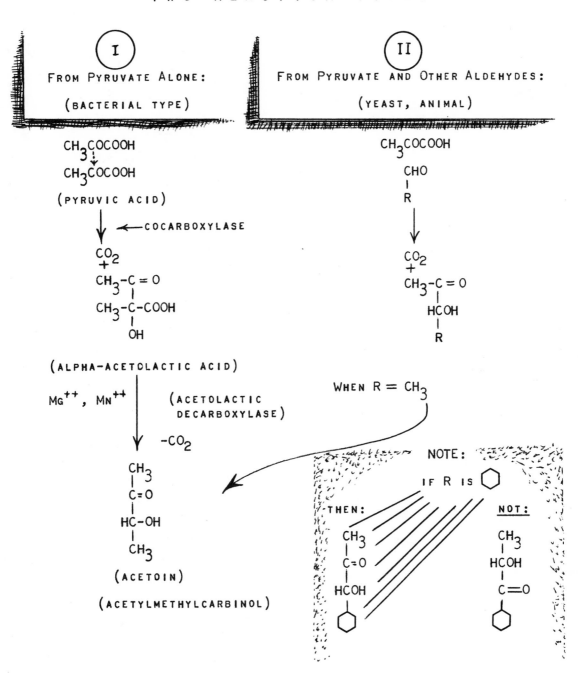

I

FROM PYRUVATE ALONE:

(BACTERIAL TYPE)

$CH_3COCOOH$
$CH_3COCOOH$

(PYRUVIC ACID)

←—— COCARBOXYLASE

CO_2
+
$CH_3-C=O$
$CH_3-C-COOH$
       OH

(ALPHA-ACETOLACTIC ACID)

Mg^{++}, Mn^{++} (ACETOLACTIC
                           DECARBOXYLASE)

$-CO_2$

CH_3
$C=O$
$HC-OH$
CH_3

(ACETOIN)

(ACETYLMETHYLCARBINOL)

II

FROM PYRUVATE AND OTHER ALDEHYDES:

(YEAST, ANIMAL)

$CH_3COCOOH$

CHO
R

CO_2
+
$CH_3-C=O$
$HCOH$
R

WHEN R = CH_3

NOTE:

IF R IS ⬡

THEN:

CH_3
$C=O$
$HCOH$
⬡

NOT:

CH_3
$HCOH$
$C=O$
⬡

MAP 66. SECTOR D - HYDROGEN, FORMIC ACID, AND ACETYL PHOSPHATE

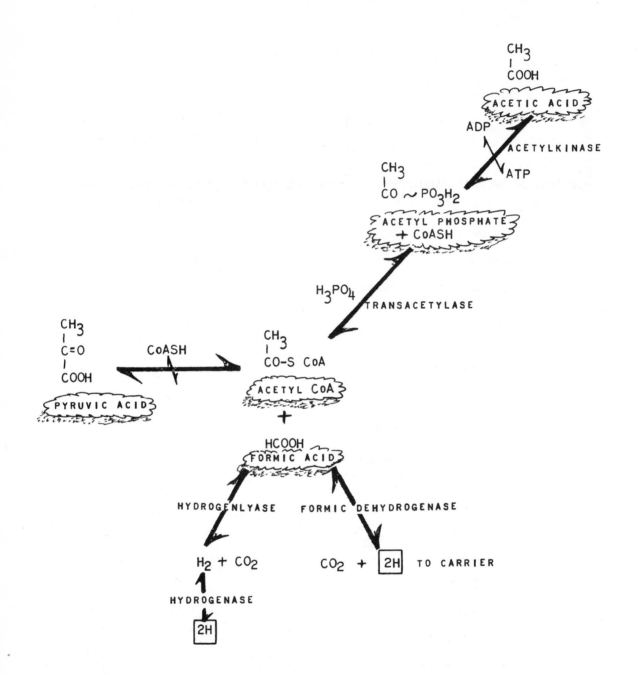

MAP 67. SECTOR E - ACETONE, BUTANOL, AND ISOPROPYL FORMATION

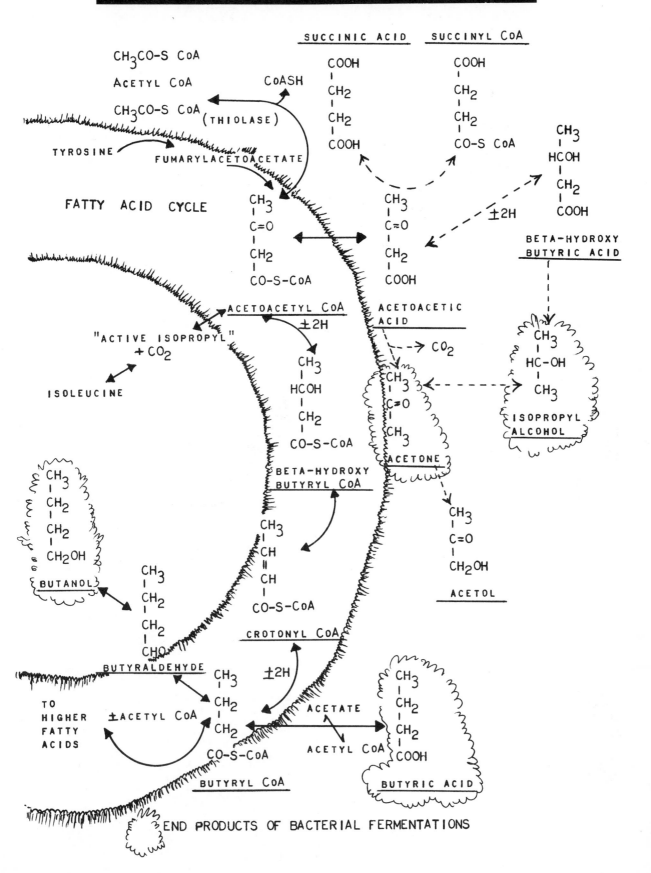

END PRODUCTS OF BACTERIAL FERMENTATIONS

MAP 68.   MALONIC ACID METABOLISM

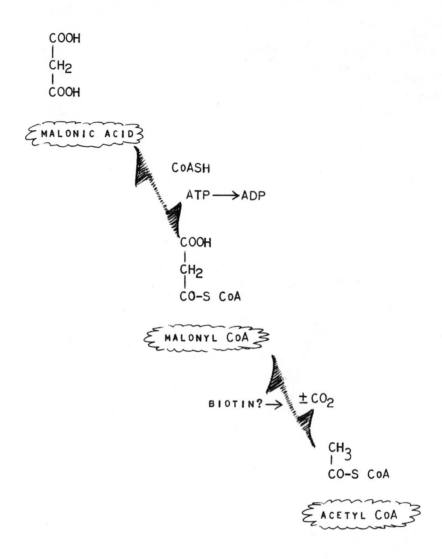

MAP 69.   PROPIONIC ACID METABOLISM

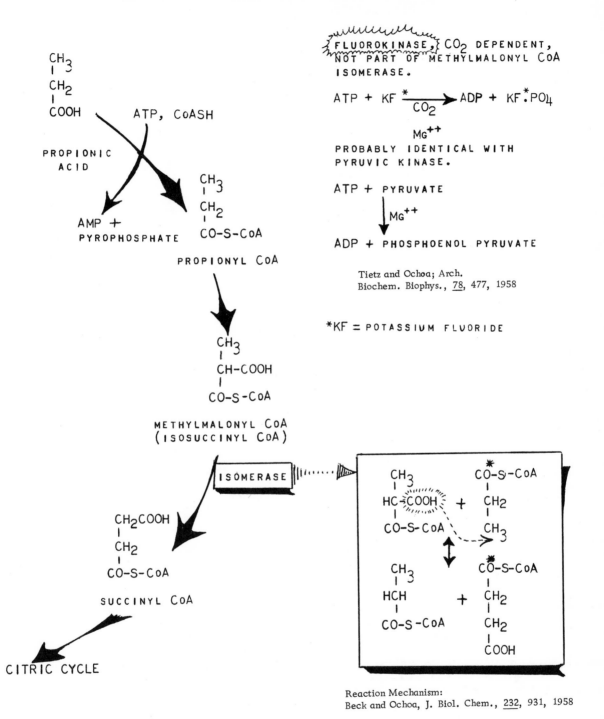

Tietz and Ochoa; Arch.
Biochem. Biophys., $\underline{78}$, 477, 1958

*KF = POTASSIUM FLUORIDE

Reaction Mechanism:
Beck and Ochoa, J. Biol. Chem., $\underline{232}$, 931, 1958

MAP 70. OTHER ROUTES TO ALPHA-KETOGLUTARIC ACID

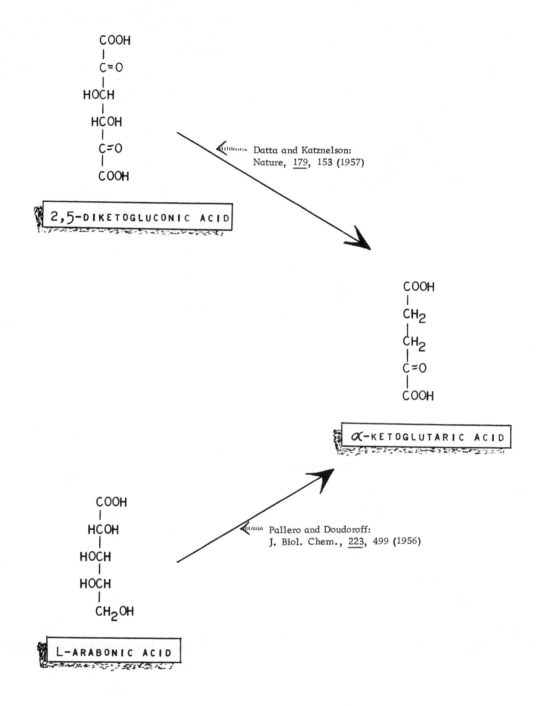

COOH
|
C=O
|
HOCH
|
HCOH
|
C=O
|
COOH

2,5-DIKETOGLUCONIC ACID

Datta and Katznelson:
Nature, 179, 153 (1957)

COOH
|
CH₂
|
CH₂
|
C=O
|
COOH

α-KETOGLUTARIC ACID

COOH
|
HCOH
|
HOCH
|
HOCH
|
CH₂OH

L-ARABONIC ACID

Pallero and Doudoroff:
J. Biol. Chem., 223, 499 (1956)

MAP 71. ACETYL CoA TO SUCCINIC ACID

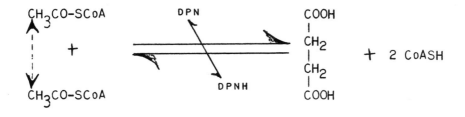

EVIDENCE:

Davis; Nature, 181, 339 (1958)
Seaman, Naschke; J. Biol. Chem., 217, 1 (1955)

NOTES

MAP 72. GLYOXALIC ACID AND GLYCOLIC ACID METABOLISM

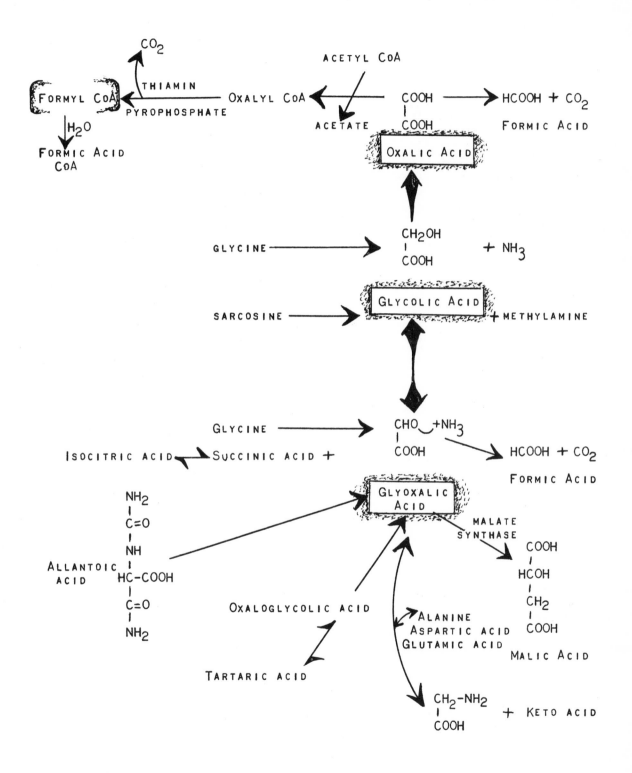

NOTES

MAP 73. TARTARIC ACID METABOLISM

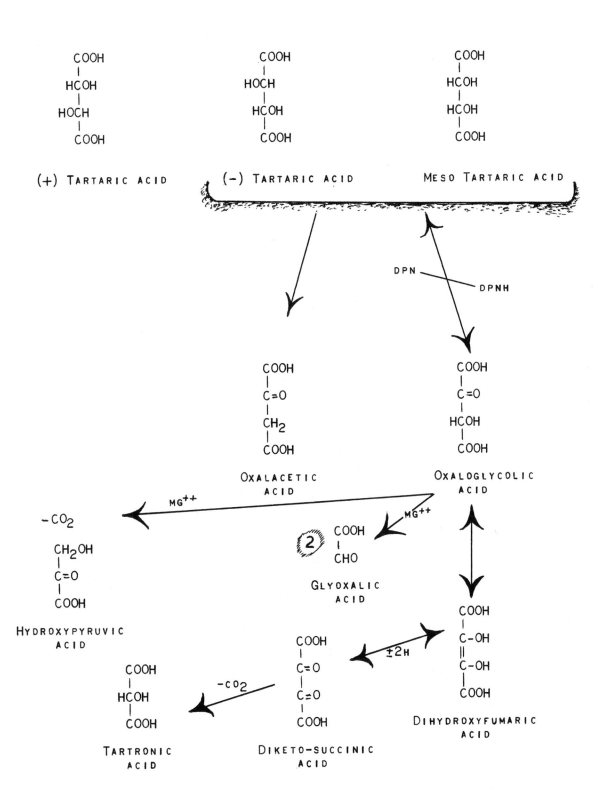

MAP 74. SYNTHESIS OF PANTOTHENIC ACID

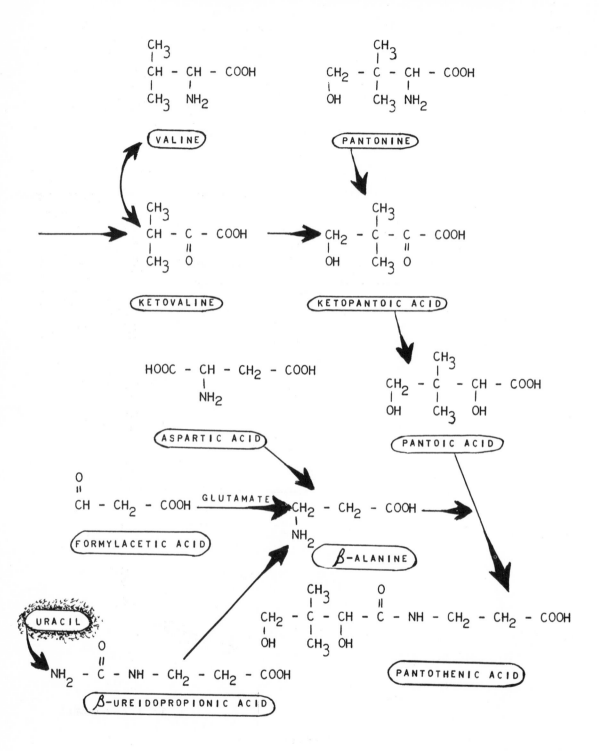

After Maas, Vol. XI, 4th Intern. Cong. Biochem., Vienna, 1958

MAP 75. METABOLISM OF COENZYME A

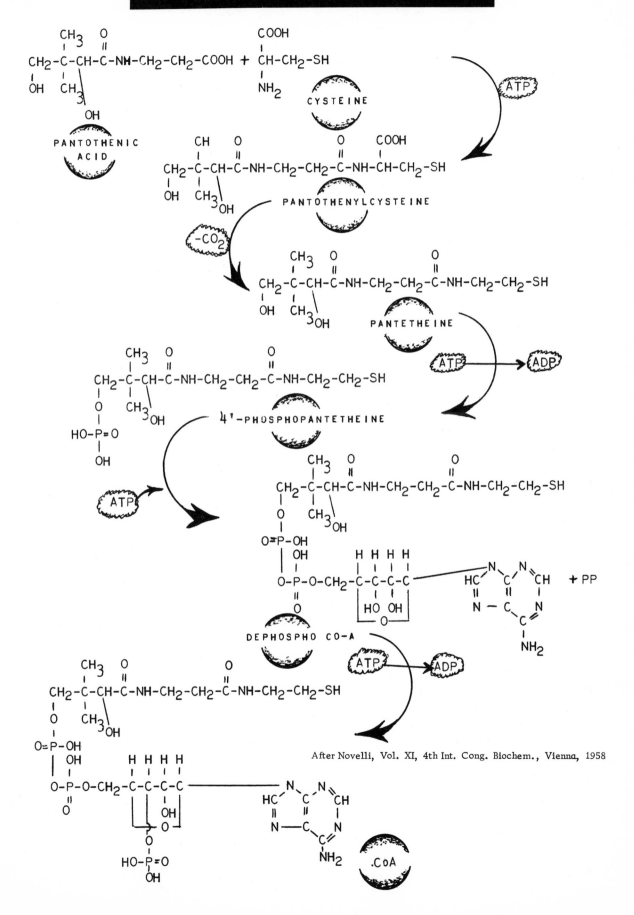

After Novelli, Vol. XI, 4th Int. Cong. Biochem., Vienna, 1958

104

NOTES

Chapter 7
THE INTRODUCTION OF NITROGEN

TABLE OF CONTENTS

Map No.	Title	Page No.
76	Inorganic Nitrogen Metabolism	107
77	Nitrogen Fixation	108
78	Nitrification	109
79	Nitrate Reduction to Nitrite	110
80	Postulated Path of Nitrate Assimilation	111
81	Denitrification	112
82	Conversion of Ammonia to Amino Groups	113
83	Aspartic Acid Metabolism	114
84	Glutamic Acid Metabolism	115
85	General Reactions of Amino Acids	116
86	The Vitamin B_6 Group	117
87	Amino Acid Activation; Protein Synthesis	119

MAP 76. INORGANIC NITROGEN METABOLISM

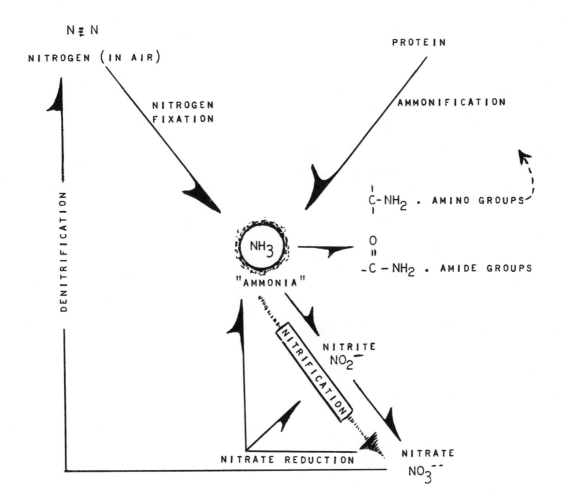

MAP 77.   NITROGEN FIXATION

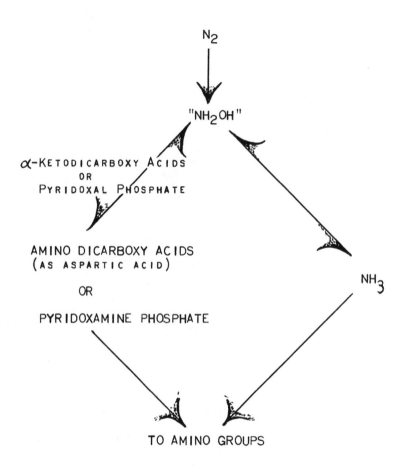

MAP 78. NITRIFICATION

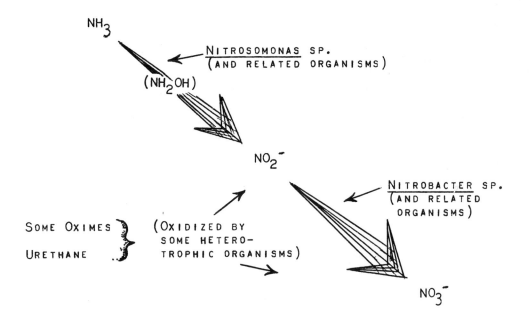

MAP 79.   NITRATE REDUCTION TO NITRITE

"NITRATE REDUCTASE"

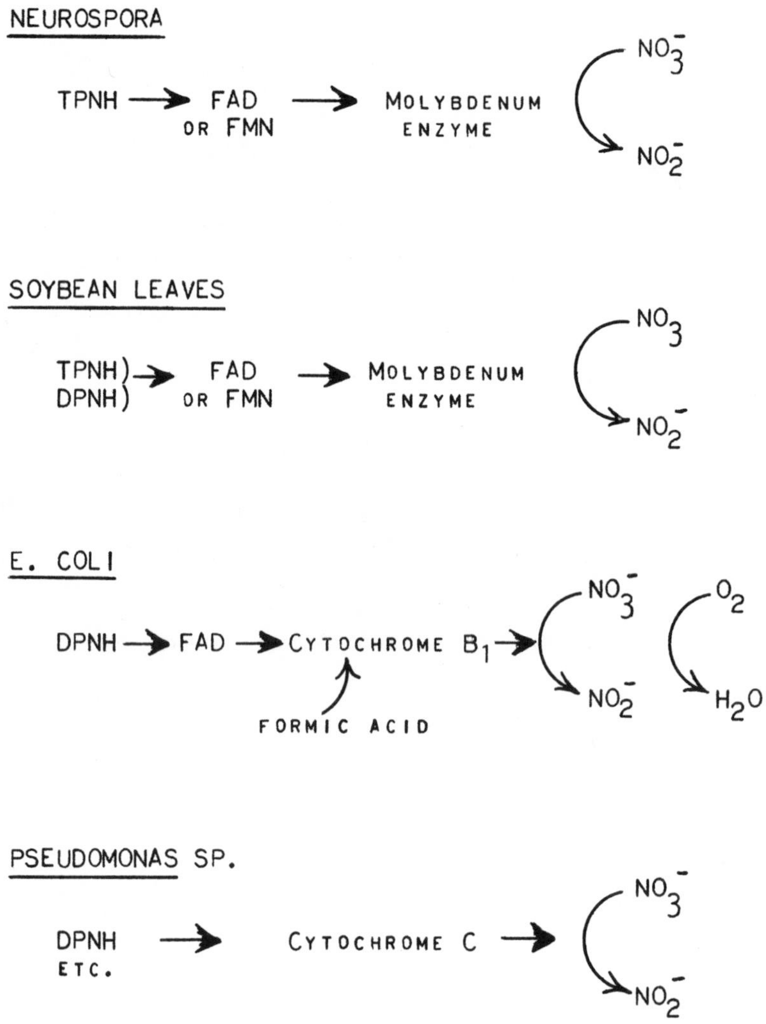

<u>NEUROSPORA</u>

$$TPNH \longrightarrow \begin{array}{c} FAD \\ OR\ FMN \end{array} \longrightarrow \begin{array}{c} MOLYBDENUM \\ ENZYME \end{array} \quad \begin{array}{c} NO_3^- \\ \\ NO_2^- \end{array}$$

<u>SOYBEAN LEAVES</u>

$$\left.\begin{array}{c} TPNH) \\ DPNH) \end{array}\right\rightarrow \begin{array}{c} FAD \\ OR\ FMN \end{array} \longrightarrow \begin{array}{c} MOLYBDENUM \\ ENZYME \end{array} \quad \begin{array}{c} NO_3 \\ \\ NO_2^- \end{array}$$

<u>E. COLI</u>

$$DPNH \longrightarrow FAD \longrightarrow CYTOCHROME\ B_1 \longrightarrow \begin{array}{c} NO_3^- \\ \\ NO_2^- \end{array} \quad \begin{array}{c} O_2 \\ \\ H_2O \end{array}$$

FORMIC ACID

<u>PSEUDOMONAS SP.</u>

$$\begin{array}{c} DPNH \\ ETC. \end{array} \longrightarrow CYTOCHROME\ C \longrightarrow \begin{array}{c} NO_3^- \\ \\ NO_2^- \end{array}$$

MAP 80. POSTULATED PATH OF NITRATE ASSIMILATION

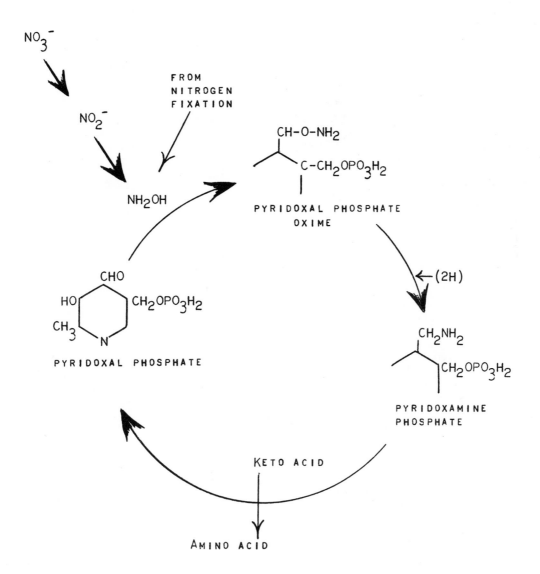

MAP 81. DENITRIFICATION

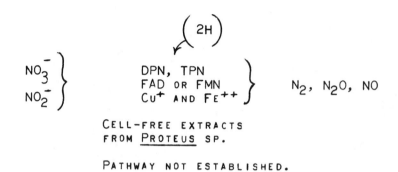

$$NO_3^- \quad \Bigg\}$$
$$NO_2^- \quad \Bigg\}$$

(2H)

DPN, TPN
FAD OR FMN
Cu^+ AND Fe^{++} $\Bigg\}$ $\quad N_2, \ N_2O, \ NO$

CELL-FREE EXTRACTS
FROM <u>PROTEUS</u> SP.

PATHWAY NOT ESTABLISHED.

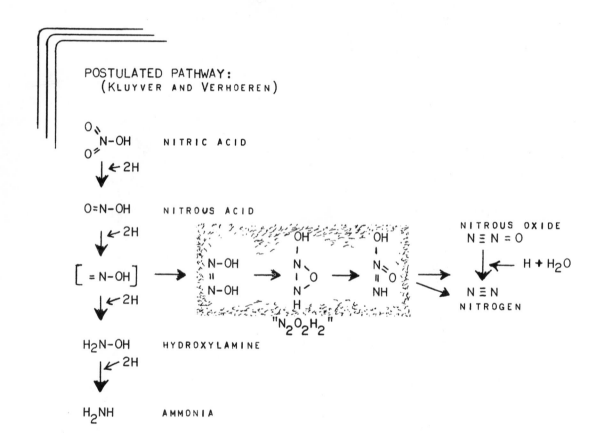

POSTULATED PATHWAY:
   (KLUYVER AND VERHOEREN)

$$O{=}N{-}OH$$
$O{=}$ NITRIC ACID

$\downarrow \leftarrow 2H$

$O{=}N{-}OH$ NITROUS ACID

$\downarrow \leftarrow 2H$

$[\ {=}N{-}OH \ ]$

$\downarrow \leftarrow 2H$

$H_2N{-}OH$ HYDROXYLAMINE

$\downarrow \leftarrow 2H$

H_2NH AMMONIA

N–OH ‖ N–OH → OH | N | O | N–H → OH | N‖O | NH

"$N_2O_2H_2$"

NITROUS OXIDE
$N{\equiv}N{=}O$

$\downarrow \leftarrow H + H_2O$

$N{\equiv}N$
NITROGEN

MAP 82. CONVERSION OF AMMONIA TO AMINO GROUPS

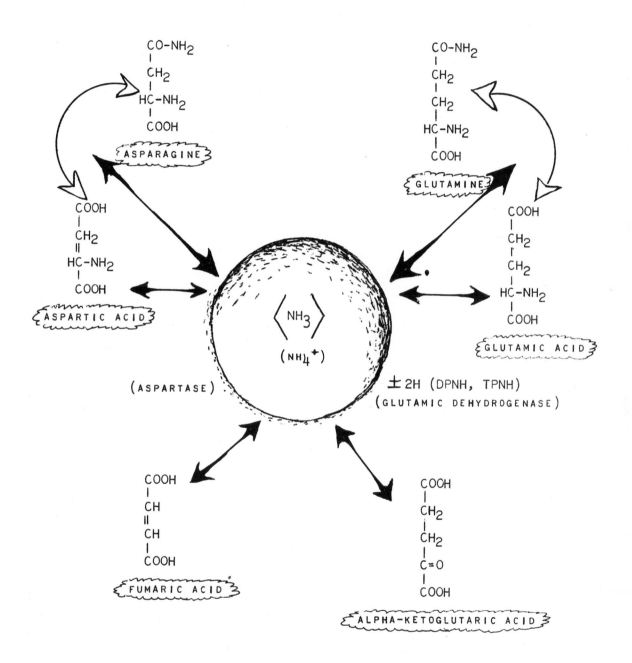

MAP 83. ASPARTIC ACID METABOLISM

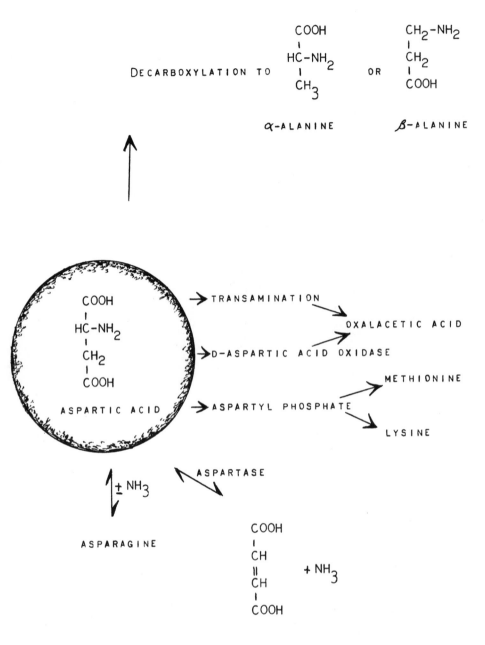

DECARBOXYLATION TO

$$\begin{array}{c} COOH \\ | \\ HC-NH_2 \\ | \\ CH_3 \end{array}$$

OR

$$\begin{array}{c} CH_2-NH_2 \\ | \\ CH_2 \\ | \\ COOH \end{array}$$

α-ALANINE

β-ALANINE

$$\begin{array}{c} COOH \\ | \\ HC-NH_2 \\ | \\ CH_2 \\ | \\ COOH \end{array}$$

ASPARTIC ACID

→ TRANSAMINATION

→ D-ASPARTIC ACID OXIDASE

OXALACETIC ACID

→ ASPARTYL PHOSPHATE

METHIONINE

LYSINE

$\pm NH_3$

ASPARTASE

ASPARAGINE

$$\begin{array}{c} COOH \\ | \\ CH \\ || \\ CH \\ | \\ COOH \end{array} + NH_3$$

FUMARIC ACID

MAP 84. GLUTAMIC ACID METABOLISM

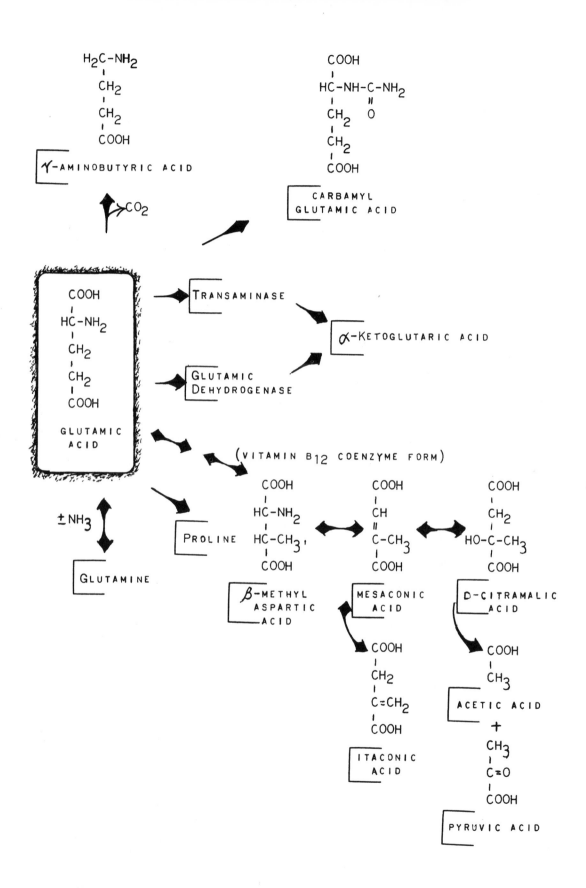

H_2C-NH_2
|
CH_2
|
CH_2
|
COOH

γ-AMINOBUTYRIC ACID

COOH
|
$HC-NH-C-NH_2$
| ‖
CH_2 O
|
CH_2
|
COOH

CARBAMYL
GLUTAMIC ACID

CO_2

COOH
|
$HC-NH_2$
|
CH_2
|
CH_2
|
COOH

GLUTAMIC
ACID

TRANSAMINASE

GLUTAMIC
DEHYDROGENASE

α-KETOGLUTARIC ACID

(VITAMIN B_{12} COENZYME FORM)

±NH_3

GLUTAMINE

PROLINE

COOH
|
$HC-NH_2$
|
$HC-CH_3$,
|
COOH

β-METHYL
ASPARTIC
ACID

COOH
|
CH
‖
$C-CH_3$
|
COOH

MESACONIC
ACID

COOH
|
CH_2
|
$HO-C-CH_3$
|
COOH

D-CITRAMALIC
ACID

COOH
|
CH_2
|
$C=CH_2$
|
COOH

ITACONIC
ACID

COOH
|
CH_3

ACETIC ACID

+

CH_3
|
C=O
|
COOH

PYRUVIC ACID

116

MAP 85. GENERAL REACTIONS OF AMINO ACIDS

DECARBOXYLATION ➡ R-CH + CO_2
　　　　　　　　　　|H (top)
　　　　　　　　　　|
　　　　　　　　　　NH_2

DECARBOXYLASES:

ARGININE
ASPARTIC ACID
CYSTEIC ACID
DIHYDROXYPHENYLALANINE
GLUTAMIC ACID
HISTIDINE
DIAMINOPIMELIC ACID

HYDROXYPHENYLSERINE
LYSINE
ORNITHINE
TRYPTOPHAN
TYROSINE
5-HYDROXYTRYPTOPHAN

H
R-C-COOH
|
NH_2

OXIDATION ➡ R-CHO + NH_3

D OR L AMINO ACID OXIDASES

MOST AMINO ACIDS

TRANSAMINATION

(+ α-KETOGLUTARIC ACID ⇌ GLUTAMIC ACID + KETO ACID)

ALANINE
ARGININE
ASPARTIC ACID
CITRULLINE
CYSTEINE
CYSTINE
GLYCINE
HISTIDINE
ISOLEUCINE
LEUCINE

LYSINE
METHIONINE
ORNITHINE
PHENYLALANINE
PROLINE
SERINE
THREONINE
TRYPTOPHAN
TYROSINE
VALINE

MAP 86. THE VITAMIN B₆ GROUP

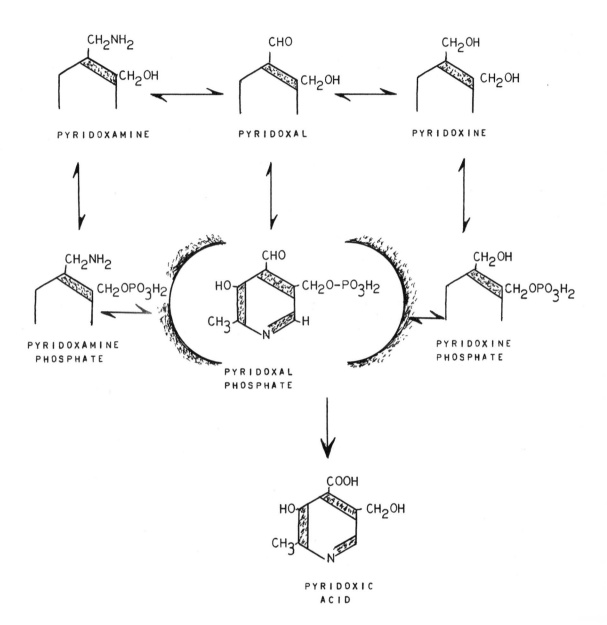

NOTES

MAP 87.   AMINO ACID ACTIVATION; PROTEIN SYNTHESIS

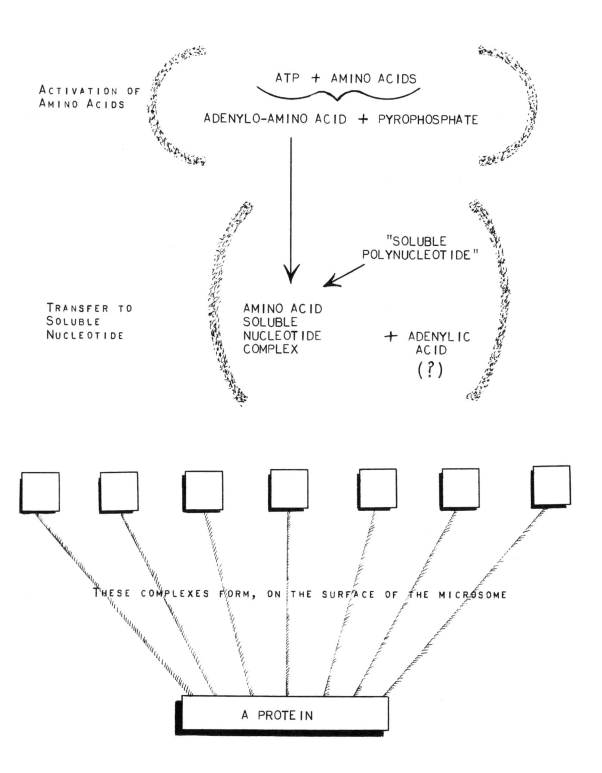

ACTIVATION OF
AMINO ACIDS

ATP + AMINO ACIDS

ADENYLO-AMINO ACID + PYROPHOSPHATE

"SOLUBLE
POLYNUCLEOTIDE"

TRANSFER TO
SOLUBLE
NUCLEOTIDE

AMINO ACID
SOLUBLE
NUCLEOTIDE
COMPLEX

+ ADENYLIC
ACID
(?)

THESE COMPLEXES FORM, ON THE SURFACE OF THE MICROSOME

A PROTEIN

NOTES

Chapter 8
SHORT-CHAIN AMINO ACIDS

TABLE OF CONTENTS

Map No.	Title	Page No.
88	Metabolism of Glycine and Serine	123
89	Synthesis of Leucine	124
90	Breakdown of Leucine	125
91	Synthesis of Isoleucine	126
92	Breakdown of Isoleucine	127
93	Synthesis of Valine	128
94	Breakdown of Valine	129
95	Example of Feedback Mechanism	130
96	Synthesis and Breakdown of Threonine	131

MAP 88. METABOLISM OF GLYCINE AND SERINE

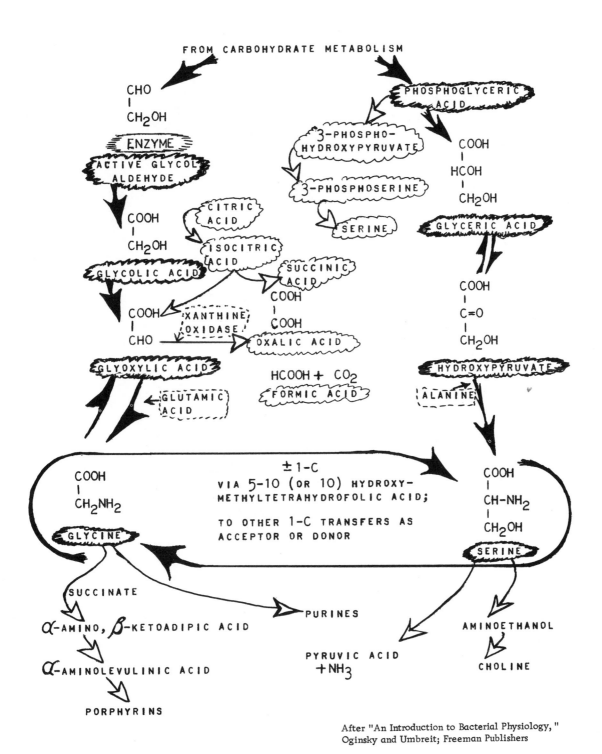

After "An Introduction to Bacterial Physiology,"
Oginsky and Umbreit; Freeman Publishers

MAP 89.   SYNTHESIS OF LEUCINE

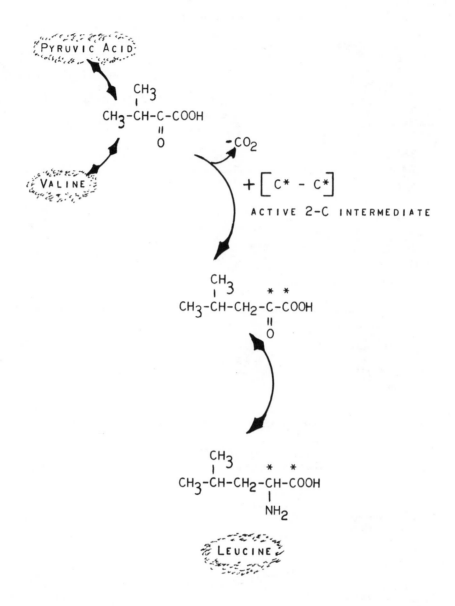

MAP 90. BREAKDOWN OF LEUCINE

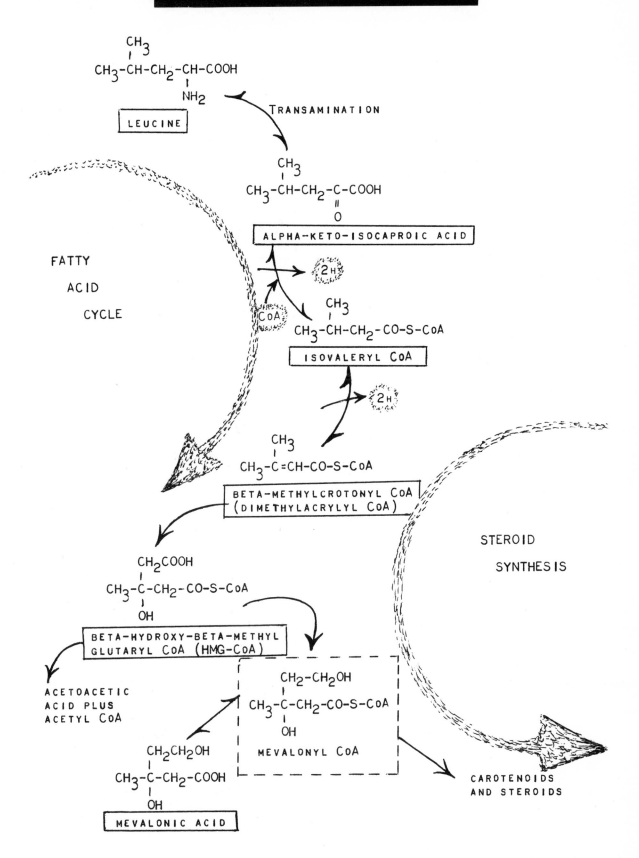

CH_3

$CH_3-CH-CH_2-CH-COOH$

NH_2

LEUCINE

TRANSAMINATION

CH_3

$CH_3-CH-CH_2-C-COOH$

O

ALPHA-KETO-ISOCAPROIC ACID

2H

FATTY

ACID

CYCLE

CoA

CH_3

$CH_3-CH-CH_2-CO-S-CoA$

ISOVALERYL CoA

2H

CH_3

$CH_3-C=CH-CO-S-CoA$

BETA-METHYLCROTONYL CoA
(DIMETHYLACRYLYL CoA)

STEROID

SYNTHESIS

CH_2COOH

$CH_3-C-CH_2-CO-S-CoA$

OH

BETA-HYDROXY-BETA-METHYL
GLUTARYL CoA (HMG-CoA)

ACETOACETIC
ACID PLUS
ACETYL CoA

CH_2-CH_2OH

$CH_3-C-CH_2-CO-S-CoA$

OH

MEVALONYL CoA

CH_2CH_2OH

CH_3-C-CH_2-COOH

OH

MEVALONIC ACID

CAROTENOIDS
AND STEROIDS

MAP 91. SYNTHESIS OF ISOLEUCINE

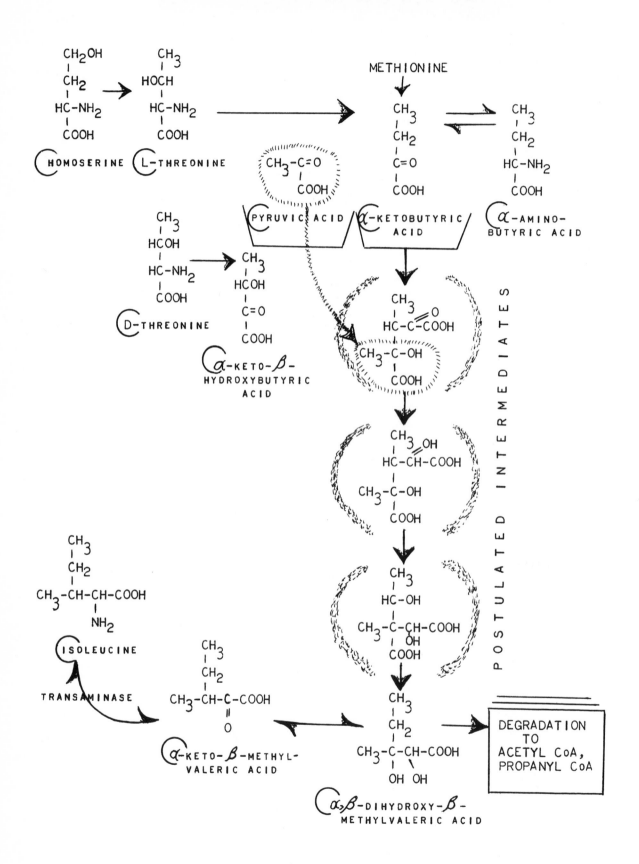

MAP 92. BREAKDOWN OF ISOLEUCINE

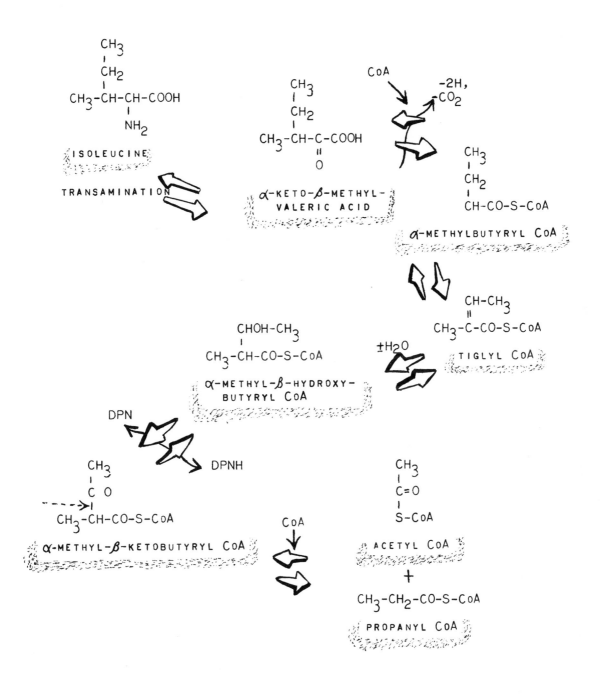

MAP 93. SYNTHESIS OF VALINE

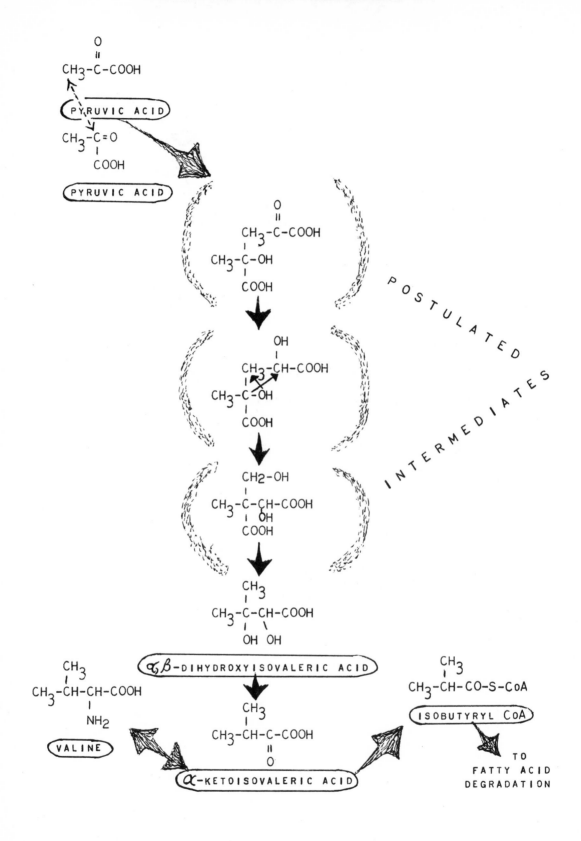

MAP 94. BREAKDOWN OF VALINE

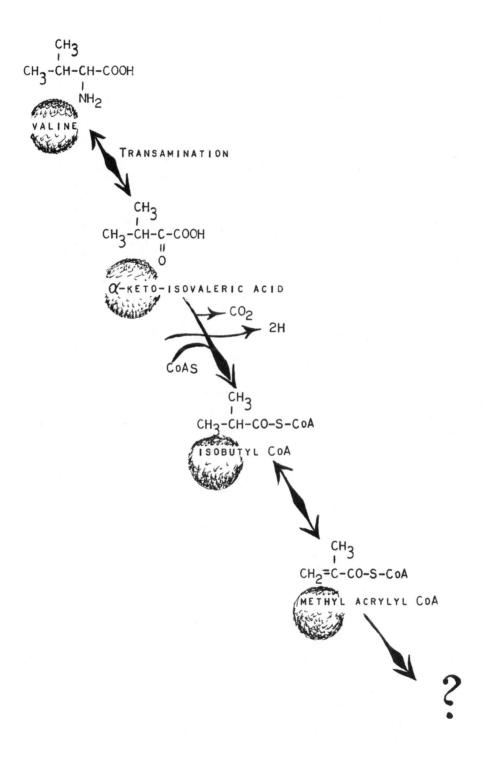

$$CH_3-CH-CH-COOH$$
with CH_3 above and NH_2 below

VALINE

TRANSAMINATION

$$CH_3-CH-C-COOH$$
with CH_3 above and O below

α-KETO-ISOVALERIC ACID

CO_2

$2H$

CoAS

$$CH_3-CH-CO-S-CoA$$
with CH_3 above

ISOBUTYL CoA

$$CH_2=C-CO-S-CoA$$
with CH_3 above

METHYL ACRYLYL CoA

?

130

MAP 95. EXAMPLE OF FEEDBACK MECHANISM

After Wormser and Pardee, Archives Biochem. Biophys. 78, 416, 1958

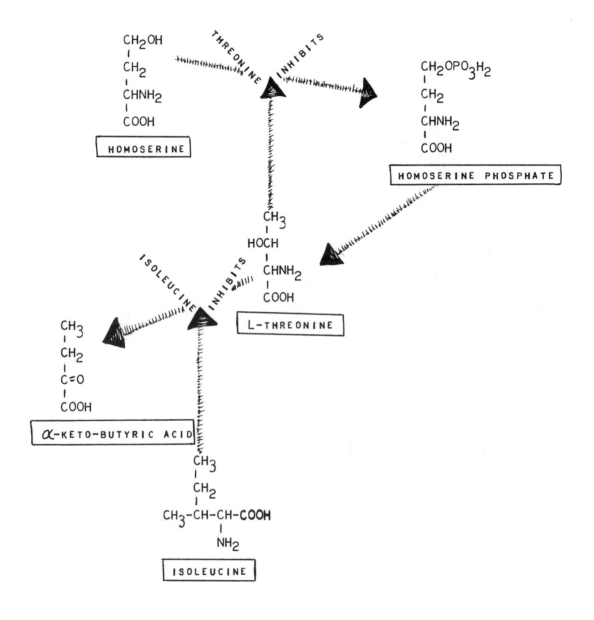

MAP 96. SYNTHESIS AND BREAKDOWN OF THREONINE

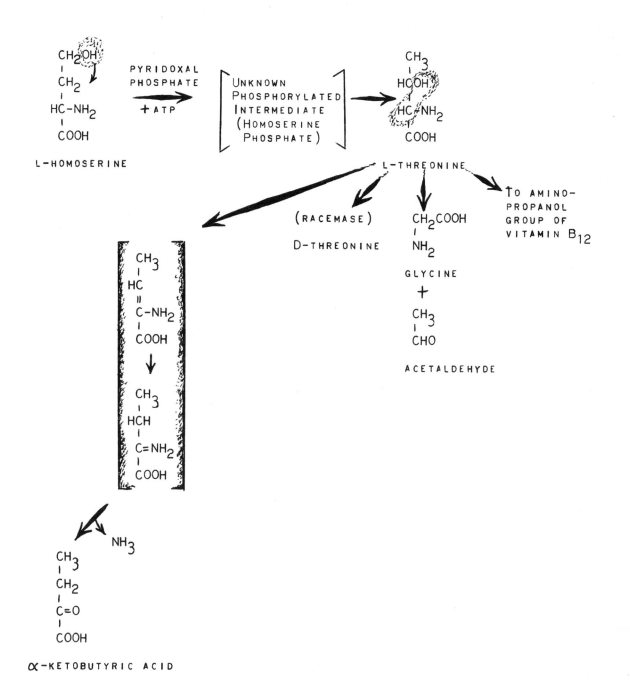

NOTES

Chapter 9
THE METABOLISM OF SULFUR

TABLE OF CONTENTS

Map No.	Title	Page No.
97	Sulfate Activation	134
98	Metabolism of Sulfur Amino Acids	135
99	Relations Between Cysteine and Homocysteine	136
100	Synthesis of Homoserine	137
101	Relations to the Choline Cycle	139

MAP 97. SULFATE ACTIVATION

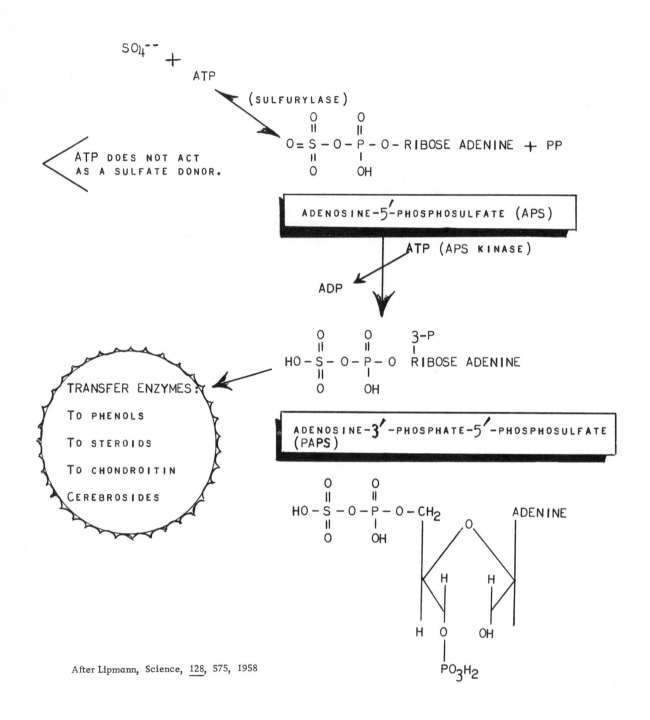

After Lipmann, Science, 128, 575, 1958

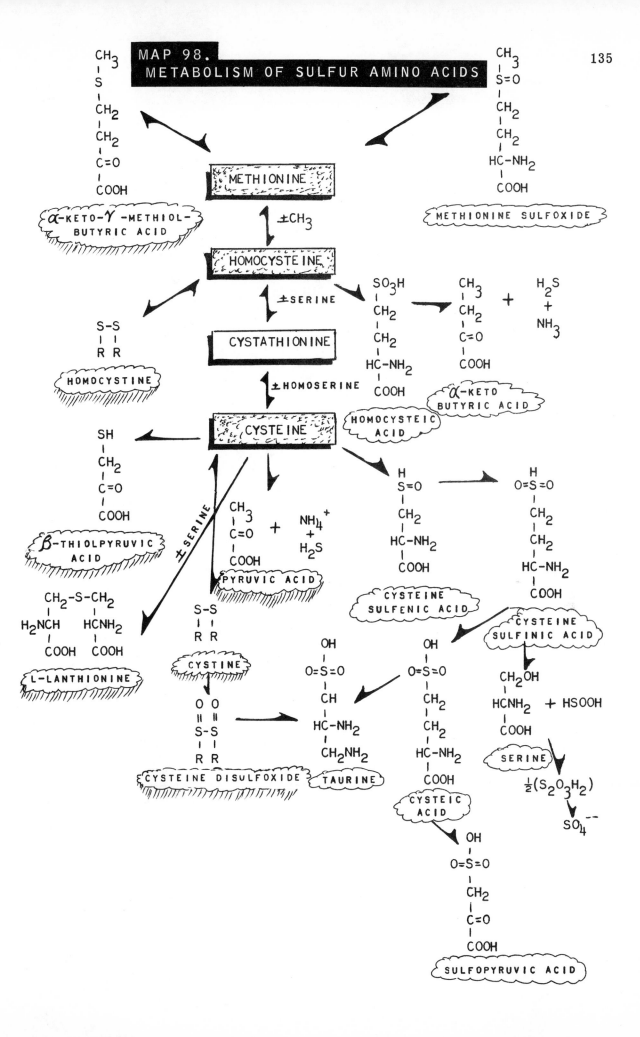

MAP 98.
METABOLISM OF SULFUR AMINO ACIDS

MAP 99. RELATIONS BETWEEN CYSTEINE AND HOMOCYSTEINE

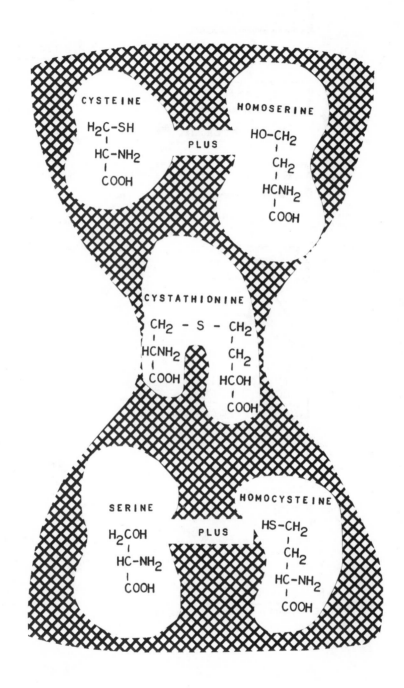

MAP 100. SYNTHESIS OF HOMOSERINE

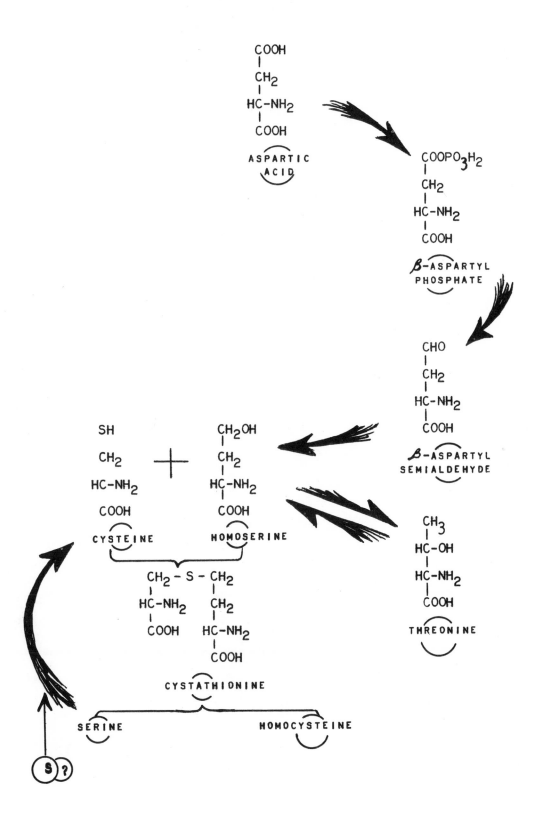

138

NOTES

MAP 101. RELATIONS TO THE CHOLINE CYCLE

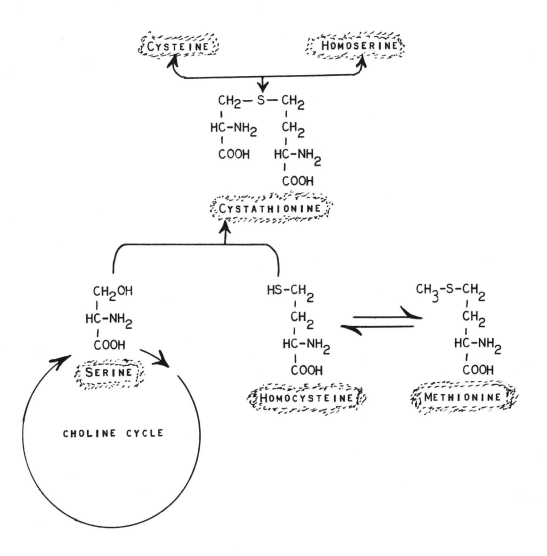

NOTES

Chapter 10
PROLINE AND ARGININE

TABLE OF CONTENTS

Map No.	Title	Page No.
102	The Citric Acid and Urea Cycles	142
103	The Proline, Urea, and Citric Acid Cycles	143
104	Metabolism of Hydroxyproline	144
105	The Proline Cycle	145
106	The Proline and Urea Cycles	147
107	Synthesis of Ornithine	148
108	Synthesis of Citrulline	149
109	Synthesis of Arginine	150
110	Metabolism of Arginine	151
111	Metabolism of Canavanine	153

MAP 102.   THE CITRIC ACID AND UREA CYCLES

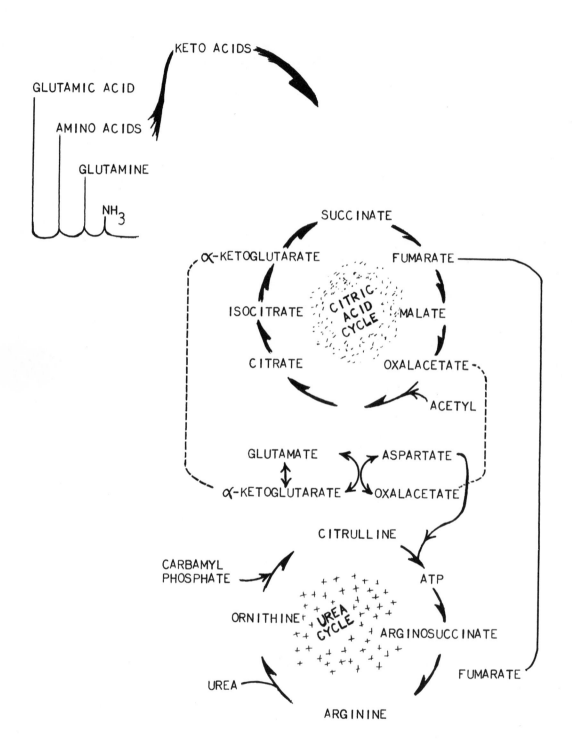

After Ratner, J. H., Amino Acid Symp. 249; Adv. Enzym., 15, 319, 1954

MAP 103. THE PROLINE, UREA, AND CITRIC ACID CYCLES

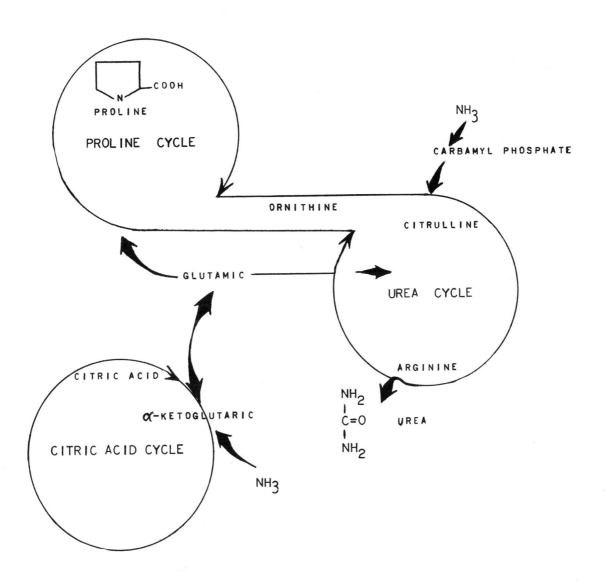

MAP 104.   METABOLISM OF HYDROXYPROLINE

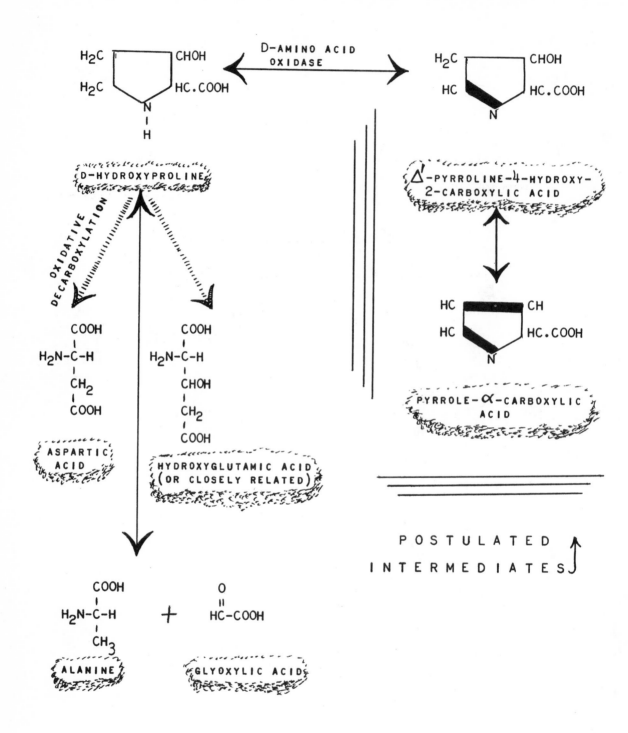

MAP 105. THE PROLINE CYCLE

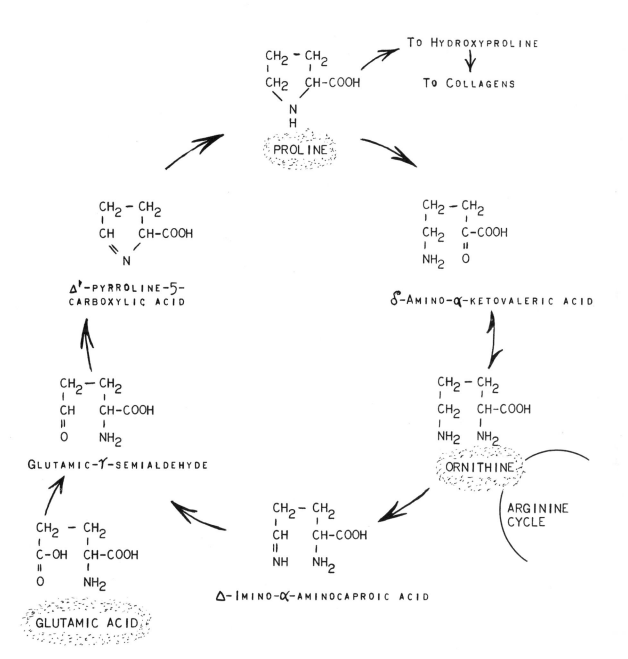

TO HYDROXYPROLINE

TO COLLAGENS

PROLINE

Δ'-PYRROLINE-5-CARBOXYLIC ACID

δ-AMINO-α-KETOVALERIC ACID

GLUTAMIC-γ-SEMIALDEHYDE

ORNITHINE

ARGININE CYCLE

Δ-IMINO-α-AMINOCAPROIC ACID

GLUTAMIC ACID

NOTES

MAP 106.   THE PROLINE AND UREA CYCLES

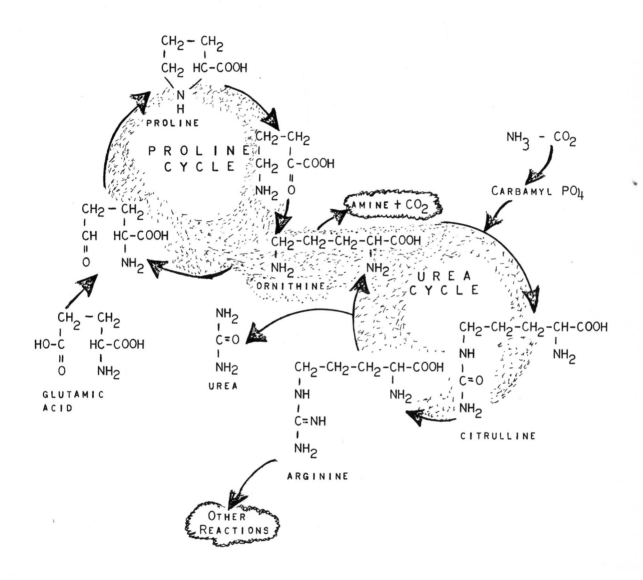

148

MAP 107.   SYNTHESIS OF ORNITHINE

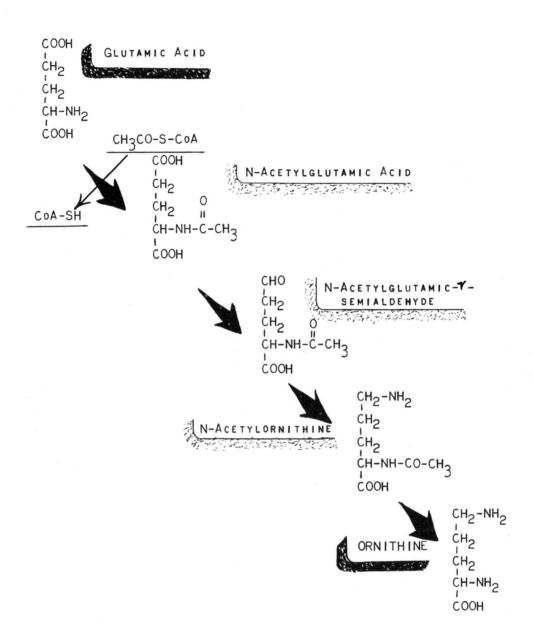

MAP 108. SYNTHESIS OF CITRULLINE

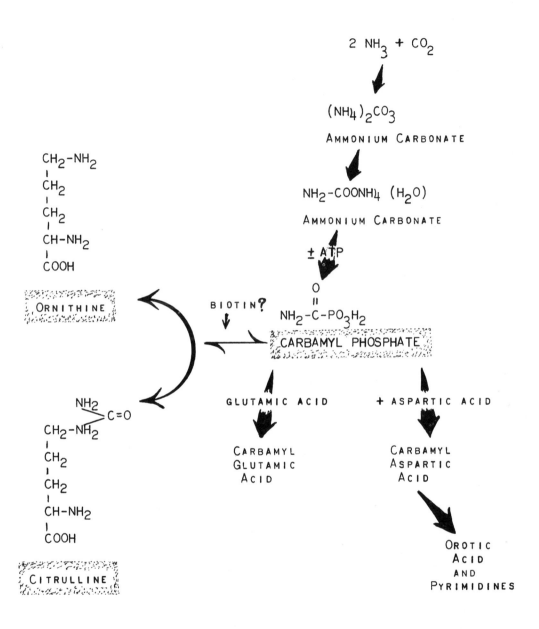

$2 \, NH_3 + CO_2$

$(NH_4)_2CO_3$

AMMONIUM CARBONATE

$NH_2-COONH_4 \, (H_2O)$

AMMONIUM CARBONATE

$\pm$ ATP

$$NH_2-\overset{\overset{\textstyle O}{\textstyle \|}}{C}-PO_3H_2$$

CARBAMYL PHOSPHATE

BIOTIN?

ORNITHINE

CH₂-NH₂
|
CH₂
|
CH₂
|
CH-NH₂
|
COOH

NH₂   C=O
CH₂-NH₂
|
CH₂
|
CH₂
|
CH-NH₂
|
COOH

CITRULLINE

GLUTAMIC ACID

CARBAMYL GLUTAMIC ACID

+ ASPARTIC ACID

CARBAMYL ASPARTIC ACID

OROTIC ACID AND PYRIMIDINES

MAP 109. SYNTHESIS OF ARGININE

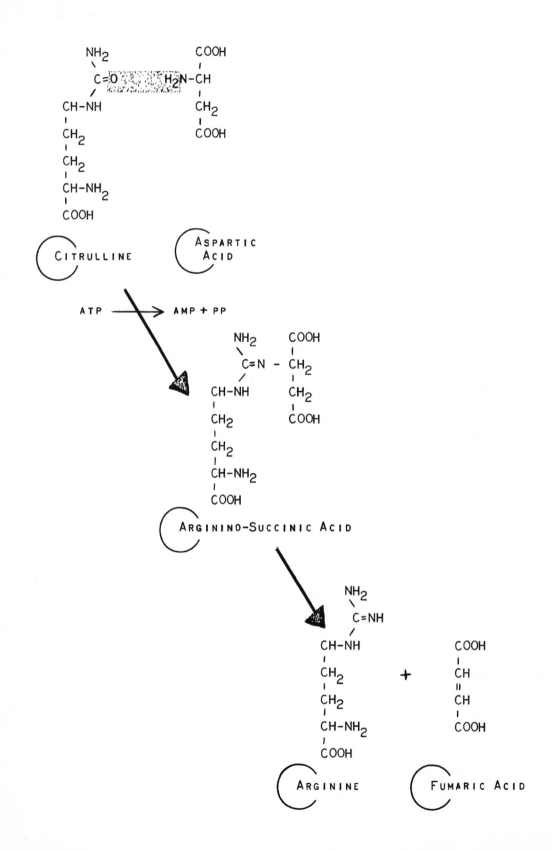

MAP 110. METABOLISM OF ARGININE

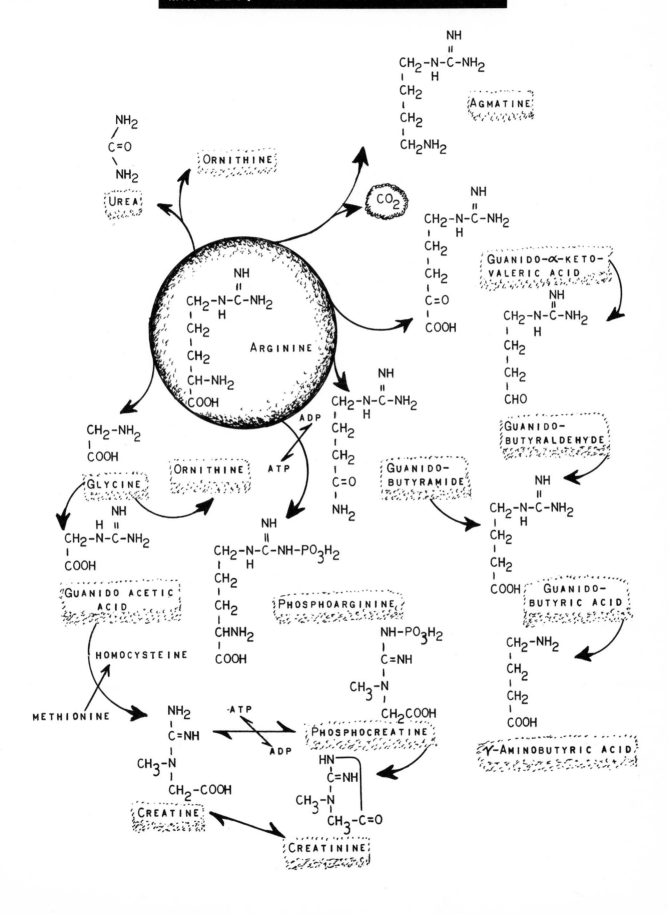

152

NOTES

MAP 111. METABOLISM OF CANAVANINE

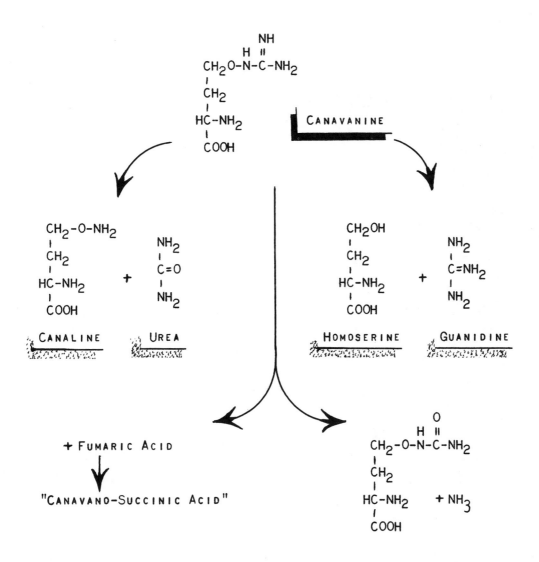

154

NOTES

Chapter II
LYSINE AND HISTIDINE

TABLE OF CONTENTS

Map No.	Title	Page No.
112	Metabolism of Lysine	157
113	Synthesis of Histidine	158
114	Main Paths of Histidine Breakdown	159
115	Minor Urocanic Acid Path	160
116	Major Urocanic Acid Path	161
117	Transamination Path	162
118	Histamine Path.	163

MAP 112. METABOLISM OF LYSINE

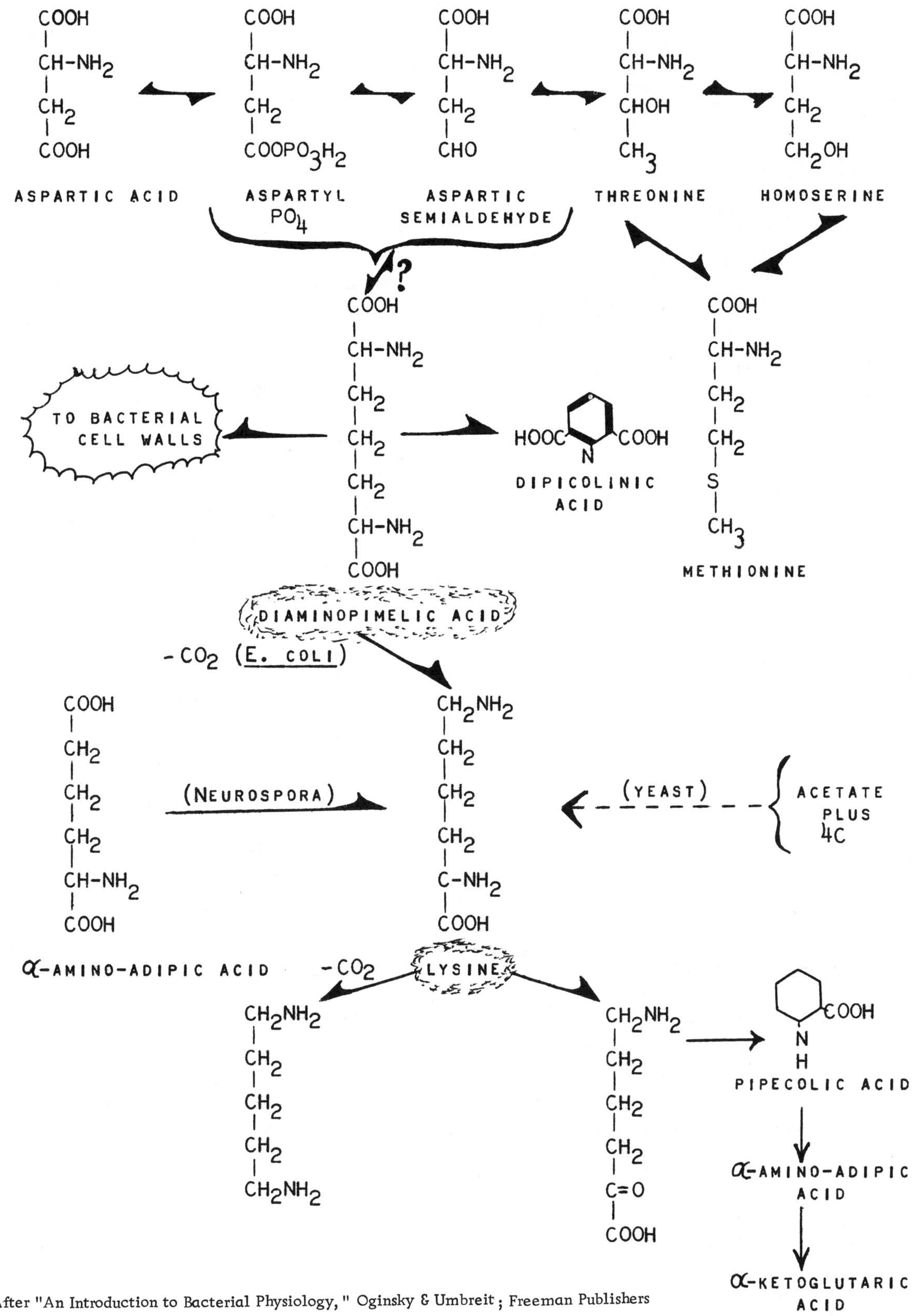

$$COOH - CH-NH_2 - CH_2 - COOH$$
ASPARTIC ACID

$$COOH - CH-NH_2 - CH_2 - COOPO_3H_2$$
ASPARTYL PO$_4$

$$COOH - CH-NH_2 - CH_2 - CHO$$
ASPARTIC SEMIALDEHYDE

$$COOH - CH-NH_2 - CHOH - CH_3$$
THREONINE

$$COOH - CH-NH_2 - CH_2 - CH_2OH$$
HOMOSERINE

?

$$COOH - CH-NH_2 - CH_2 - CH_2 - CH_2 - CH_2 - CH-NH_2 - COOH$$

TO BACTERIAL CELL WALLS

$$HOOC - N - COOH$$
DIPICOLINIC ACID

$$COOH - CH-NH_2 - CH_2 - CH_2 - S - CH_3$$
METHIONINE

DIAMINOPIMELIC ACID

$-CO_2$ (_E. COLI_)

$$CH_2NH_2 - CH_2 - CH_2 - CH_2 - C-NH_2 - COOH$$

$$COOH - CH_2 - CH_2 - CH_2 - CH-NH_2 - COOH$$
α-AMINO-ADIPIC ACID

(NEUROSPORA)

(YEAST) — ACETATE PLUS 4C

LYSINE

$-CO_2$

$$CH_2NH_2 - CH_2 - CH_2 - CH_2 - CH_2NH_2$$

$$CH_2NH_2 - CH_2 - CH_2 - CH_2 - C=O - COOH$$

$$COOH - N - H$$
PIPECOLIC ACID

α-AMINO-ADIPIC ACID

α-KETOGLUTARIC ACID

After "An Introduction to Bacterial Physiology," Oginsky & Umbreit; Freeman Publishers

MAP 113. SYNTHESIS OF HISTIDINE

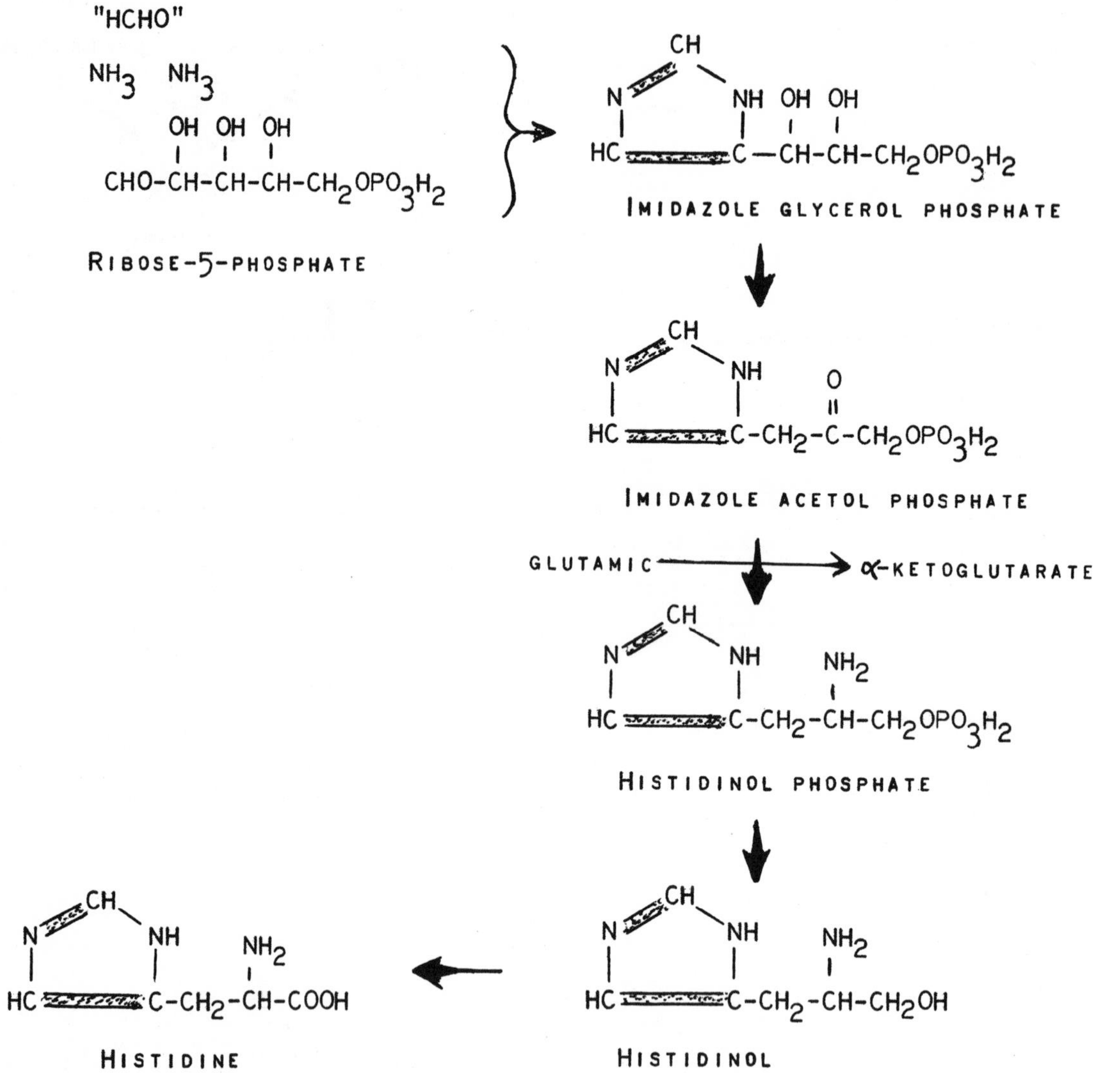

"HCHO"

NH_3 NH_3

$$CHO-CH-CH-CH-CH_2OPO_3H_2$$
(OH OH OH)

RIBOSE-5-PHOSPHATE

$$HC=C-CH-CH-CH_2OPO_3H_2$$

IMIDAZOLE GLYCEROL PHOSPHATE

$$HC=C-CH_2-C-CH_2OPO_3H_2$$

IMIDAZOLE ACETOL PHOSPHATE

GLUTAMIC $\longrightarrow$ α-KETOGLUTARATE

$$HC=C-CH_2-CH-CH_2OPO_3H_2$$

HISTIDINOL PHOSPHATE

$$HC=C-CH_2-CH-CH_2OH$$

HISTIDINOL

$$HC=C-CH_2-CH-COOH$$

HISTIDINE

After "An Introduction to Bacterial Physiology," Oginsky and Umbreit, page 304 ; Freeman Publishers

MAP 114. MAIN PATHS OF HISTIDINE BREAKDOWN

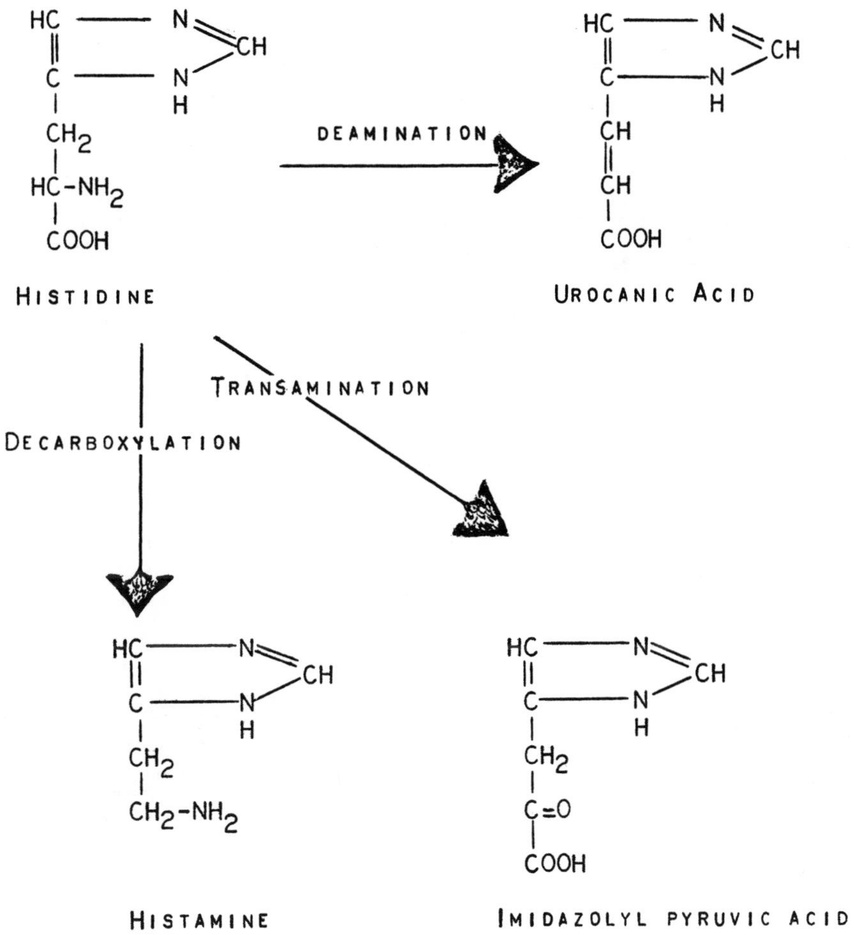

HISTIDINE

DEAMINATION

UROCANIC ACID

TRANSAMINATION

DECARBOXYLATION

HISTAMINE

IMIDAZOLYL PYRUVIC ACID

MAP 115. MINOR UROCANIC ACID PATH

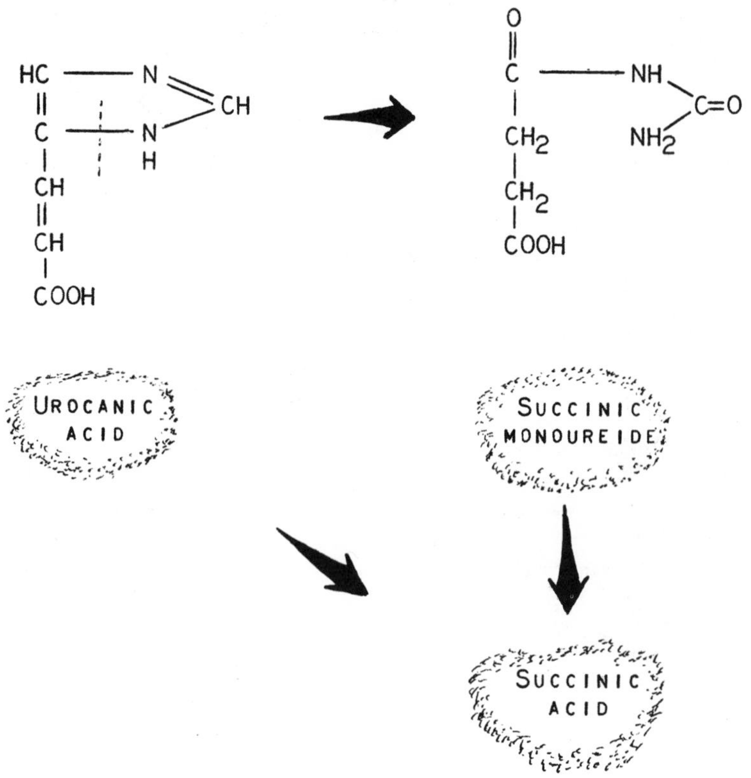

MAP 116.   MAJOR UROCANIC ACID PATH

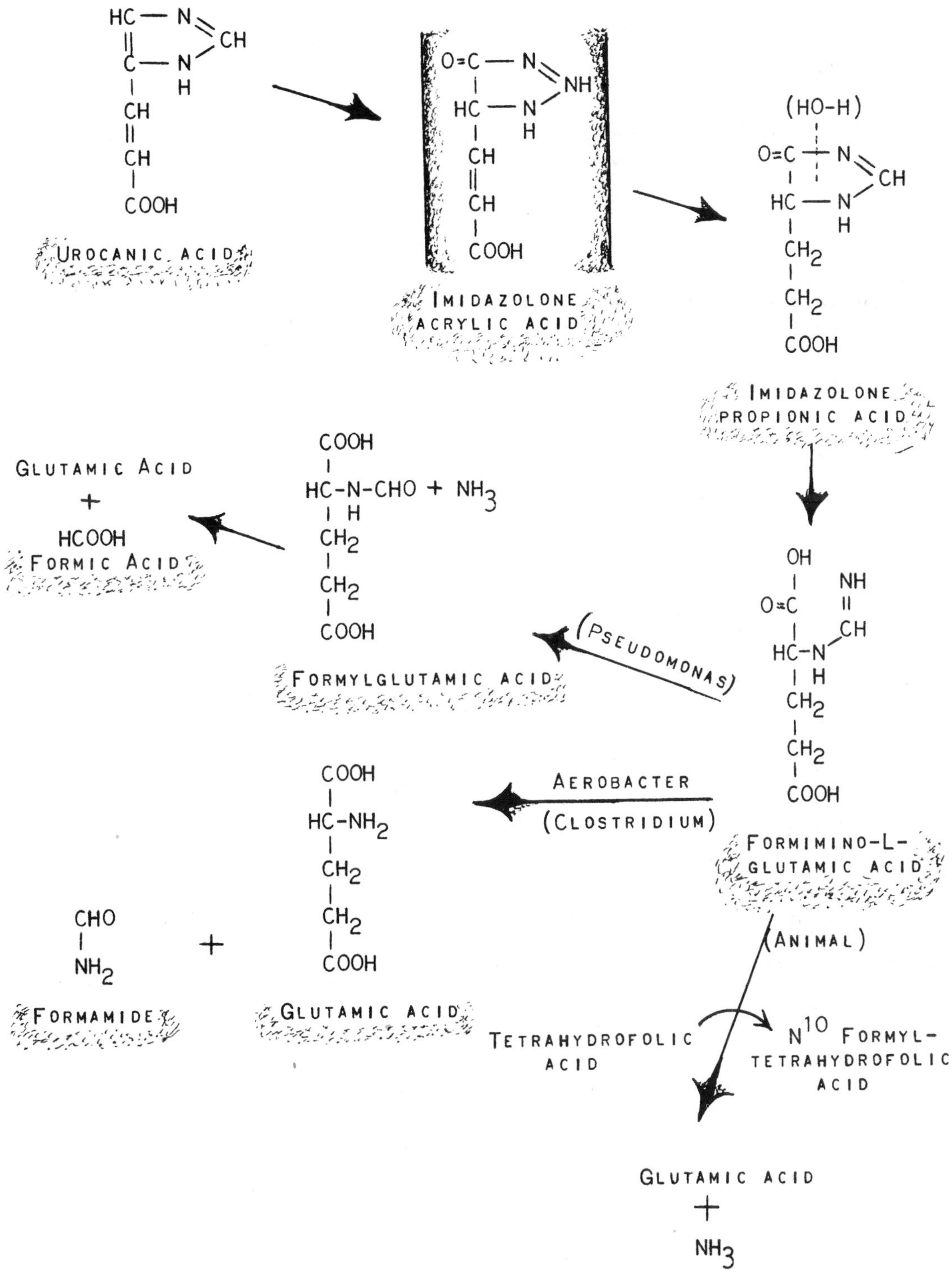

UROCANIC ACID

IMIDAZOLONE ACRYLIC ACID

IMIDAZOLONE PROPIONIC ACID

GLUTAMIC ACID
+
HCOOH
FORMIC ACID

FORMYLGLUTAMIC ACID

(PSEUDOMONAS)

AEROBACTER
(CLOSTRIDIUM)

FORMIMINO-L-GLUTAMIC ACID

FORMAMIDE   +   GLUTAMIC ACID

(ANIMAL)

TETRAHYDROFOLIC ACID

N^{10} FORMYL-TETRAHYDROFOLIC ACID

GLUTAMIC ACID
+
NH_3

MAP 117.   TRANSAMINATION PATH

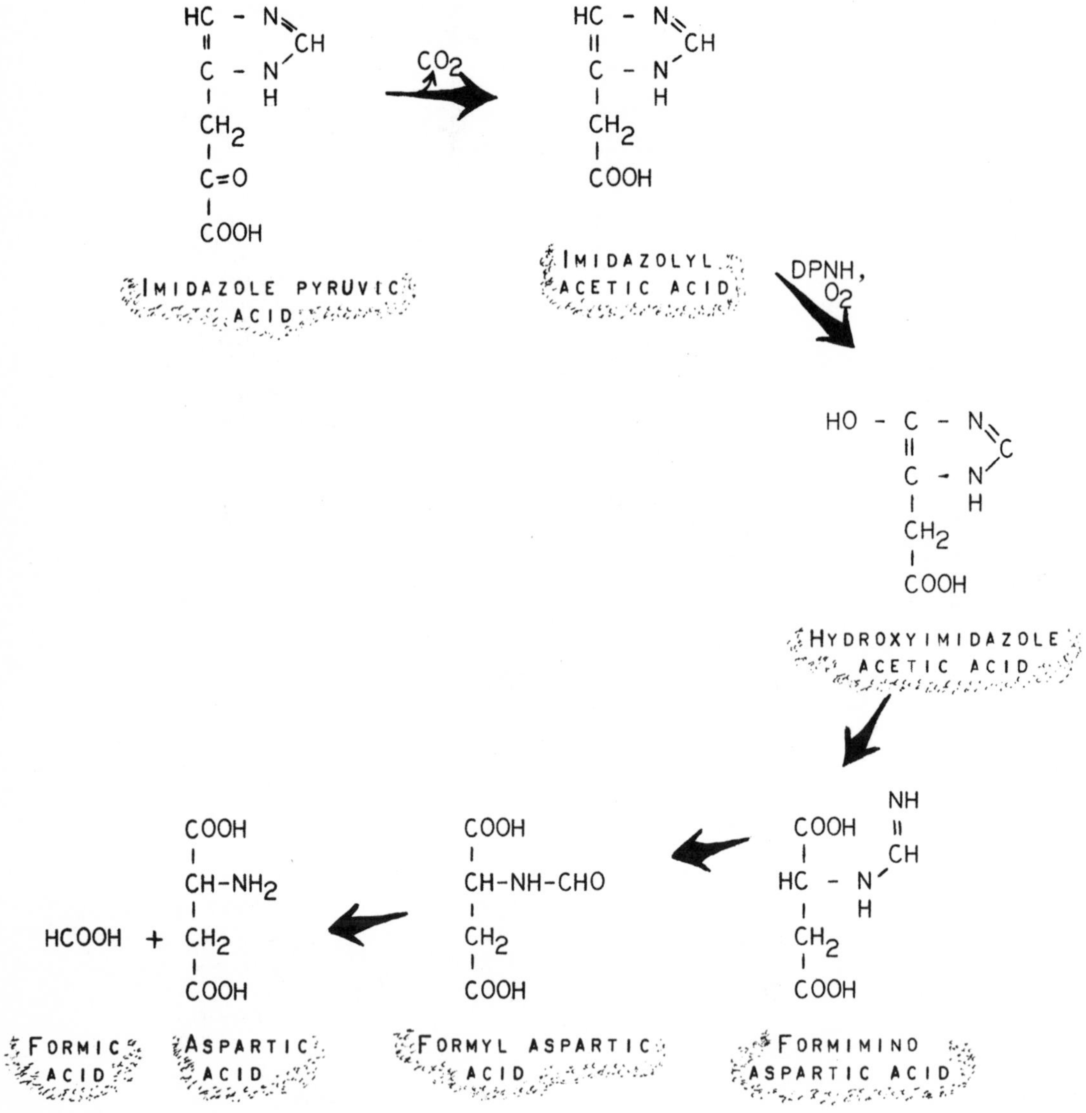

IMIDAZOLE PYRUVIC ACID

$\xrightarrow{CO_2}$

IMIDAZOLYL ACETIC ACID

$\xrightarrow{DPNH, O_2}$

HYDROXYIMIDAZOLE ACETIC ACID

FORMIMINO ASPARTIC ACID

FORMYL ASPARTIC ACID

FORMIC ACID   +   ASPARTIC ACID

MAP 118. HISTAMINE PATH

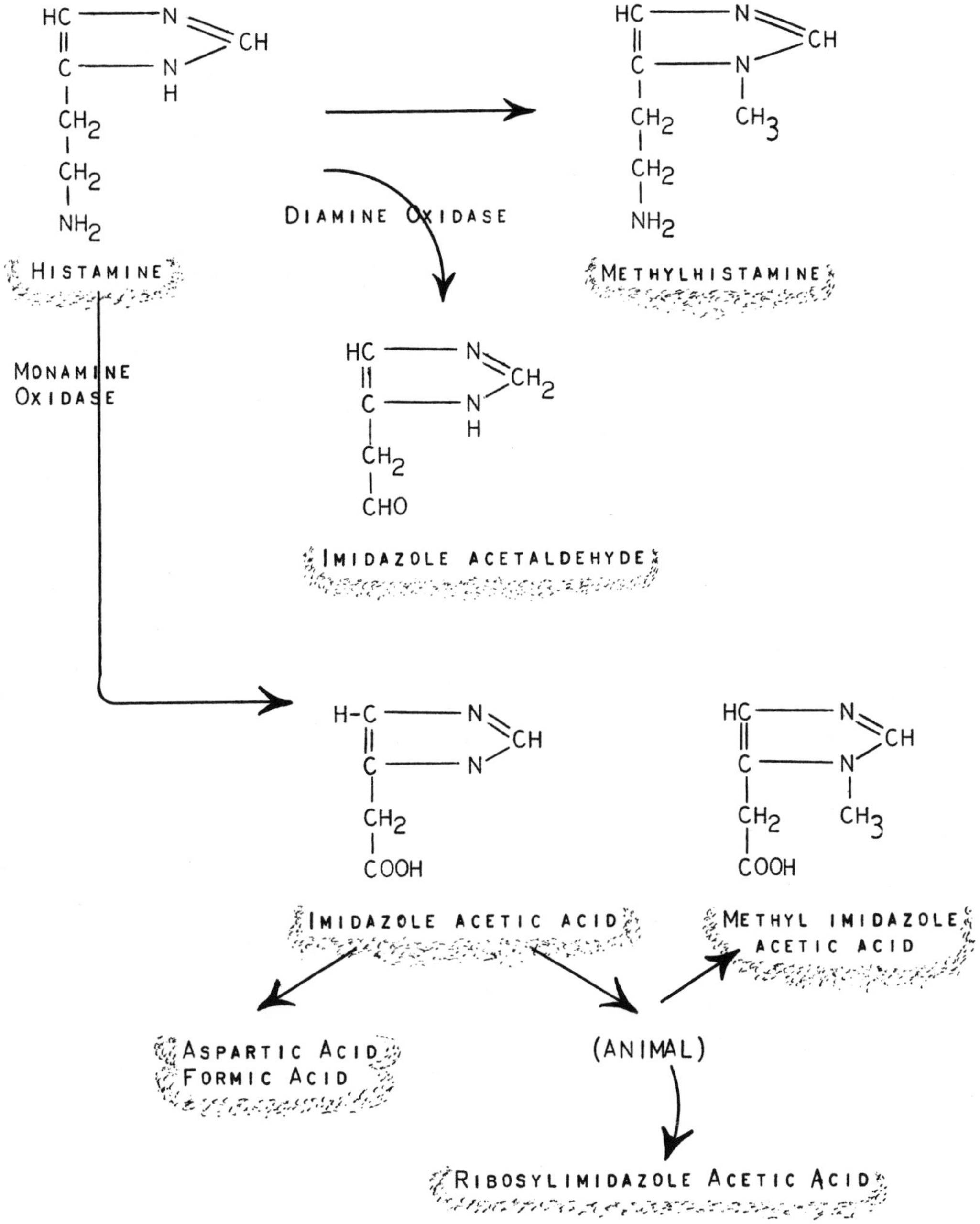

HISTAMINE

DIAMINE OXIDASE

MONAMINE OXIDASE

METHYLHISTAMINE

IMIDAZOLE ACETALDEHYDE

IMIDAZOLE ACETIC ACID

METHYL IMIDAZOLE ACETIC ACID

ASPARTIC ACID
FORMIC ACID

(ANIMAL)

RIBOSYLIMIDAZOLE ACETIC ACID

NOTES

Chapter 12
AROMATIC RING STRUCTURES

TABLE OF CONTENTS

Map No.	Title	Page No.
119	Synthesis of Aromatic Rings	167
120	Catechol Path of Aromatic Breakdown	168
121	Protocatechuic Path of Aromatic Breakdown	169
122	Path to Keto-adipic Acid	170
123	Homogentisic Acid	171
124	Analogous Oxidations	172
125	Naphthalene Breakdown	173
126	Phenylpyruvic Acid Metabolism	174
127	Related Structures Arranged in Order of Possible Origin	175
128	Synthesis of Kojic Acid	177

MAP 119.   SYNTHESIS OF AROMATIC RINGS

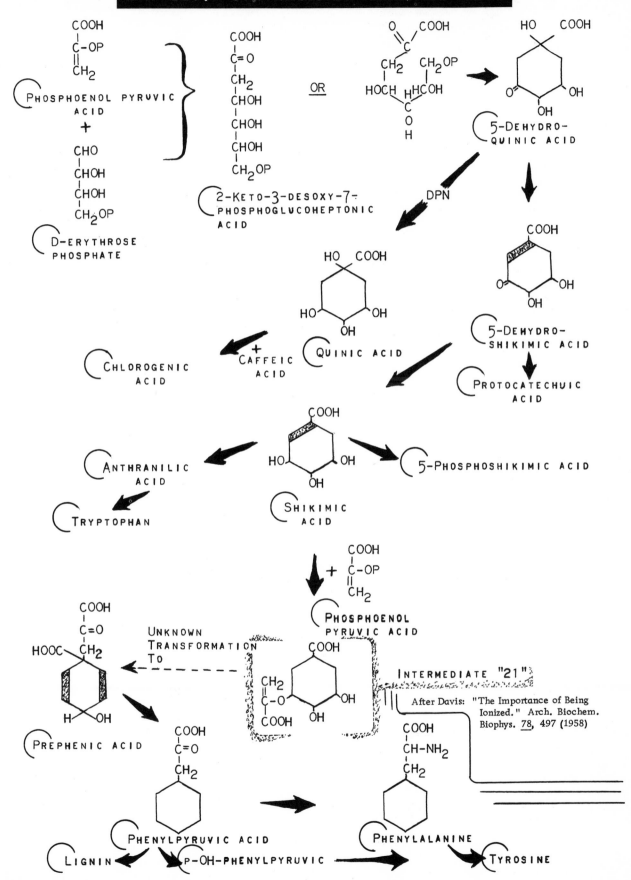

PHOSPHOENOL PYRUVIC ACID

+

D-ERYTHROSE PHOSPHATE

OR

2-KETO-3-DESOXY-7-PHOSPHOGLUCOHEPTONIC ACID

5-DEHYDRO-QUINIC ACID

DPN

5-DEHYDRO-SHIKIMIC ACID

PROTOCATECHUIC ACID

CHLOROGENIC ACID

+ CAFFEIC ACID

QUINIC ACID

ANTHRANILIC ACID

TRYPTOPHAN

SHIKIMIC ACID

5-PHOSPHOSHIKIMIC ACID

PHOSPHOENOL PYRUVIC ACID

UNKNOWN TRANSFORMATION TO

INTERMEDIATE "21"

After Davis: "The Importance of Being Ionized." Arch. Biochem. Biophys. 78, 497 (1958)

PREPHENIC ACID

PHENYLALANINE

PHENYLPYRUVIC ACID

LIGNIN

P-OH-PHENYLPYRUVIC

TYROSINE

MAP 120. CATECHOL PATH OF AROMATIC BREAKDOWN

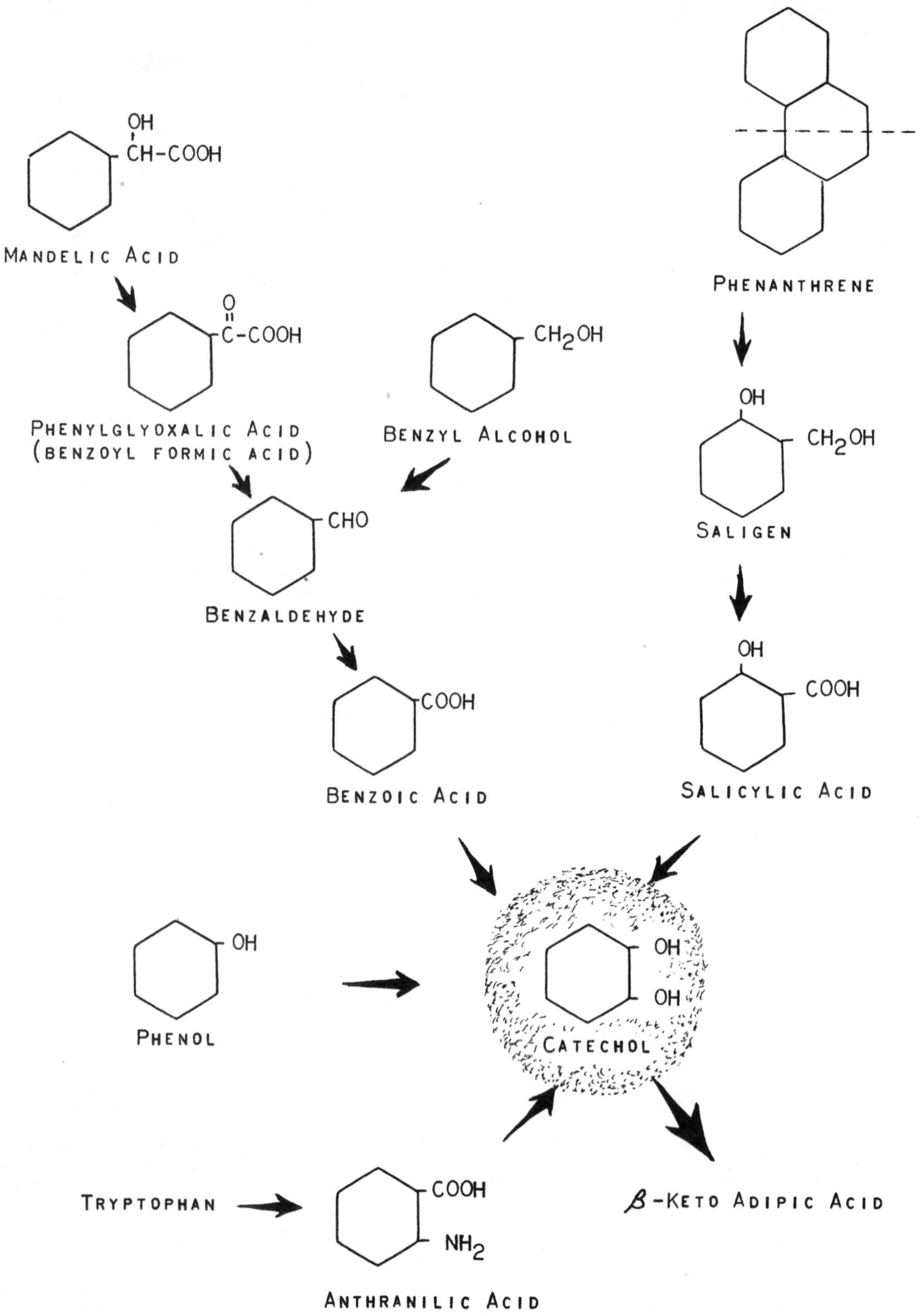
OH
CH-COOH
MANDELIC ACID
O
C-COOH
PHENYLGLYOXALIC ACID
(BENZOYL FORMIC ACID)
CH2OH
BENZYL ALCOHOL
CHO
BENZALDEHYDE
COOH
BENZOIC ACID
PHENANTHRENE
OH
CH2OH
SALIGEN
OH
COOH
SALICYLIC ACID
OH
PHENOL
OH
OH
CATECHOL
TRYPTOPHAN
COOH
NH2
ANTHRANILIC ACID
β-KETO ADIPIC ACID

MAP 121. PROTOCATECHUIC PATH OF AROMATIC BREAKDOWN

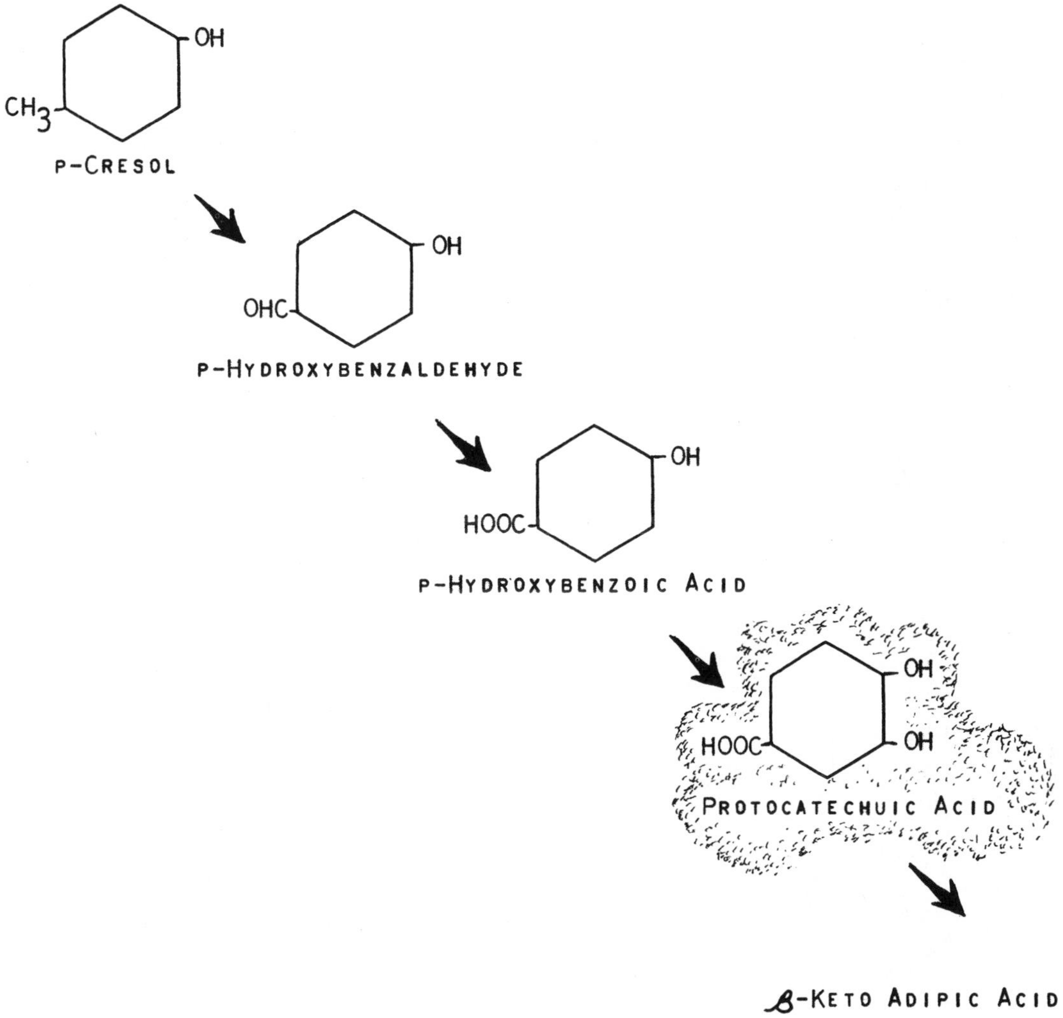
OH
CH_3
p-Cresol
OH
OHC
p-Hydroxybenzaldehyde
OH
HOOC
p-Hydroxybenzoic Acid
OH
OH
HOOC
Protocatechuic Acid
β-Keto Adipic Acid

MAP 122. PATH TO KETO-ADIPIC ACID

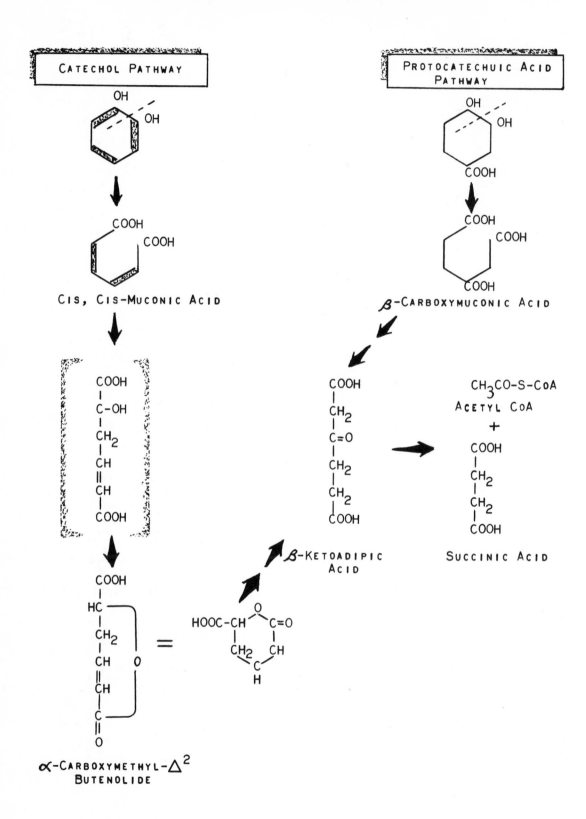

MAP 123. HOMOGENTISIC ACID

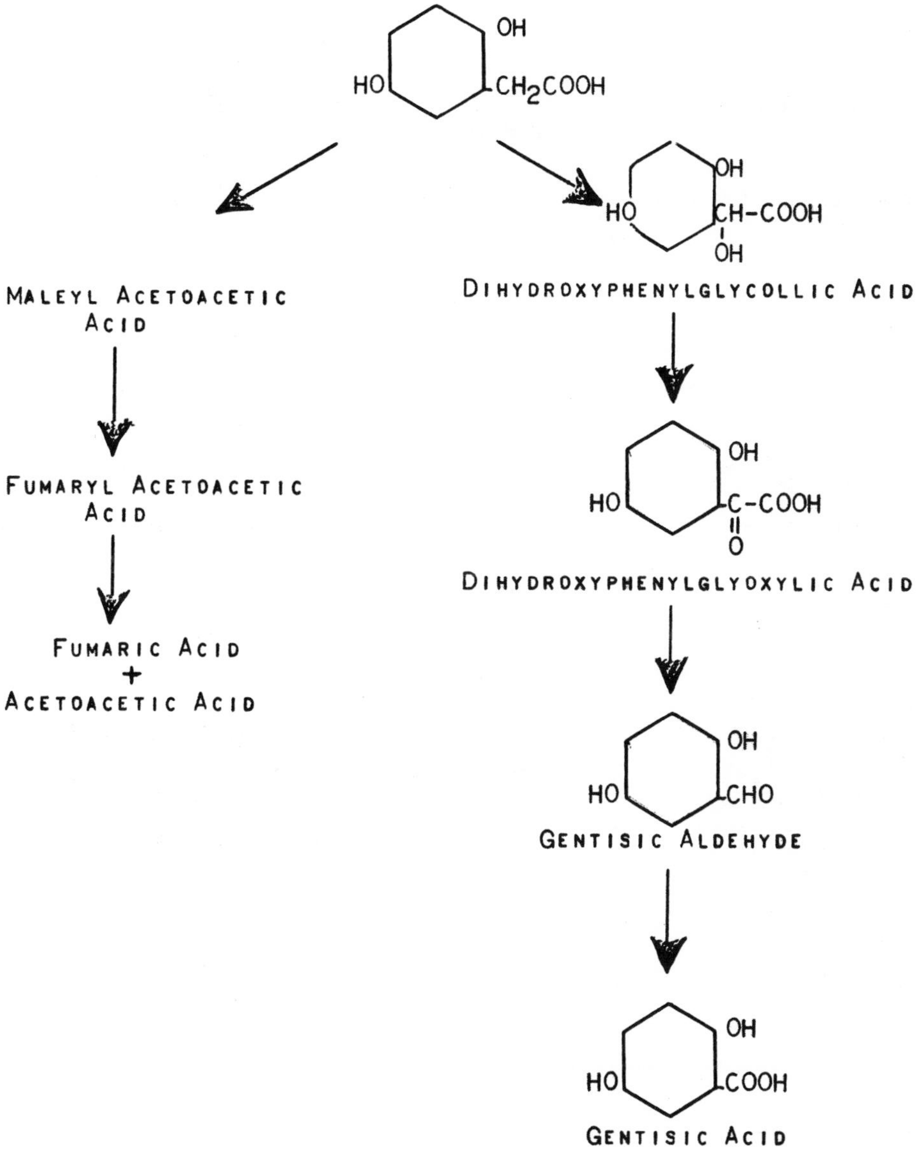
OH
HO
CH2COOH
Maleyl Acetoacetic Acid
Fumaryl Acetoacetic Acid
Fumaric Acid + Acetoacetic Acid
OH
HO
CH-COOH
OH
Dihydroxyphenylglycollic Acid
OH
HO
C-COOH
O
Dihydroxyphenylglyoxylic Acid
OH
HO
CHO
Gentisic Aldehyde
OH
HO
COOH
Gentisic Acid

MAP 124. ANALOGOUS OXIDATIONS

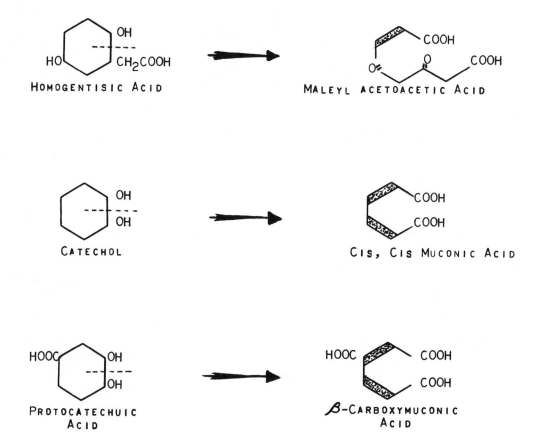

HOMOGENTISIC ACID → MALEYL ACETOACETIC ACID

CATECHOL → CIS, CIS MUCONIC ACID

PROTOCATECHUIC ACID → β-CARBOXYMUCONIC ACID

MAP 125. NAPHTHALENE BREAKDOWN

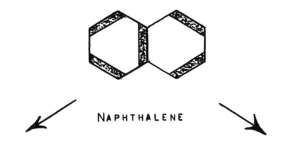

NAPHTHALENE

(MICROSOME FRACTION,
LIVER, TPN, G-6-P,
NICOTINAMIDE)

$CH_2 - S - S - CH_2$

$NH_2C-COOH$ $NH_2C-COOH$

H H

CYSTINE

-OH

-OH

1,2-DIHYDRONAPHTHALENE-1,2-DIOL

"PREMERCAPTURIC ACIDS"

(HYDROLYSIS)

(HYDROLYSIS)

-OH

$S - CH_2$

$CHNH-OC-CH_3$

$COOH$

NAPHTHYL-MERCAPTURIC ACID

α-NAPHTHOL

MAP 126. PHENYLPYRUVIC ACID METABOLISM

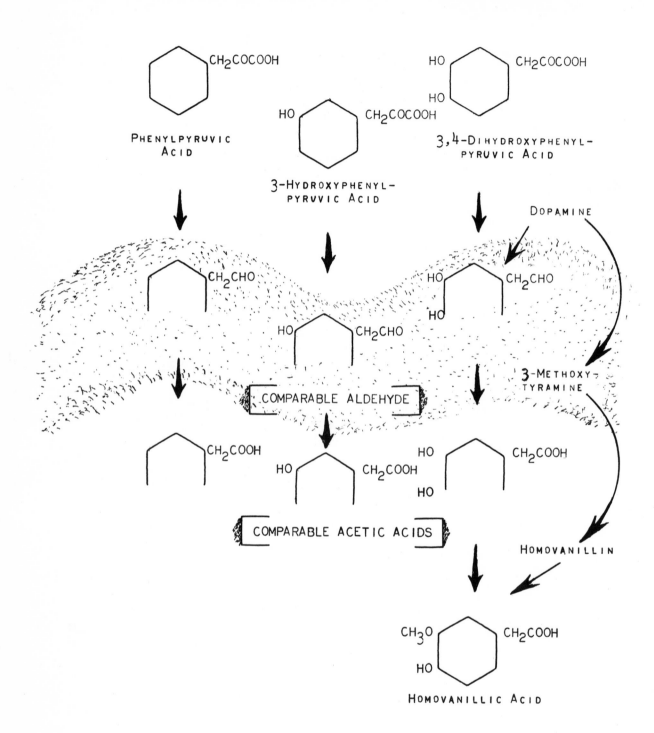

MAP 127. RELATED STRUCTURES ARRANGED IN ORDER OF POSSIBLE ORIGIN

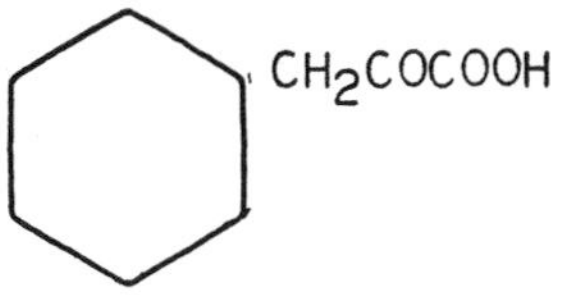

PHENYLPYRUVIC ACID

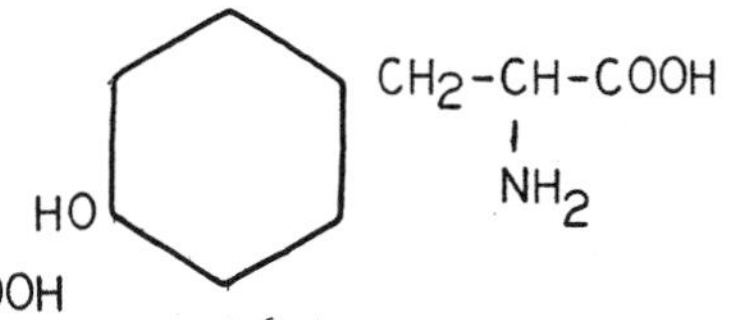

TYROSINE

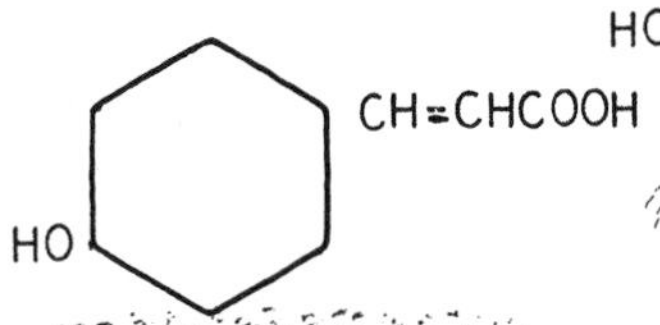

P-COUMARIC ACID

METABOLIC RELATIONS BETWEEN STRUCTURES UNCERTAIN.

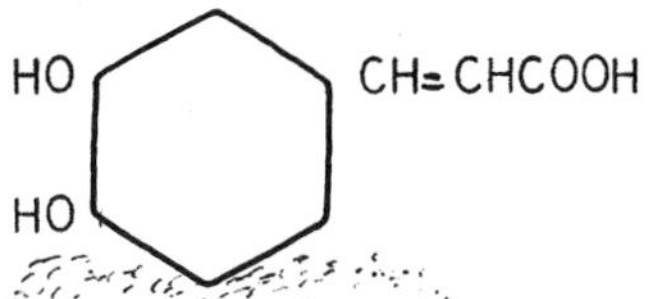

CAFFEIC ACID

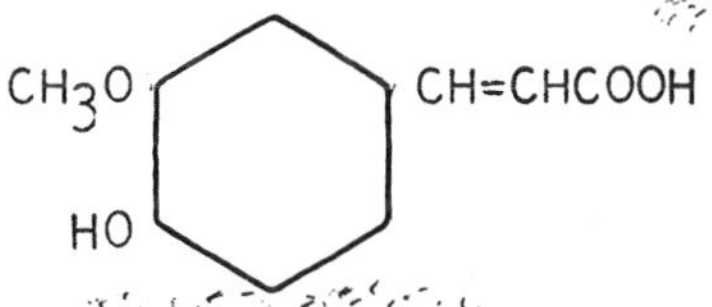

FERULIC ACID

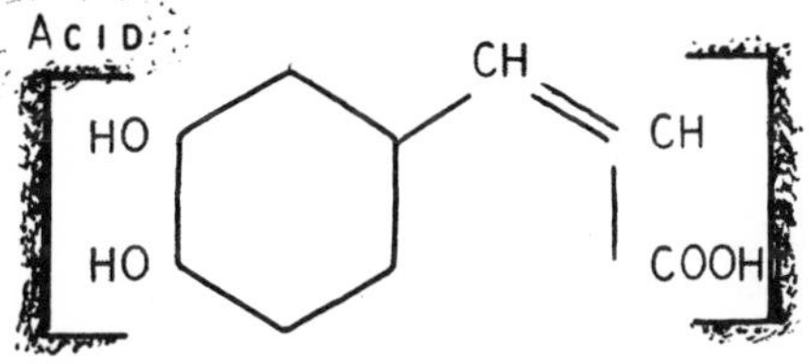

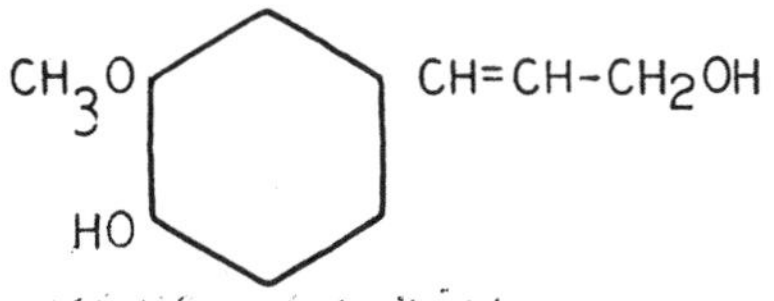

CONIFERYL ALCOHOL

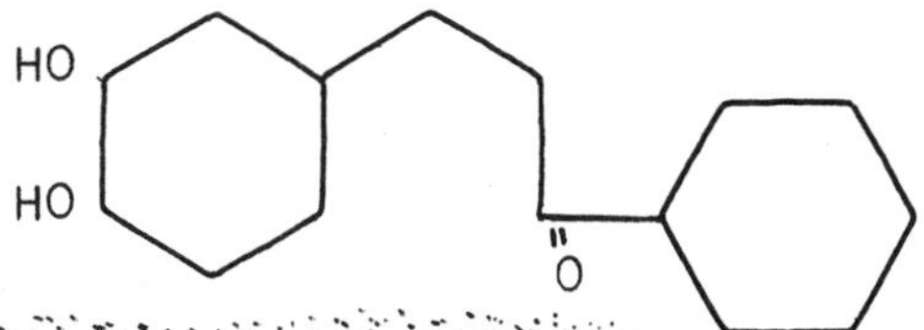

3,4-DIHYDROXYCHALCONE

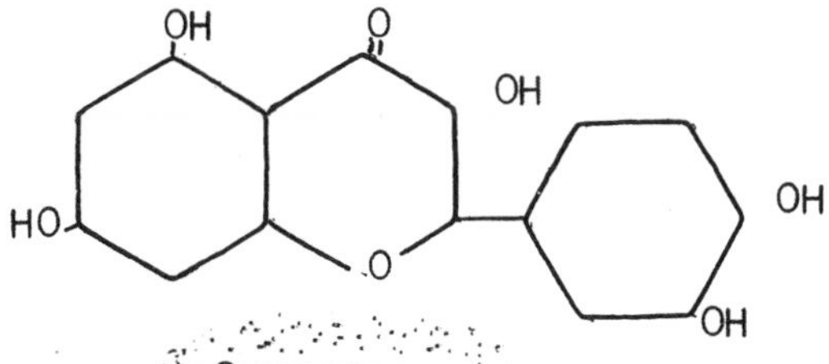

QUERCETIN

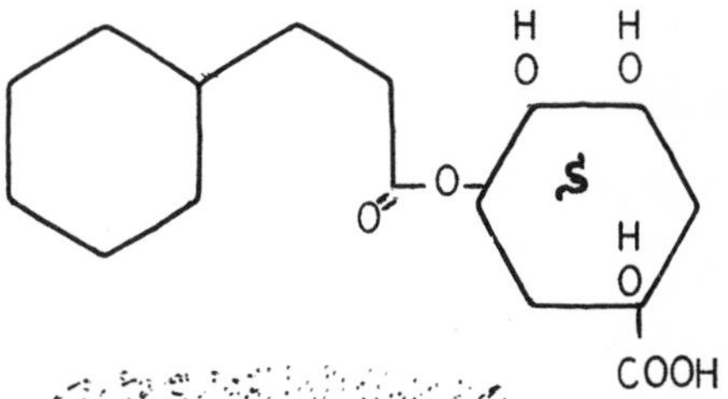

CHLOROGENIC ACID

NOTES

MAP 128. SYNTHESIS OF KOJIC ACID

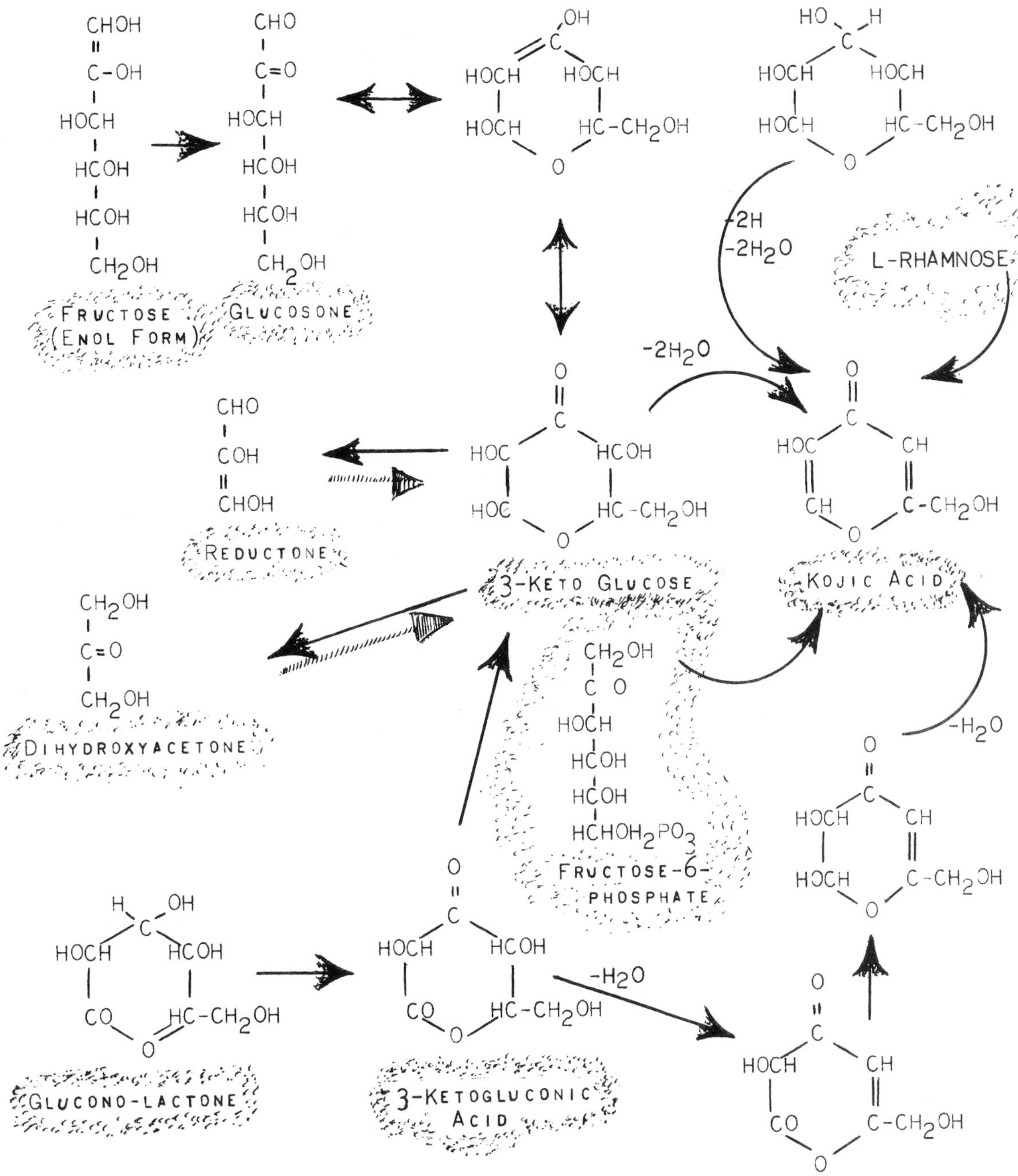

FRUCTOSE (ENOL FORM)

GLUCOSONE

L-RHAMNOSE

-2H
-2H$_2$O

-2H$_2$O

REDUCTONE

DIHYDROXYACETONE

3-KETO GLUCOSE

KOJIC ACID

FRUCTOSE-6-PHOSPHATE

-H$_2$O

GLUCONO-LACTONE

3-KETOGLUCONIC ACID

-H$_2$O

NOTES

Chapter 13
AROMATIC AMINO ACIDS

TABLE OF CONTENTS

Map No.	Title	Page No.
129	Synthesis of Tyrosine and Phenylalanine	181
130	Main Routes of Tyrosine Metabolism	182
131	Paths through Dihydroxyphenylalanine	183
132	Paths through Adrenaline	184
133	Paths through Thyroxine	185
134	Paths through Phenylpyruvic Acid	186
135	Comparison between Tyrosine and Phenols	187
136	Phenylalanine Metabolism (Other than to Tyrosine)	188
137	Main Routes of Tryptophan Metabolism	189
138	Tryptophan Activation	190
139	Tryptophan Synthesis	191
140	Path through Indole	192
141	Path to Indole Acetic Acid	193
142	Path to Kynurenine and Hydroxyanthranilic Acid	194
143	Serotonin Path	195
144	Kynurenine Metabolism	196
145	Hydroxyanthranilic Acid Metabolism	197
146	Nicotinic Acid Metabolism	199

MAP 129. SYNTHESIS OF TYROSINE AND PHENYLALANINE

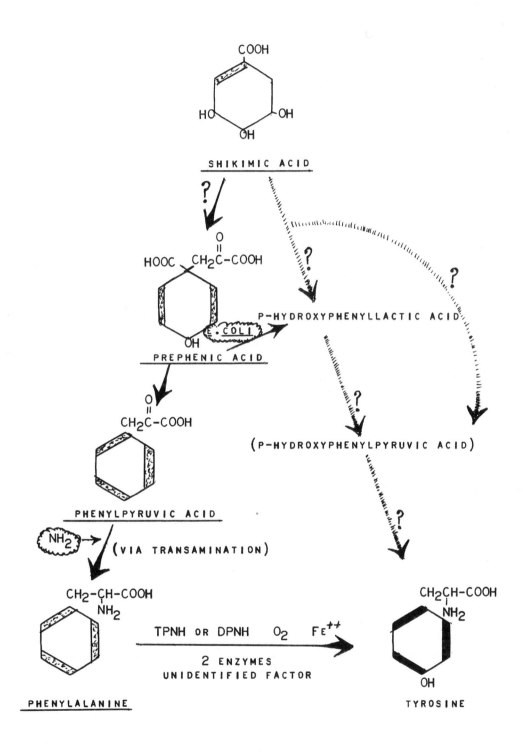

MAP 130. MAIN ROUTES OF TYROSINE METABOLISM

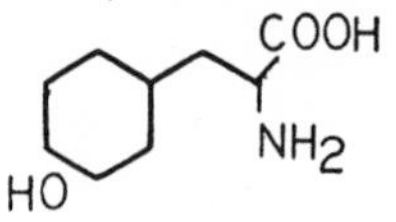

COOH
NH2
HO

TYROSINE

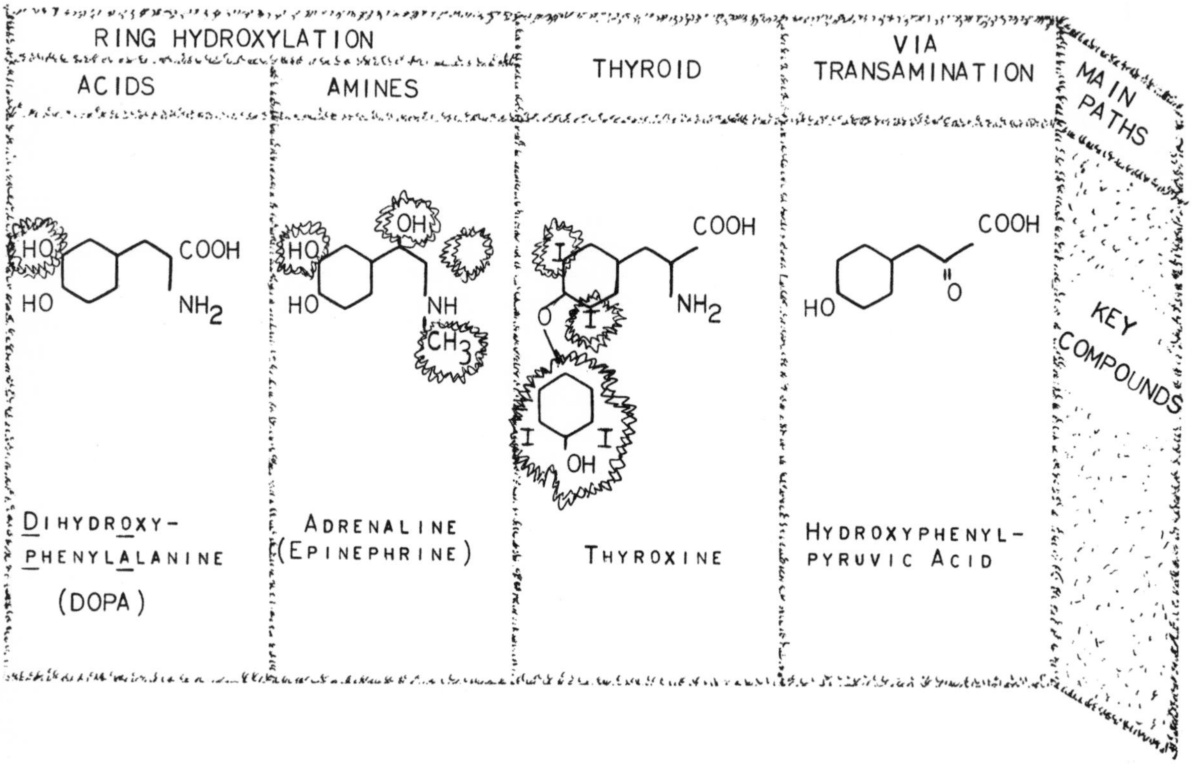

RING HYDROXYLATION
ACIDS
AMINES
THYROID
VIA TRANSAMINATION
MAIN PATHS
KEY COMPOUNDS
HO
HO
COOH
NH2
HO
HO
OH
NH
CH3
I
I
O
I
I
OH
COOH
NH2
COOH
HO
O
DIHYDROXY-PHENYLALANINE (DOPA)
ADRENALINE (EPINEPHRINE)
THYROXINE
HYDROXYPHENYL-PYRUVIC ACID

MAP 131. PATHS THROUGH DIHYDROXYPHENYLALANINE

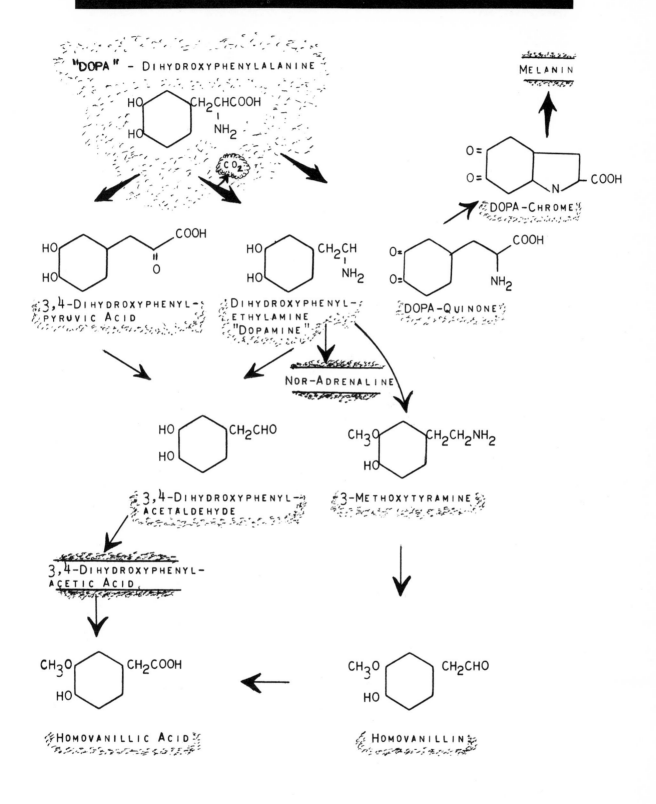

"DOPA" - DIHYDROXYPHENYLALANINE

MELANIN

DOPA-CHROME

3,4-DIHYDROXYPHENYL-PYRUVIC ACID

DIHYDROXYPHENYL-ETHYLAMINE "DOPAMINE"

DOPA-QUINONE

NOR-ADRENALINE

3,4-DIHYDROXYPHENYL-ACETALDEHYDE

3-METHOXYTYRAMINE

3,4-DIHYDROXYPHENYL-ACETIC ACID

HOMOVANILLIC ACID

HOMOVANILLIN

MAP 132. PATHS THROUGH ADRENALINE

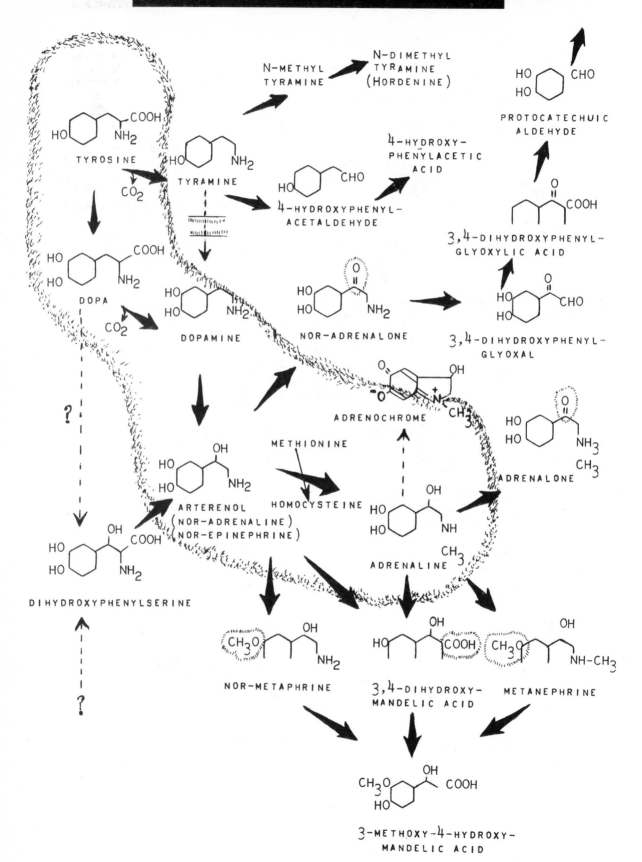

MAP 133.   PATHS THROUGH THYROXINE

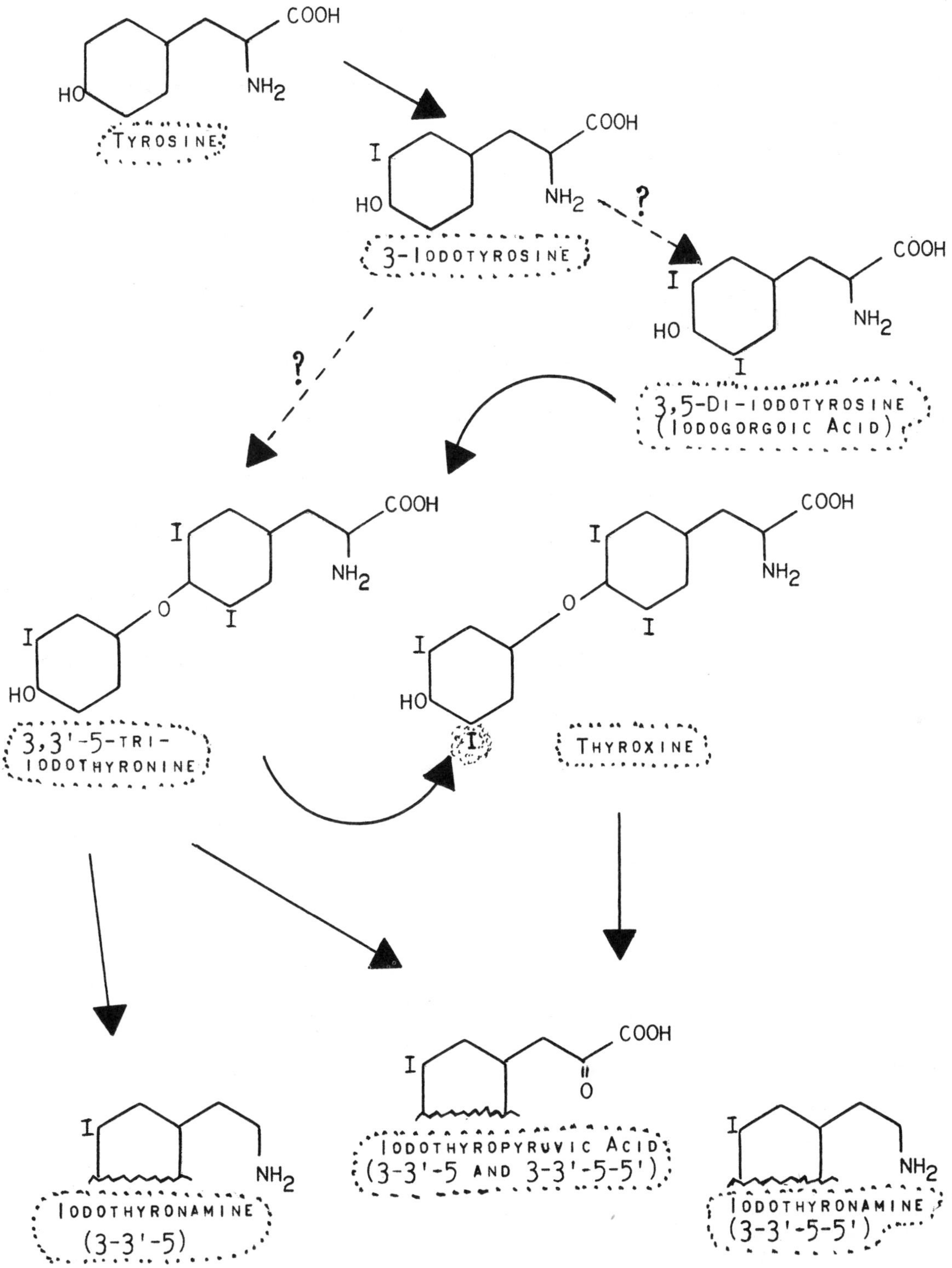

MAP 134. PATHS THROUGH PHENYLPYRUVIC ACID

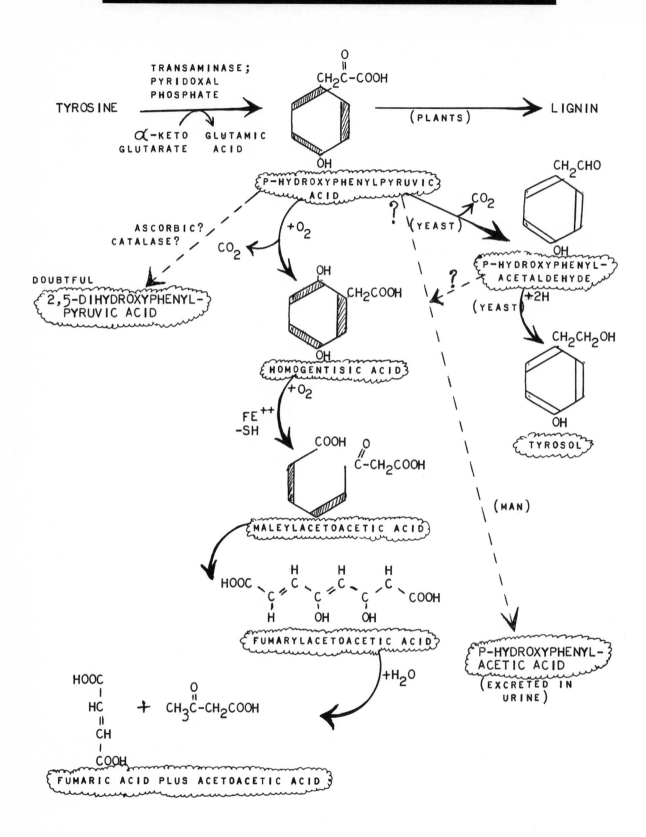

MAP 135. COMPARISON BETWEEN TYROSINE AND PHENOLS

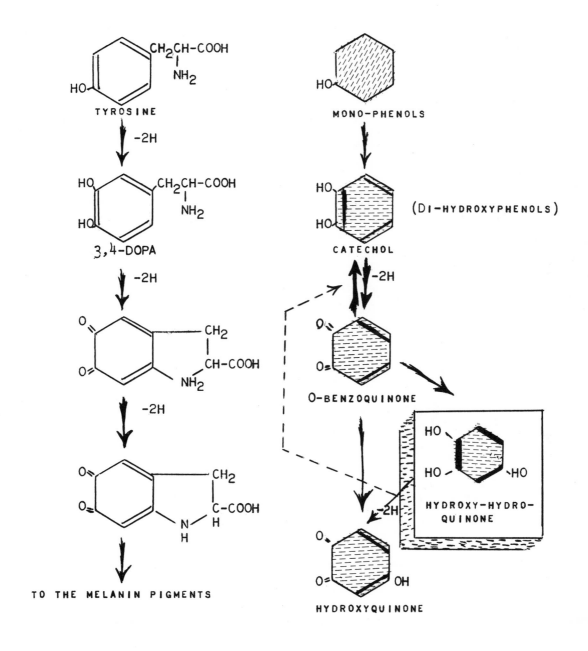

TYROSINE

-2H

3,4-DOPA

-2H

-2H

TO THE MELANIN PIGMENTS

MONO-PHENOLS

(DI-HYDROXYPHENOLS)

CATECHOL

-2H

O-BENZOQUINONE

HYDROXY-HYDRO-QUINONE

-2H

HYDROXYQUINONE

188

MAP 136. PHENYLALANINE METABOLISM
(OTHER THAN TO TYROSINE)

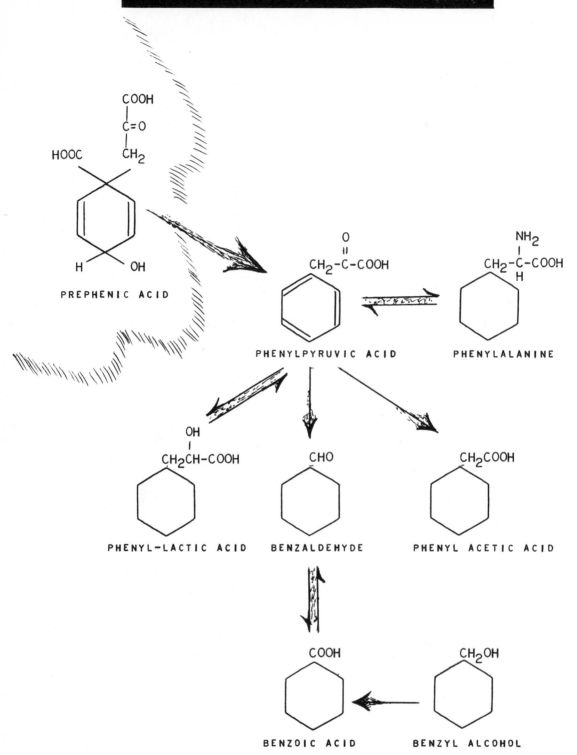

PREPHENIC ACID

PHENYLPYRUVIC ACID

PHENYLALANINE

PHENYL-LACTIC ACID

BENZALDEHYDE

PHENYL ACETIC ACID

BENZOIC ACID

BENZYL ALCOHOL

189

MAP 137.   MAIN ROUTES OF TRYPTOPHAN METABOLISM

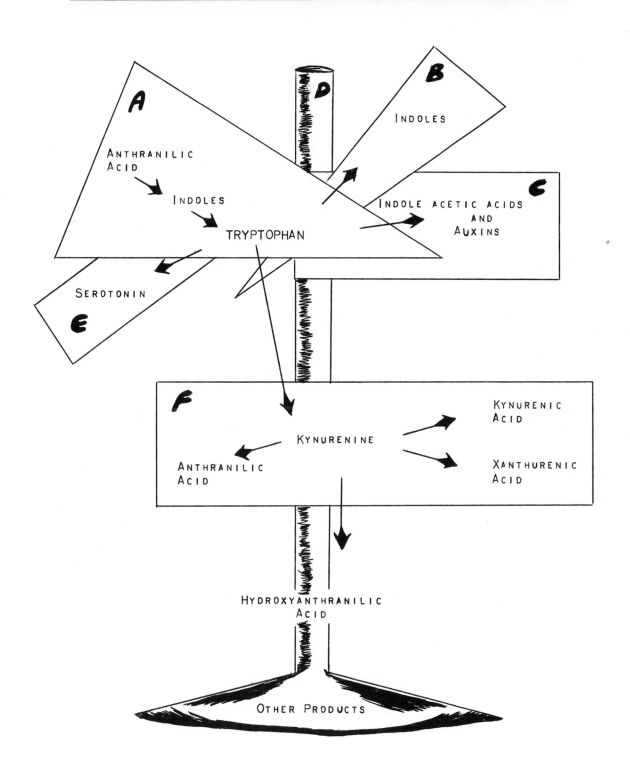

MAP 138. TRYPTOPHAN ACTIVATION

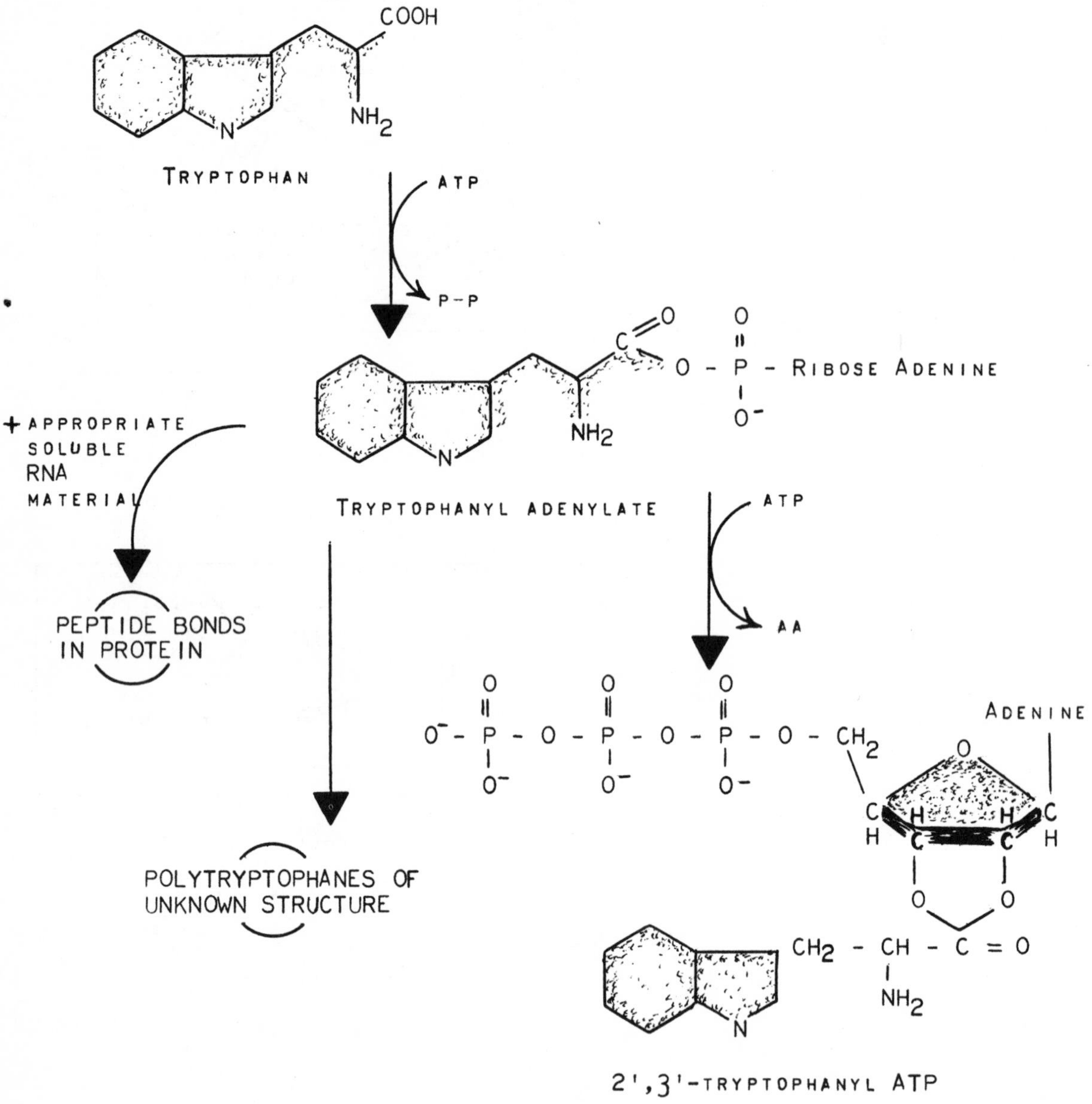
COOH
NH2
N
TRYPTOPHAN
ATP
P-P
O
C
O - P - RIBOSE ADENINE
O-
NH2
N
TRYPTOPHANYL ADENYLATE
+ APPROPRIATE SOLUBLE RNA MATERIAL
PEPTIDE BONDS IN PROTEIN
ATP
AA
POLYTRYPTOPHANES OF UNKNOWN STRUCTURE
O- - P - O - P - O - P - O - CH2
ADENINE
CH2 - CH - C = O
NH2
N
2',3'-TRYPTOPHANYL ATP

MAP 139. TRYPTOPHAN SYNTHESIS

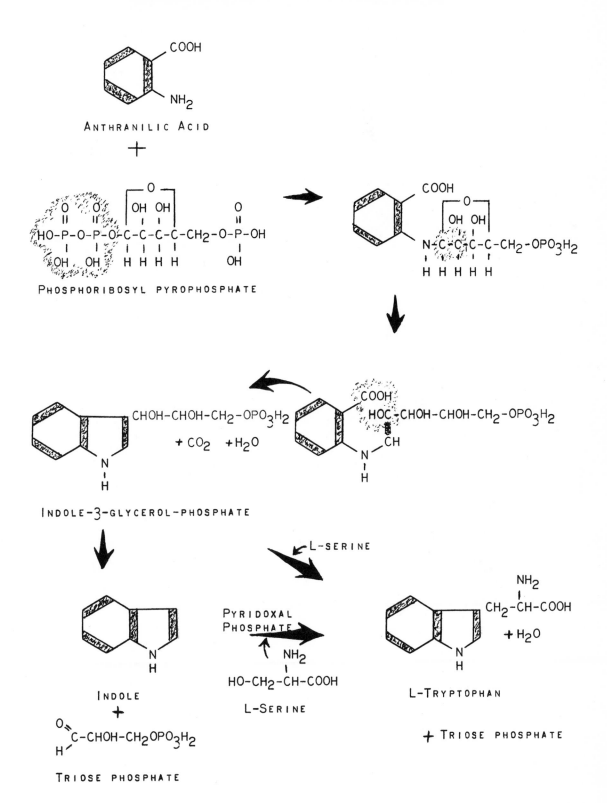

ANTHRANILIC ACID

+

PHOSPHORIBOSYL PYROPHOSPHATE

INDOLE-3-GLYCEROL-PHOSPHATE

+ CO_2 + H_2O

L-SERINE

INDOLE

+

TRIOSE PHOSPHATE

PYRIDOXAL PHOSPHATE

L-SERINE

L-TRYPTOPHAN

+ H_2O

+ TRIOSE PHOSPHATE

MAP 140. PATH THROUGH INDOLE

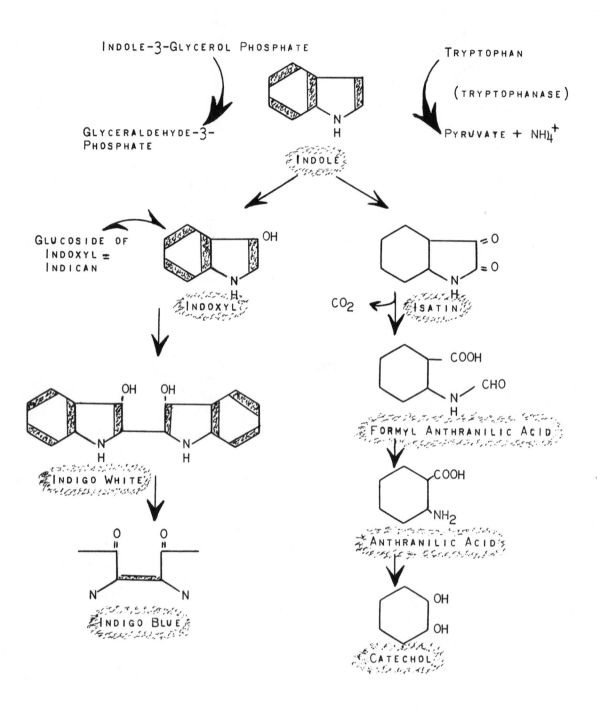

INDOLE-3-GLYCEROL PHOSPHATE

GLYCERALDEHYDE-3-PHOSPHATE

TRYPTOPHAN

(TRYPTOPHANASE)

PYRUVATE + NH_4^+

INDOLE

GLUCOSIDE OF INDOXYL = INDICAN

INDOXYL

CO_2

ISATIN

FORMYL ANTHRANILIC ACID

ANTHRANILIC ACID

CATECHOL

INDIGO WHITE

INDIGO BLUE

193

MAP 141.   PATH TO INDOLE ACETIC ACID

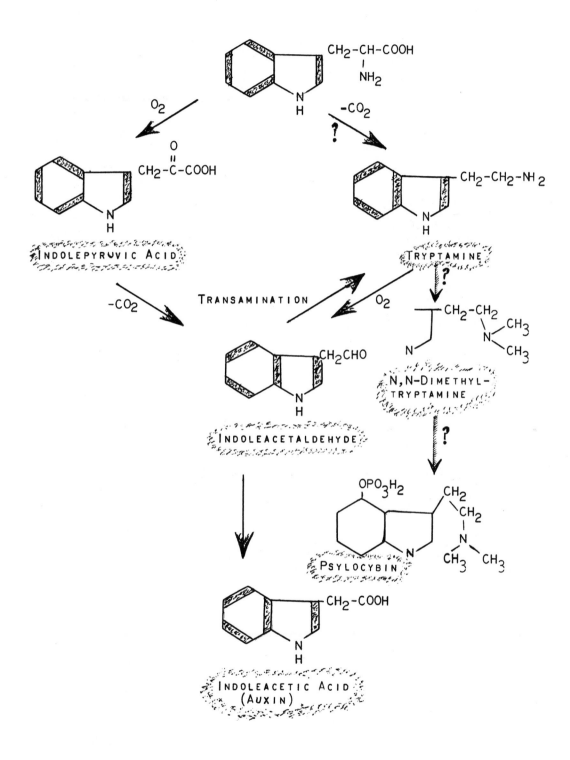

MAP 142. PATH TO KYNURENINE AND HYDROXYANTHRANILIC ACID

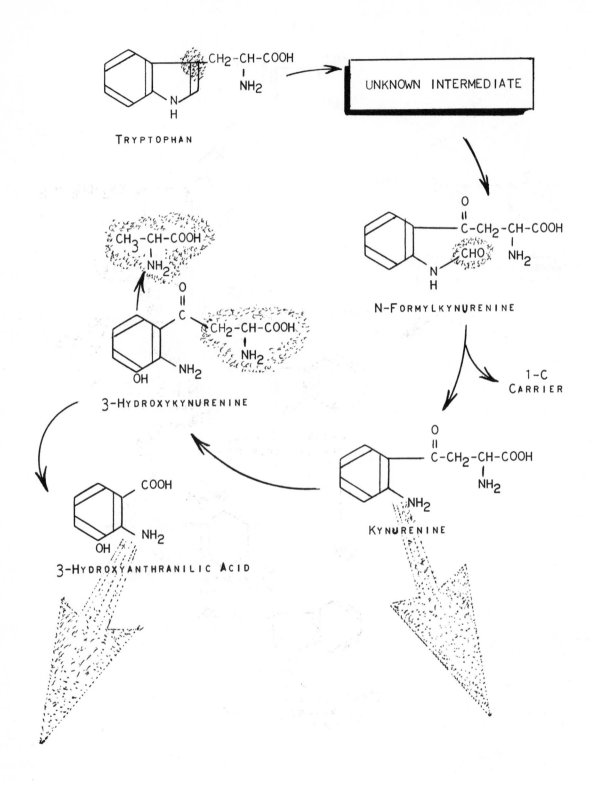

TRYPTOPHAN

UNKNOWN INTERMEDIATE

N-FORMYLKYNURENINE

1-C CARRIER

3-HYDROXYKYNURENINE

3-HYDROXYANTHRANILIC ACID

KYNURENINE

MAP 143. SEROTONIN PATH

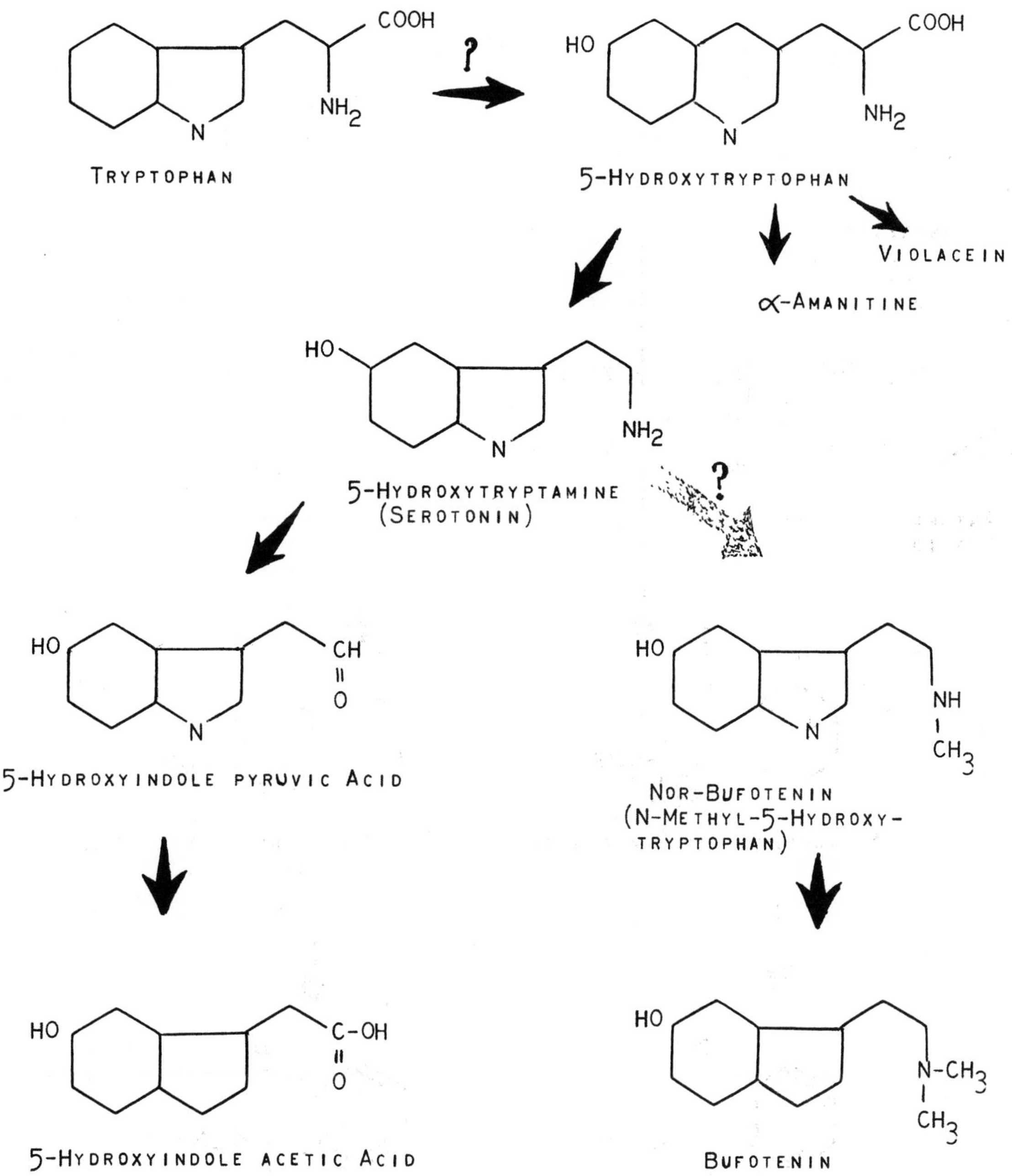
COOH
NH2
N
TRYPTOPHAN
?
HO
COOH
NH2
N
5-HYDROXYTRYPTOPHAN
VIOLACEIN
α-AMANITINE
HO
NH2
N
5-HYDROXYTRYPTAMINE
(SEROTONIN)
?
HO
CH
O
N
5-HYDROXYINDOLE PYRUVIC ACID
HO
NH
CH3
N
NOR-BUFOTENIN
(N-METHYL-5-HYDROXY-
TRYPTOPHAN)
HO
C-OH
O
5-HYDROXYINDOLE ACETIC ACID
HO
N-CH3
CH3
BUFOTENIN

MAP 144.   KYNURENINE METABOLISM

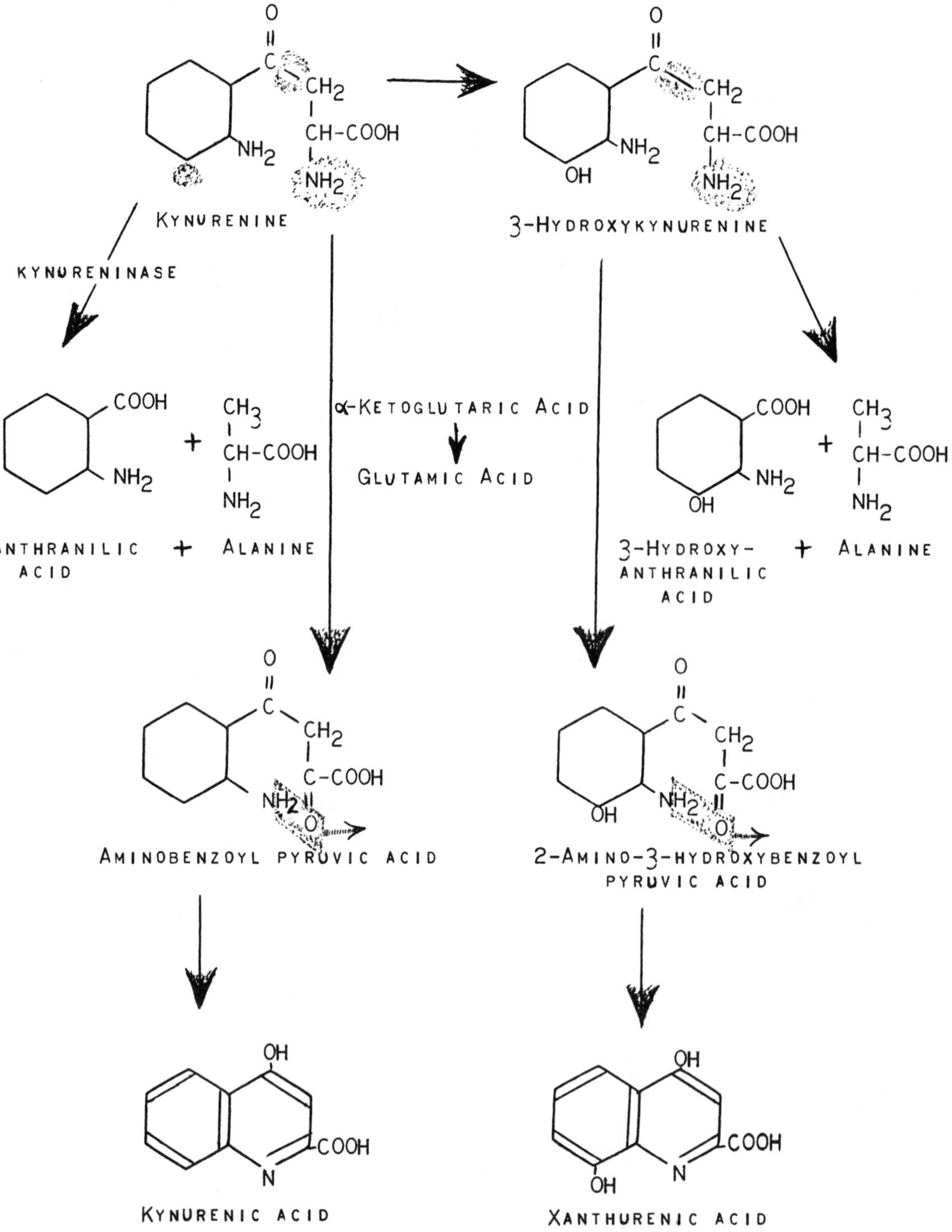

KYNURENINE

KYNURENINASE

3-HYDROXYKYNURENINE

α-KETOGLUTARIC ACID

GLUTAMIC ACID

ANTHRANILIC + ALANINE
ACID

3-HYDROXY- + ALANINE
ANTHRANILIC
ACID

AMINOBENZOYL PYRUVIC ACID

2-AMINO-3-HYDROXYBENZOYL
PYRUVIC ACID

KYNURENIC ACID

XANTHURENIC ACID

MAP 145. HYDROXYANTHRANILIC ACID METABOLISM

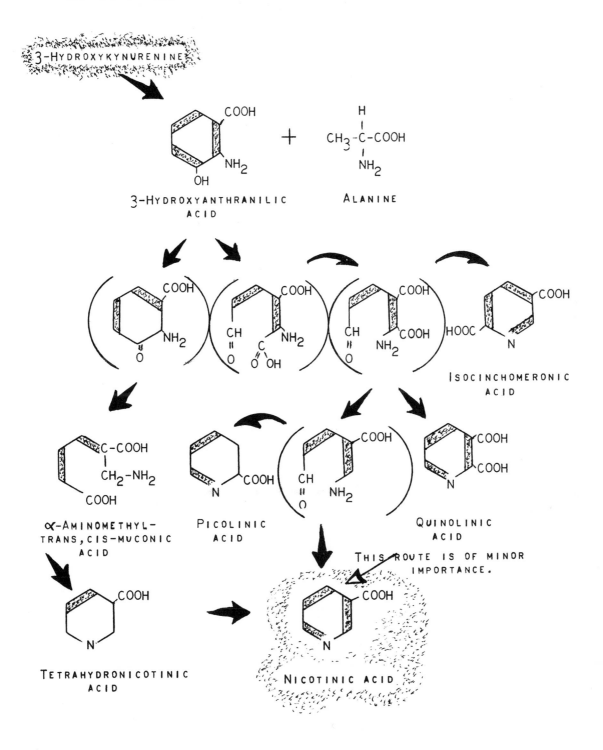

3-HYDROXYKYNURENINE

3-HYDROXYANTHRANILIC ACID

ALANINE

ISOCINCHOMERONIC ACID

α-AMINOMETHYL-TRANS,CIS-MUCONIC ACID

PICOLINIC ACID

QUINOLINIC ACID

TETRAHYDRONICOTINIC ACID

NICOTINIC ACID

THIS ROUTE IS OF MINOR IMPORTANCE.

NOTES

MAP 146. NICOTINIC ACID METABOLISM

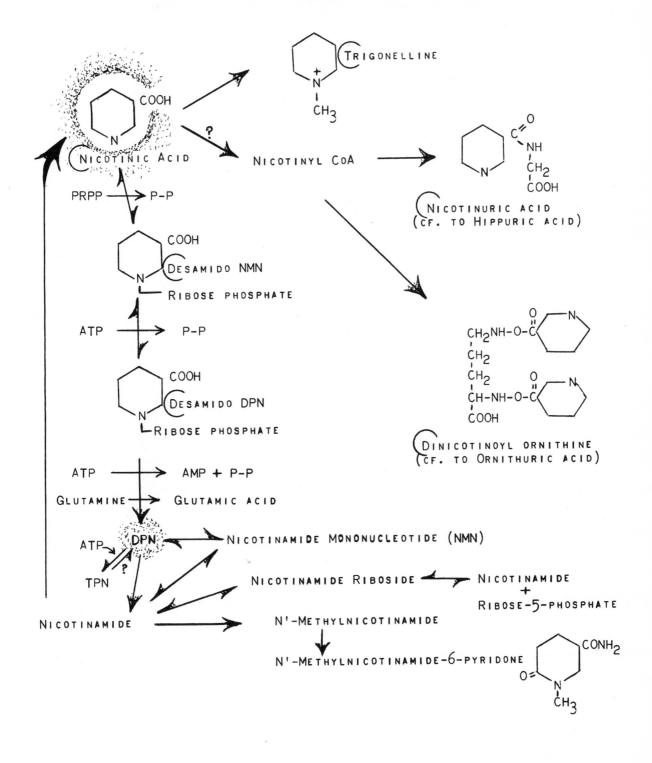

NOTES

Chapter 14
PURINES, PYRIMIDINES, NUCLEIC ACID

TABLE OF CONTENTS

Map No.		Title	Page No.

METABOLISM OF PURINES

147	Synthesis:	Amination of Ribose Phosphates (to "PRA").	203
148	Synthesis:	To Imidazole Ribotide (to "AIR")	204
149	Synthesis:	To Inosinic Acid	205
150	Synthesis:	Interconversion of Ribotides.	207
151	Breakdown:	To Uric Acid	208
152	Breakdown:	Uric Acid Metabolism	209

METABOLISM OF PYRIMIDINES

153	Synthesis:	Origins of Carbamyl Phosphate	210
154	Synthesis:	Uridine Synthesis.	211
155	Synthesis:	Cytidine Series.	212
156	Synthesis:	Thymine	213
157	Breakdown:	Uracil	214
158	Breakdown:	Thymine	215
159	Interconversion:	Ribotides to Deoxyribotides	217

NUCLEIC ACIDS

160	Synthesis:	Ribose Nucleic Acids.	219
161	Synthesis:	Deoxyribose Nucleic Acids	220
162	Replication:	Deoxyribose Nucleic Acids	221
163	Replication:	Separate Strands Yield Initial Structure	222
164	Replication:	Second Stage of Single Strand	223

MAP 147. PURINE SYNTHESIS: AMINATION OF RIBOSE PHOSPHATES (TO "PRA")

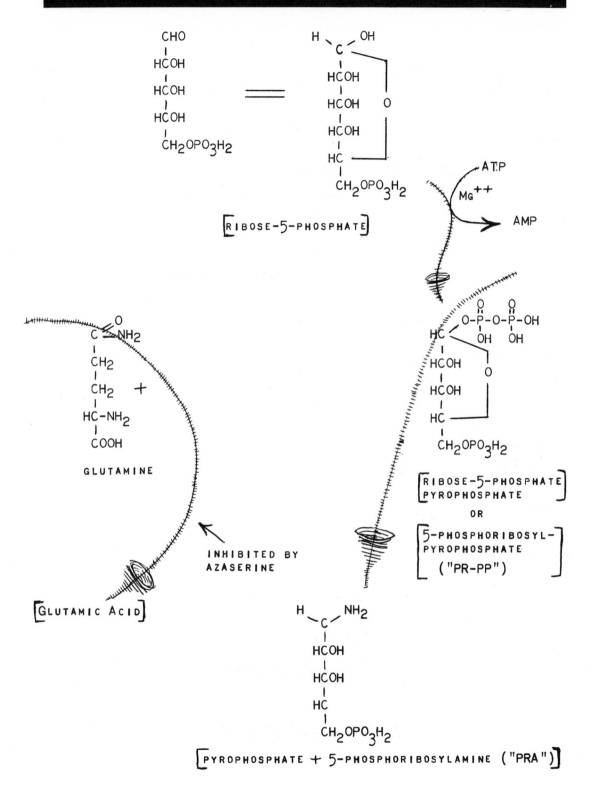

CHO
HCOH
HCOH
HCOH
CH₂OPO₃H₂

=

H—C—OH
HCOH
HCOH
HCOH
HC
CH₂OPO₃H₂

[RIBOSE-5-PHOSPHATE]

ATP
Mg⁺⁺
AMP

O   O
O-P-O-P-OH
OH OH
HC
HCOH
HCOH
HC
CH₂OPO₃H₂

[RIBOSE-5-PHOSPHATE
PYROPHOSPHATE]
OR
[5-PHOSPHORIBOSYL-
PYROPHOSPHATE]
("PR-PP")

O
C—NH₂
CH₂
CH₂   +
HC-NH₂
COOH

GLUTAMINE

INHIBITED BY
AZASERINE

[GLUTAMIC ACID]

H—C—NH₂
HCOH
HCOH
HC
CH₂OPO₃H₂

[PYROPHOSPHATE + 5-PHOSPHORIBOSYLAMINE ("PRA")]

MAP 148. PURINE SYNTHESIS: TO IMIDAZOLE RIBOTIDE (TO "AIR")

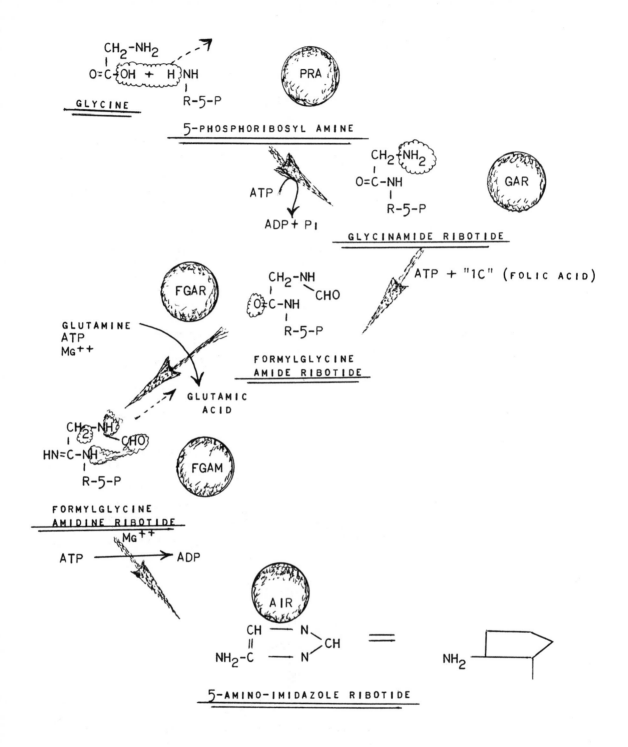

GLYCINE

5-PHOSPHORIBOSYL AMINE

PRA

ATP

ADP + Pi

GLYCINAMIDE RIBOTIDE

GAR

ATP + "1C" (FOLIC ACID)

FGAR

FORMYLGLYCINE AMIDE RIBOTIDE

GLUTAMINE
ATP
Mg++

GLUTAMIC ACID

FGAM

FORMYLGLYCINE AMIDINE RIBOTIDE

Mg++

ATP → ADP

AIR

5-AMINO-IMIDAZOLE RIBOTIDE

MAP 149.   PURINE SYNTHESIS: TO INOSINIC ACID

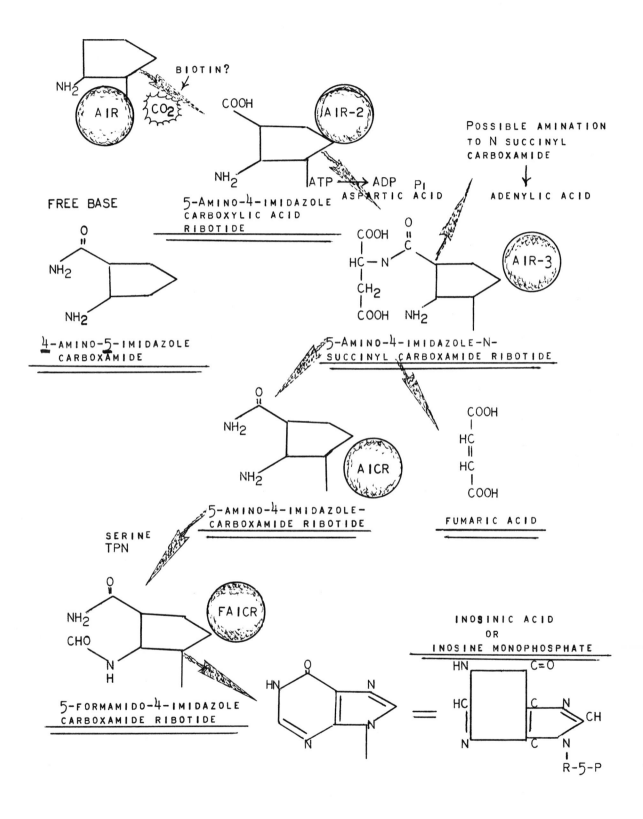

BIOTIN?

CO_2

COOH

AIR

AIR-2

ATP → ADP Pi

POSSIBLE AMINATION
TO N SUCCINYL
CARBOXAMIDE

ADENYLIC ACID

ASPARTIC ACID

FREE BASE

5-AMINO-4-IMIDAZOLE
CARBOXYLIC ACID
RIBOTIDE

O

NH₂

NH₂

4-AMINO-5-IMIDAZOLE
CARBOXAMIDE

COOH

HC — N

CH₂

COOH

NH₂

AIR-3

5-AMINO-4-IMIDAZOLE-N-
SUCCINYL CARBOXAMIDE RIBOTIDE

O

NH₂

NH₂

AICR

5-AMINO-4-IMIDAZOLE-
CARBOXAMIDE RIBOTIDE

COOH

HC

HC

COOH

FUMARIC ACID

SERINE
TPN

O

NH₂

CHO

NH
H

FAICR

5-FORMAMIDO-4-IMIDAZOLE
CARBOXAMIDE RIBOTIDE

O

HN   N

N

N

INOSINIC ACID
OR
INOSINE MONOPHOSPHATE

HN   C=O

HC   C   N

CH

N   C   N

R-5-P

206

NOTES

MAP 150.   PURINE SYNTHESIS: INTERCONVERSION OF RIBOTIDES

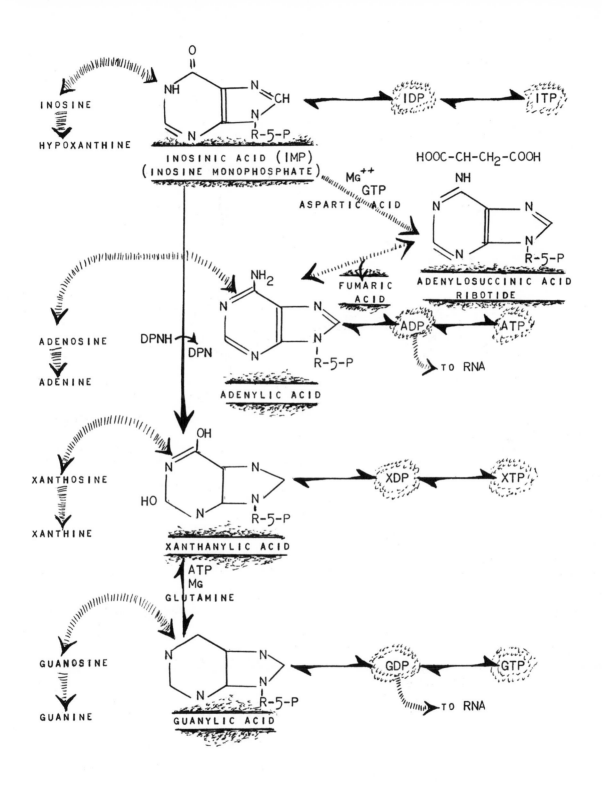

208

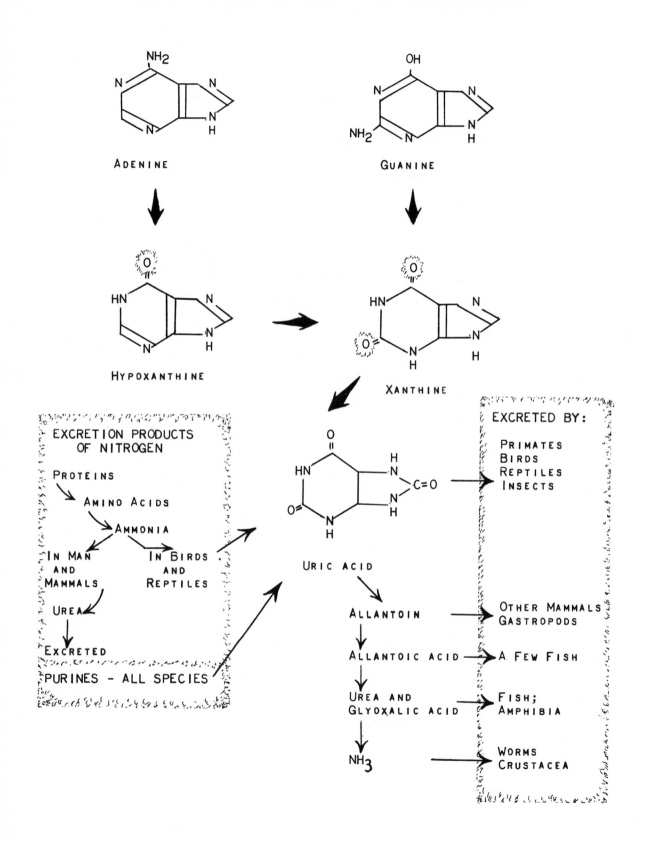

MAP 151.   PURINE BREAKDOWN: TO URIC ACID

MAP 152.   PURINE BREAKDOWN: URIC ACID METABOLISM

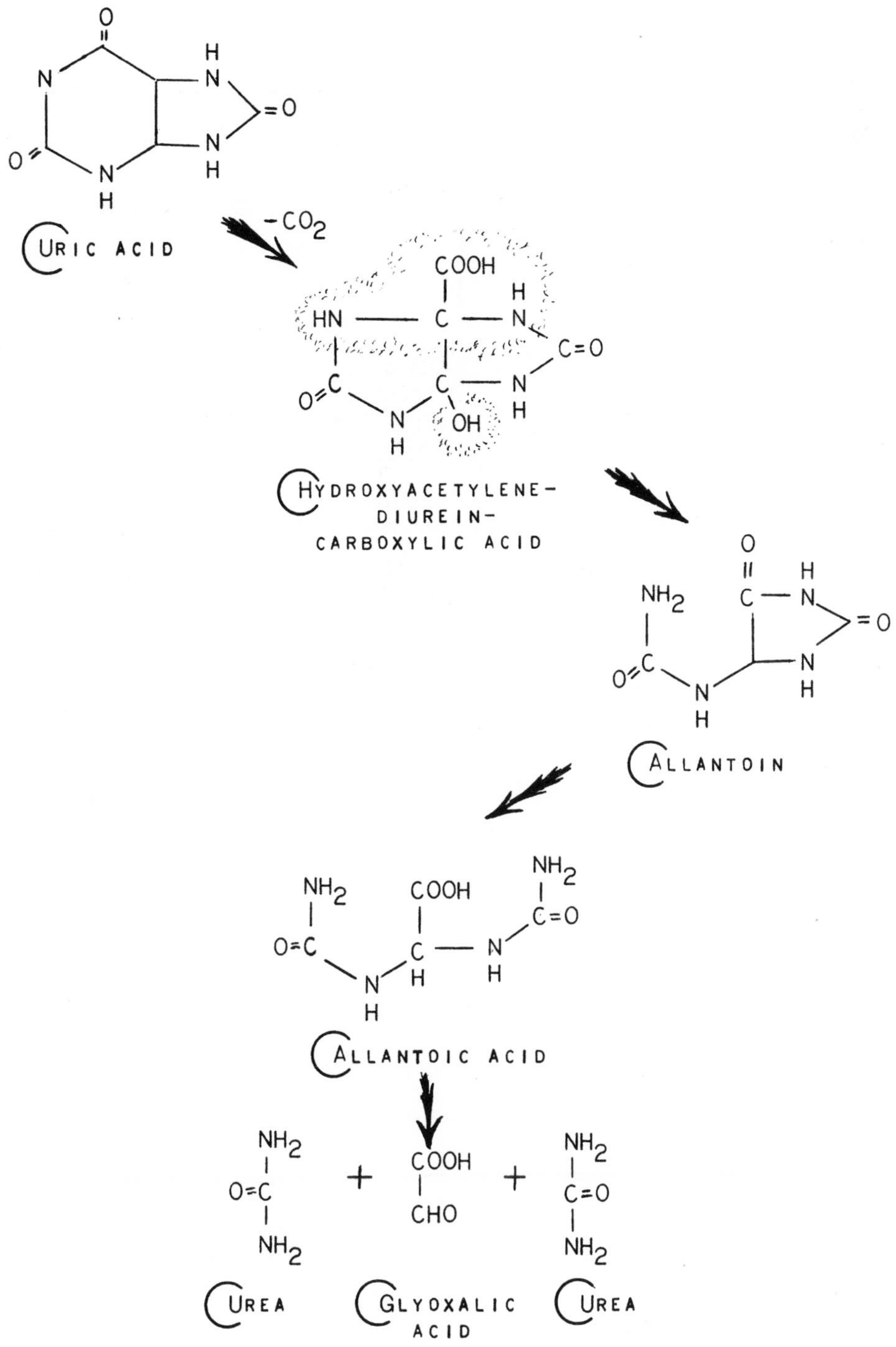

URIC ACID

−CO₂

HYDROXYACETYLENE−
DIUREIN−
CARBOXYLIC ACID

ALLANTOIN

ALLANTOIC ACID

UREA + GLYOXALIC ACID + UREA

MAP 153. PYRIMIDINE SYNTHESIS: ORIGINS OF CARBAMYL PHOSPHATE

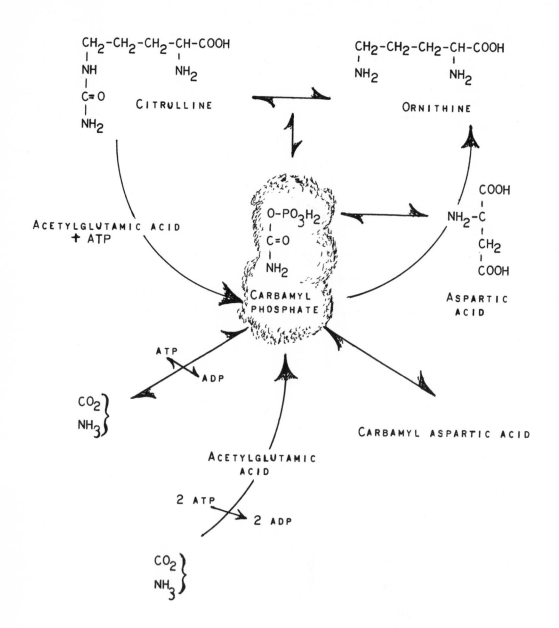

MAP 154. PYRIMIDINE SYNTHESIS: URIDINE SYNTHESIS

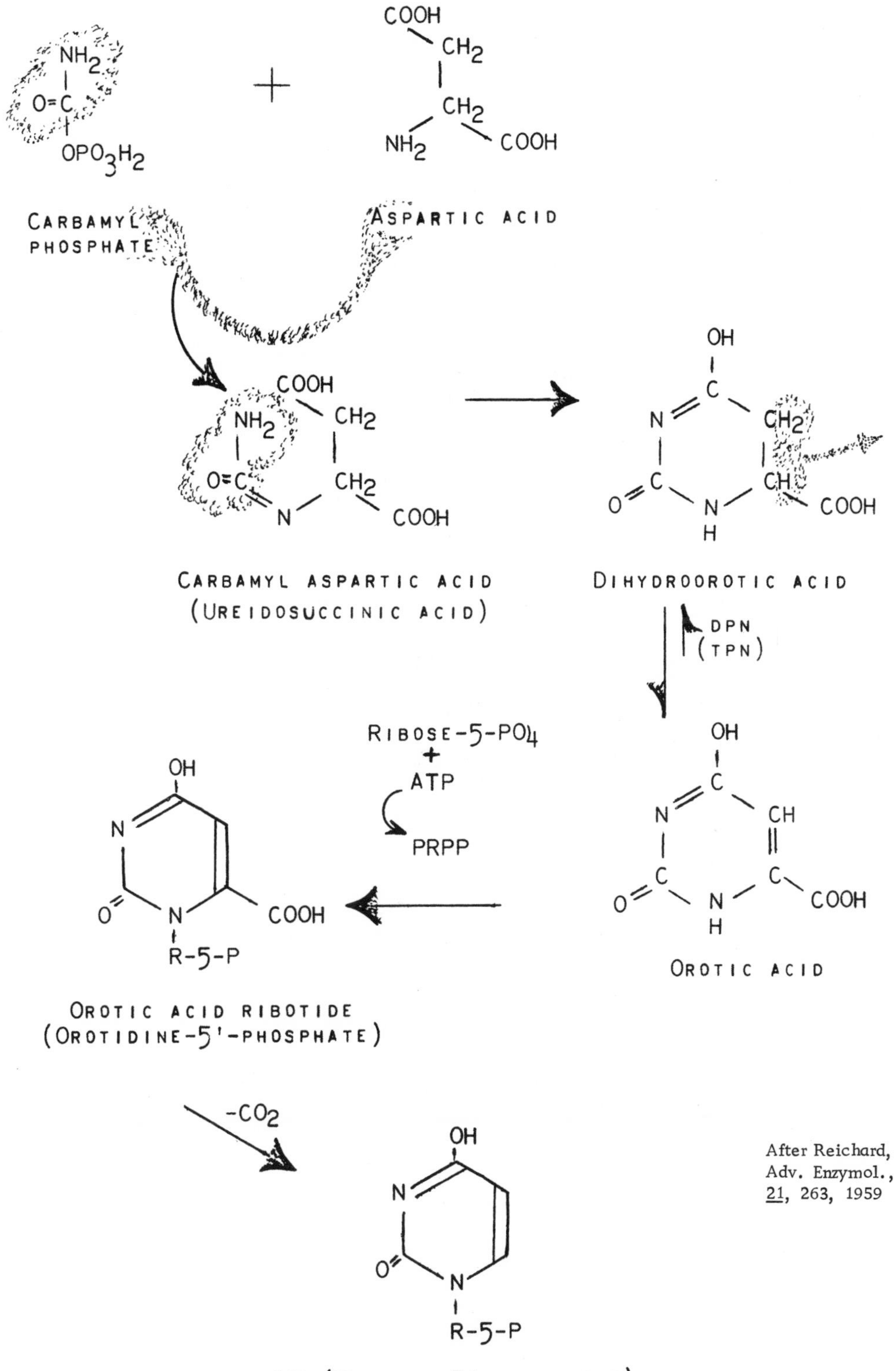

CARBAMYL PHOSPHATE

ASPARTIC ACID

CARBAMYL ASPARTIC ACID
(UREIDOSUCCINIC ACID)

DIHYDROOROTIC ACID

DPN
(TPN)

RIBOSE-5-PO₄
+
ATP

PRPP

OROTIC ACID RIBOTIDE
(OROTIDINE-5'-PHOSPHATE)

OROTIC ACID

-CO₂

After Reichard,
Adv. Enzymol.,
21, 263, 1959

UMP (URIDINE-5'-PHOSPHATE)

MAP 155. PYRIMIDINE SYNTHESIS: CYTIDINE SERIES

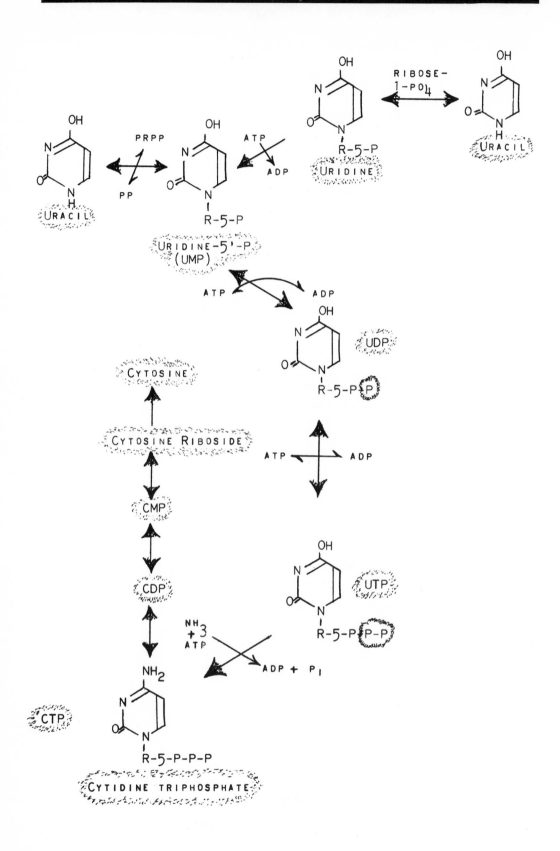

MAP 156. PYRIMIDINE SYNTHESIS: THYMINE

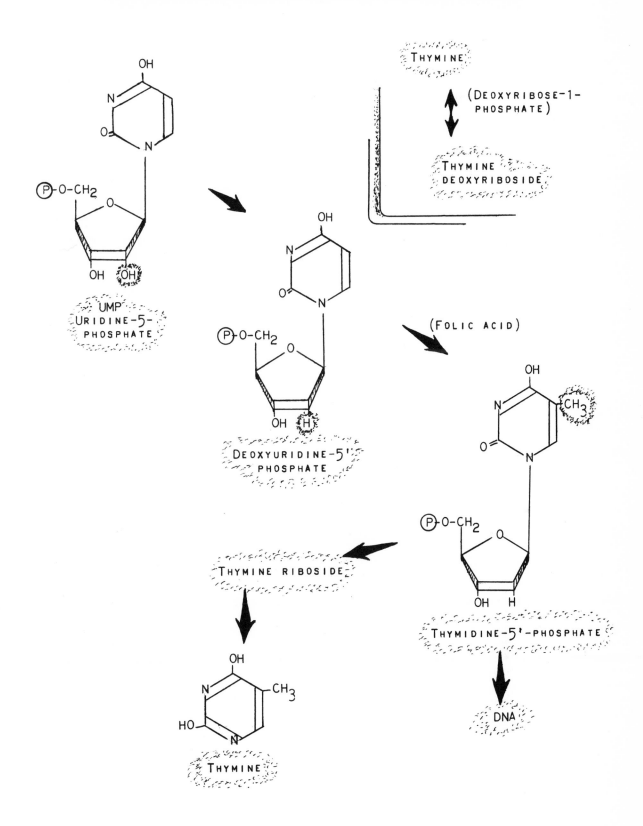

MAP 157. PYRIMIDINE BREAKDOWN: URACIL

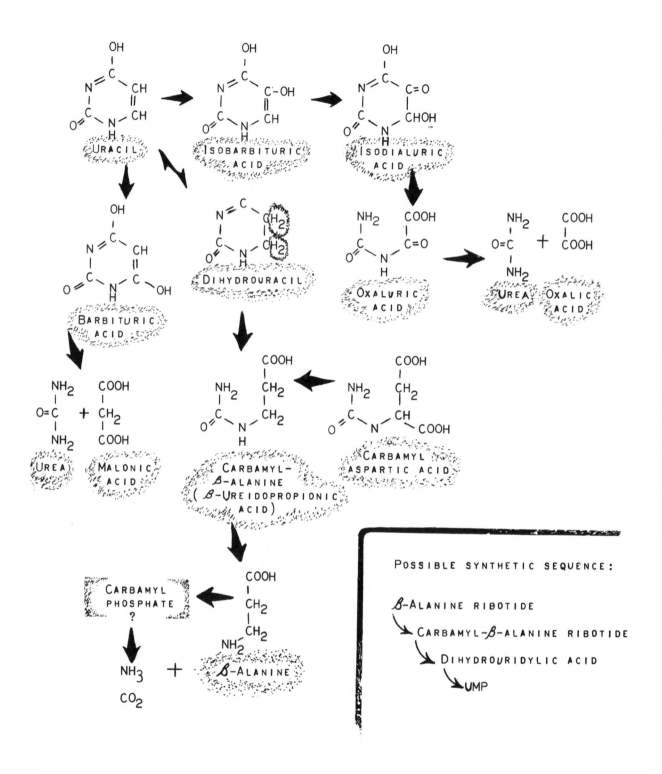

MAP 158. PYRIMIDINE BREAKDOWN: THYMINE

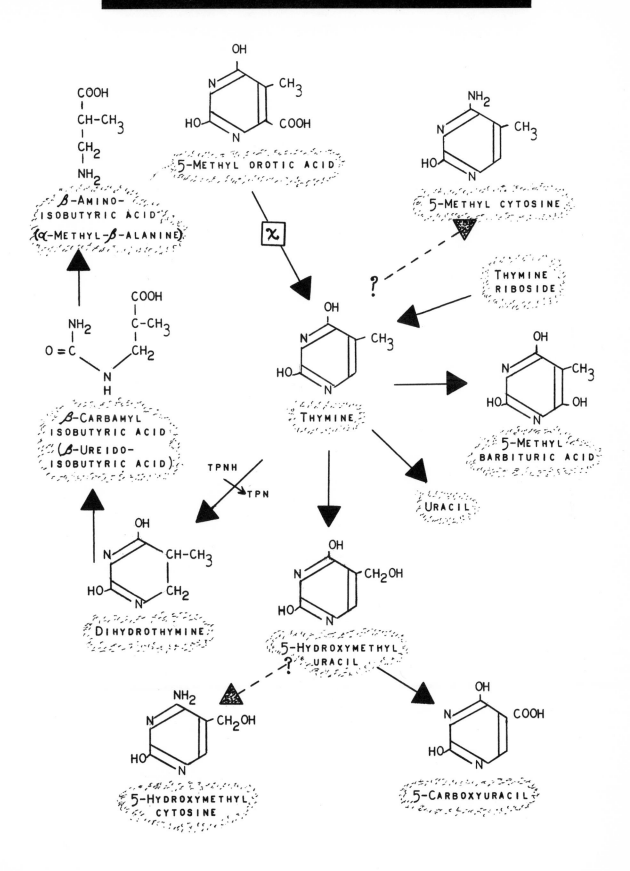

5-METHYL OROTIC ACID

5-METHYL CYTOSINE

β-AMINO-
ISOBUTYRIC ACID
(α-METHYL-β-ALANINE)

THYMINE
RIBOSIDE

β-CARBAMYL
ISOBUTYRIC ACID
(β-UREIDO-
ISOBUTYRIC ACID)

THYMINE

5-METHYL
BARBITURIC ACID

URACIL

TPNH
TPN

DIHYDROTHYMINE

5-HYDROXYMETHYL
URACIL

5-HYDROXYMETHYL
CYTOSINE

5-CARBOXYURACIL

NOTES

MAP 159. PYRIMIDINE INTERCONVERSION: RIBOTIDES TO DEOXYRIBOTIDES

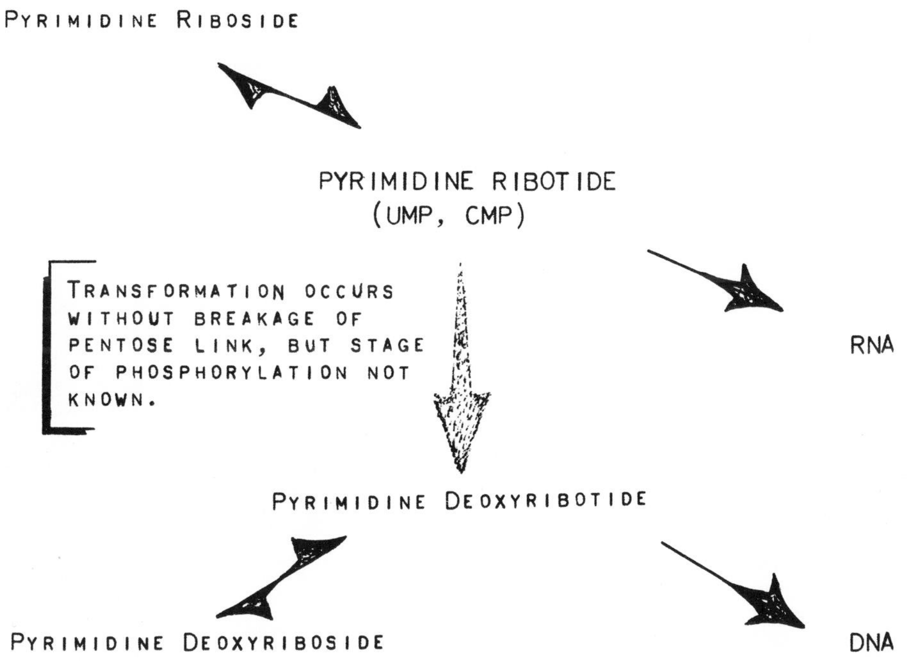

PYRIMIDINE RIBOSIDE

PYRIMIDINE RIBOTIDE
(UMP, CMP)

TRANSFORMATION OCCURS
WITHOUT BREAKAGE OF
PENTOSE LINK, BUT STAGE
OF PHOSPHORYLATION NOT
KNOWN.

RNA

PYRIMIDINE DEOXYRIBOTIDE

PYRIMIDINE DEOXYRIBOSIDE

DNA

NOTES

MAP 160.　SYNTHESIS OF RIBOSE NUCLEIC ACIDS

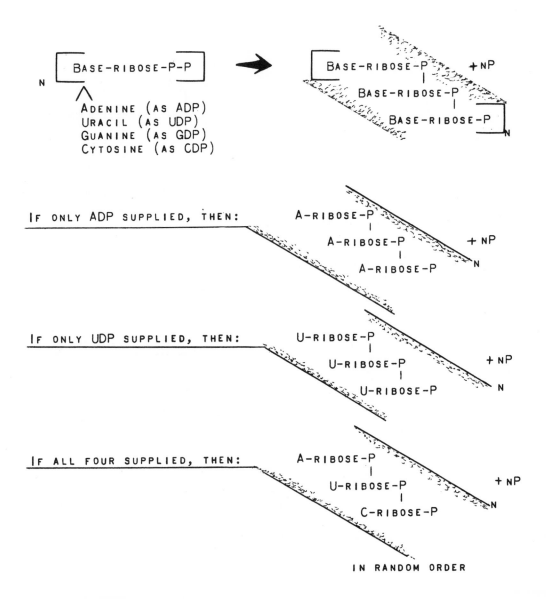

220

MAP 161.   SYNTHESIS OF DEOXYRIBOSE NUCLEIC ACIDS

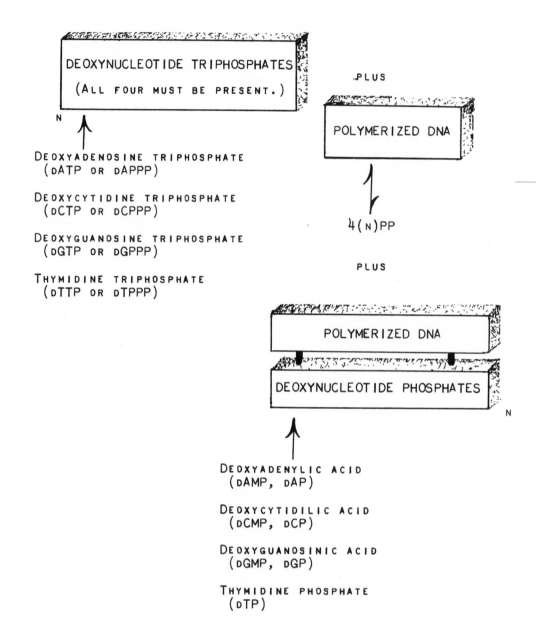

DEOXYNUCLEOTIDE TRIPHOSPHATES

(ALL FOUR MUST BE PRESENT.)

N

PLUS

POLYMERIZED DNA

4(N)PP

PLUS

DEOXYADENOSINE TRIPHOSPHATE
(DATP OR DAPPP)

DEOXYCYTIDINE TRIPHOSPHATE
(DCTP OR DCPPP)

DEOXYGUANOSINE TRIPHOSPHATE
(DGTP OR DGPPP)

THYMIDINE TRIPHOSPHATE
(DTTP OR DTPPP)

POLYMERIZED DNA

DEOXYNUCLEOTIDE PHOSPHATES

N

DEOXYADENYLIC ACID
(DAMP, DAP)

DEOXYCYTIDILIC ACID
(DCMP, DCP)

DEOXYGUANOSINIC ACID
(DGMP, DGP)

THYMIDINE PHOSPHATE
(DTP)

MAP 162. REPLICATION OF DEOXYRIBOSE NUCLEIC ACIDS

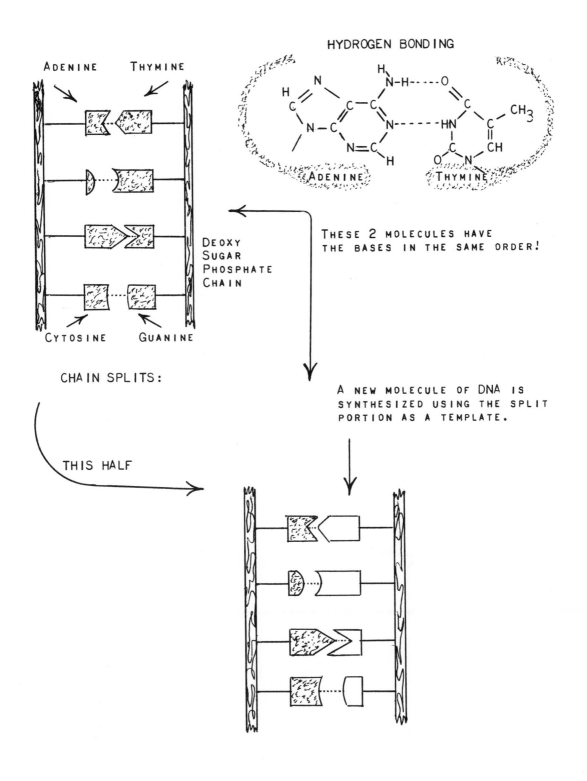

HYDROGEN BONDING

ADENINE   THYMINE

DEOXY
SUGAR
PHOSPHATE
CHAIN

THESE 2 MOLECULES HAVE
THE BASES IN THE SAME ORDER!

CYTOSINE   GUANINE

CHAIN SPLITS:

THIS HALF

A NEW MOLECULE OF DNA IS
SYNTHESIZED USING THE SPLIT
PORTION AS A TEMPLATE.

MAP 163.   REPLICATION OF SEPARATE STRANDS
YIELDS INITIAL STRUCTURE

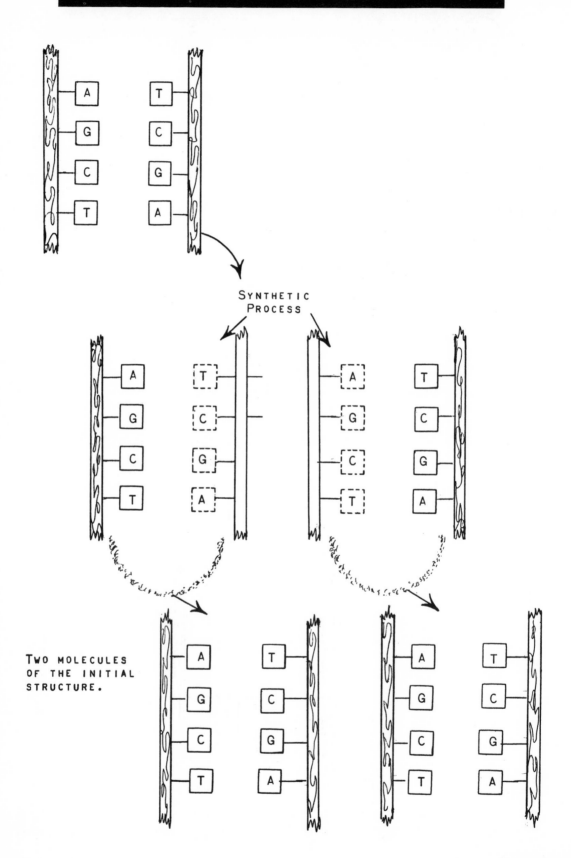

MAP 164. SECOND STAGE REPLICATION OF A SINGLE STRAND

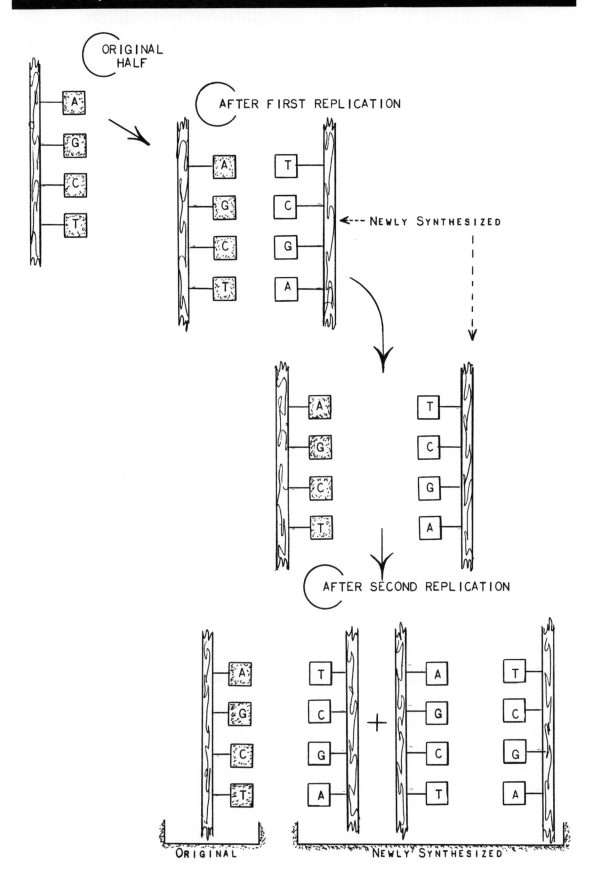

NOTES

Chapter 15
FATTY ACID AND STEROID METABOLISM

(by J. A. Johnston)

TABLE OF CONTENTS

Map No.	Title	Page No.
165	Synthesis and Degradation of Fatty Acids	227
166	Fate of Propanyl-CoA	228
167	Fate of Acetoacetyl CoA; Mevalonic Acid Synthesis	229
168	Squalene (to Farnesyl Phosphates)	230
169	Squalene	231
170	Cyclization of Squalene	233
171	Conformation and Configuration of Steroids	234-7
172	Nomenclature of Steroids	238-41
173	Carotenoids	243
174	Synthesis of Triglycerides and Phosphatides	244
175	Synthesis of Complex Lipids	245

MAP 165. SYNTHESIS AND DEGRADATION OF FATTY ACIDS

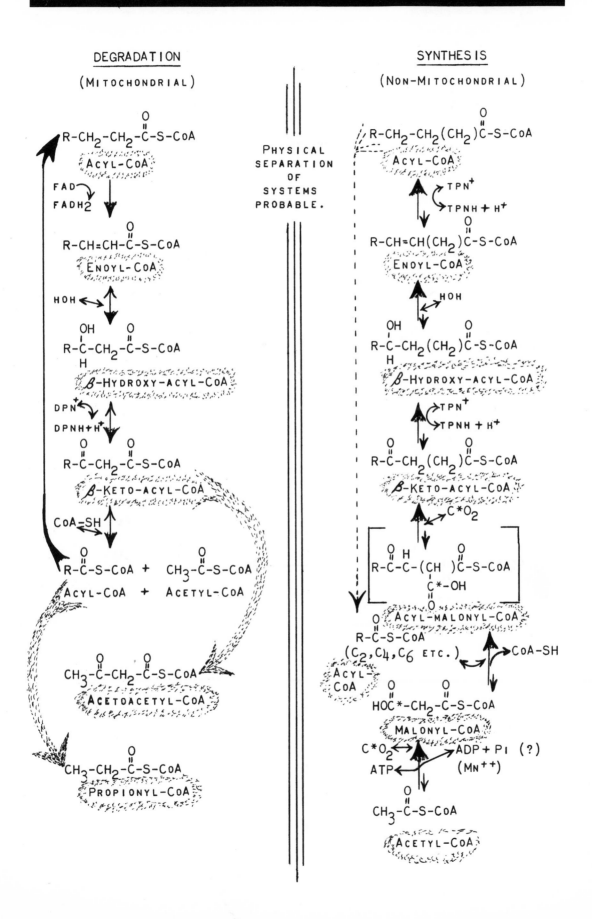

DEGRADATION (MITOCHONDRIAL)

SYNTHESIS (NON-MITOCHONDRIAL)

PHYSICAL SEPARATION OF SYSTEMS PROBABLE.

228

MAP 166. FATE OF PROPANYL-CoA

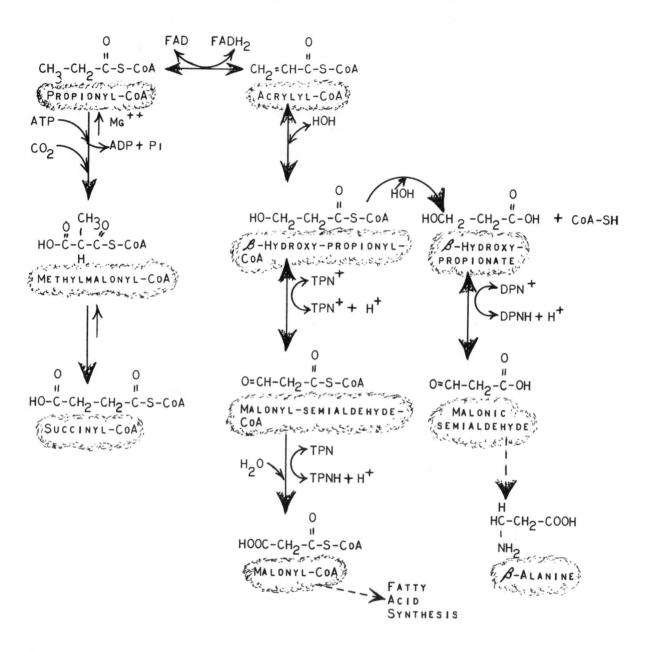

J. Biol. Chem., 229: 997 (1957)

J. Biol. Chem., 234" 2272 (1959)

J. Biol. Chem., 234: 1666 (1959)

J. Biol. Chem., 234: 1394 (1959)

MAP 167.   FATE OF ACETOACETYL CoA: MEVALONIC ACID SYNTHESIS

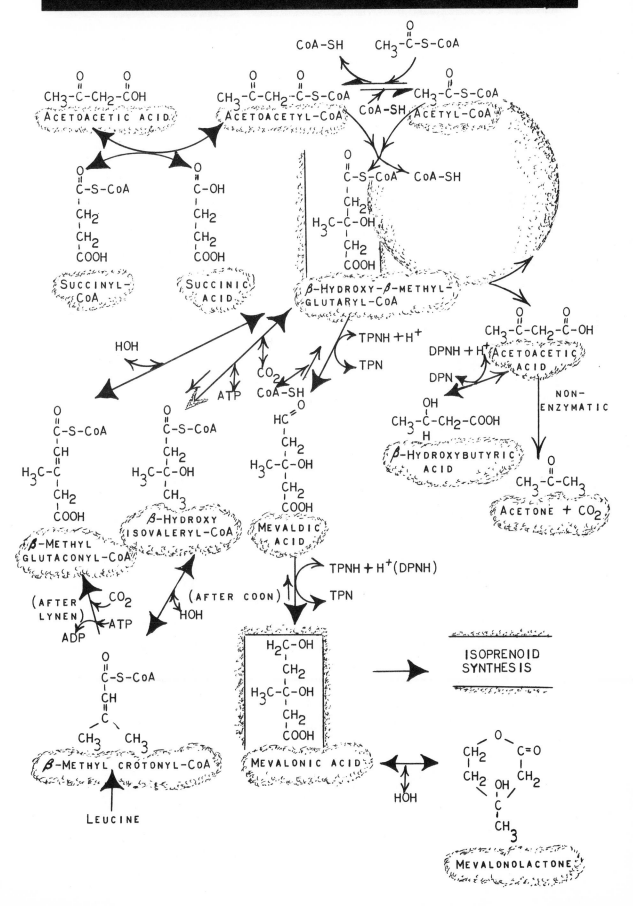

230

MAP 168.   BIOSYNTHESIS OF SQUALENE (TO FARNESYL PYROPHOSPHATE)

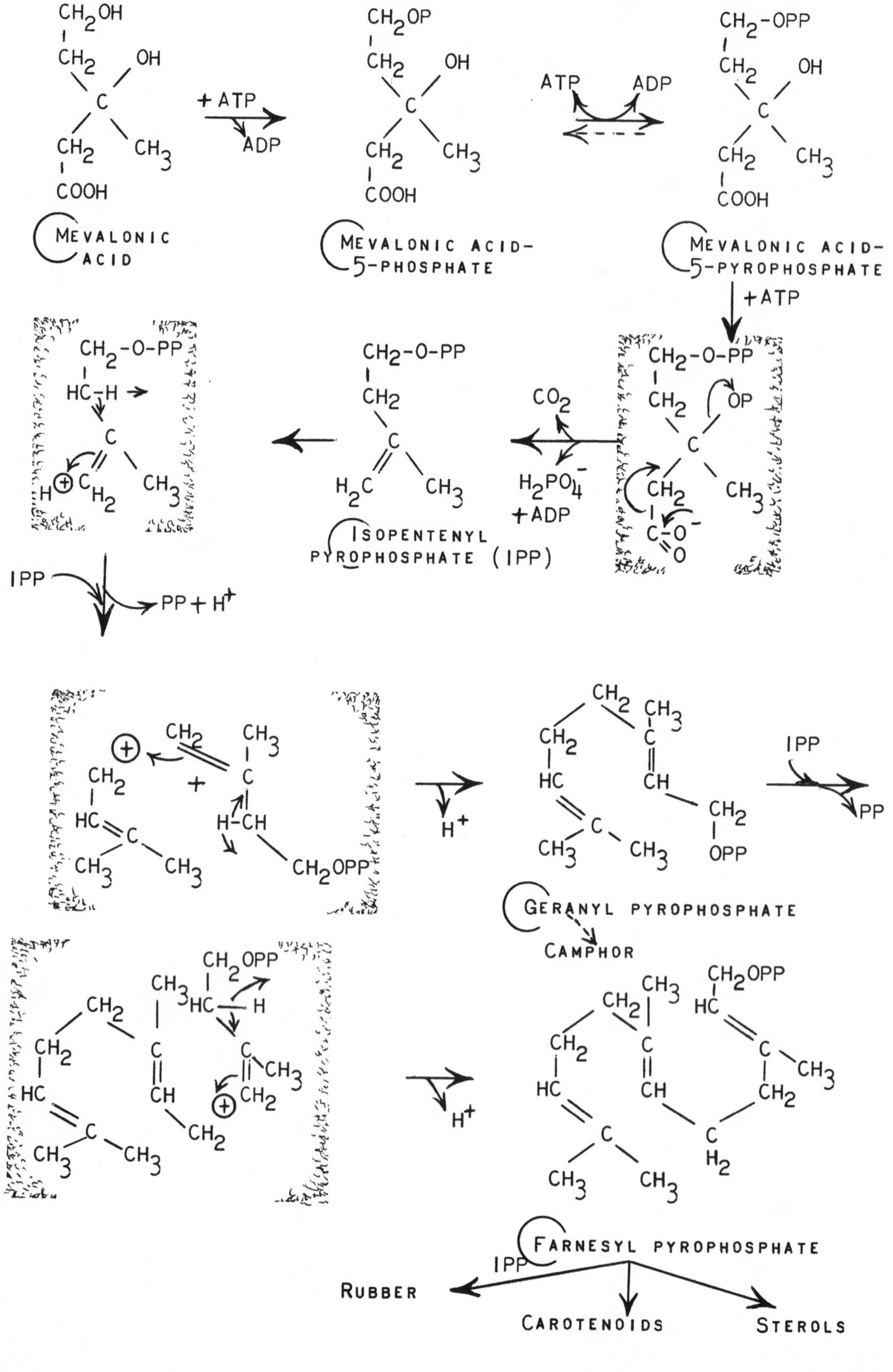

MAP 169.   BIOSYNTHESIS OF SQUALENE (TO SQUALENE)

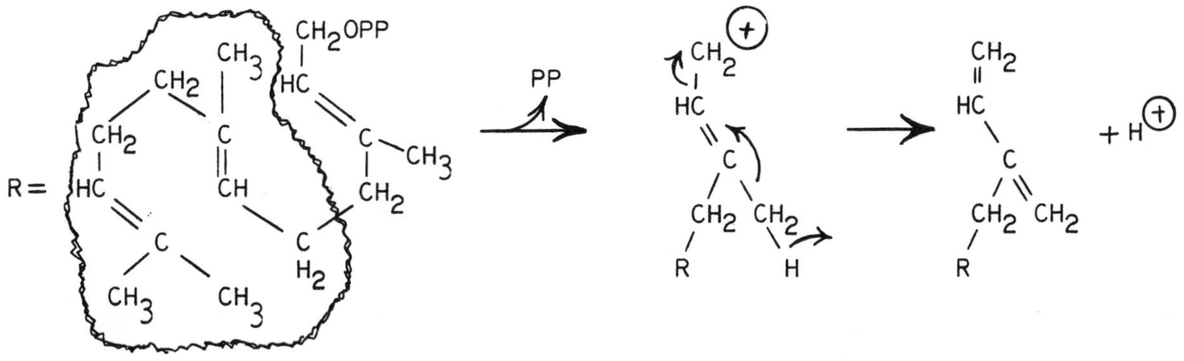

FARNESYL PYROPHOSPHATE

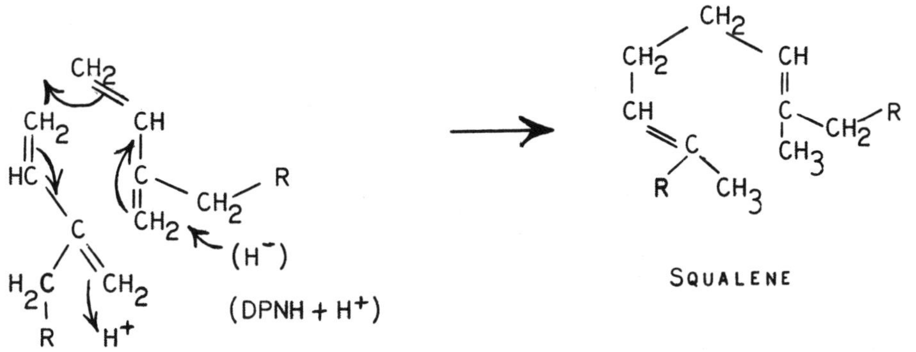

2 FARNESYL PYROPHOSPHATES

(H⁻)

(DPNH + H⁺)

SQUALENE

NOTES

MAP 170. CYCLIZATION OF SQUALENE

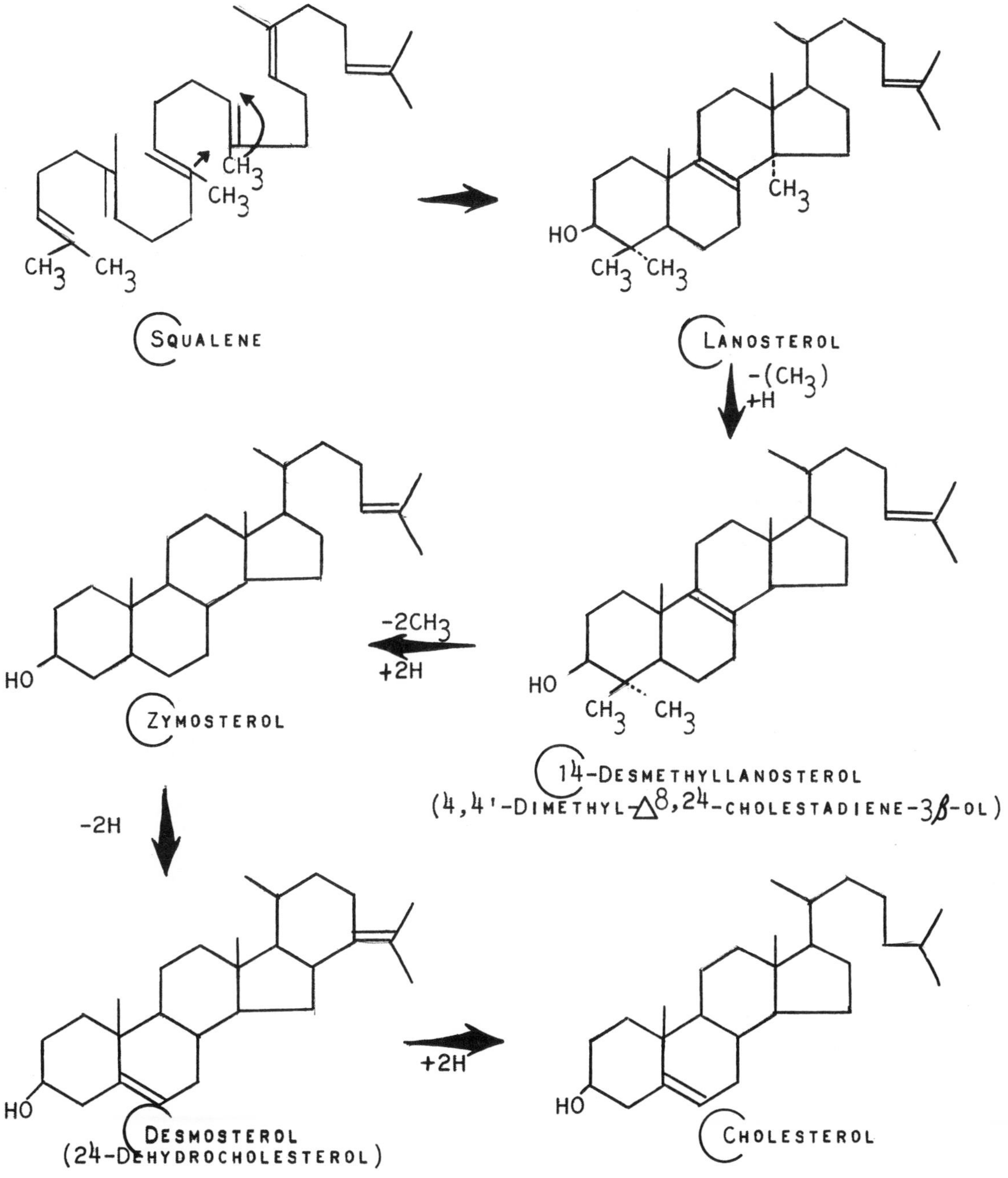
CH3
CH3
CH3 CH3
SQUALENE
HO
CH3
CH3 CH3
LANOSTEROL
-(CH3)
+H
HO
CH3 CH3
14-DESMETHYLLANOSTEROL
(4,4'-DIMETHYL-Δ8,24-CHOLESTADIENE-3β-OL)
-2CH3
+2H
HO
ZYMOSTEROL
-2H
HO
DESMOSTEROL
(24-DEHYDROCHOLESTEROL)
+2H
HO
CHOLESTEROL

MAP 171. CONFORMATION AND CONFIGURATION OF STEROIDS

1. THE STEROIDS ARE COMPOUNDS CHEMICALLY RELATED TO CHOLESTEROL. THE FUNDAMENTAL CARBON SKELETON OF THESE COMPOUNDS IS THE CYCLO-PENTANO-PERHYDRO-PHENANTHRENE RING.

CYCLO-PENTANO-PERHYDRO-PHENANTHRENE

2. ASSUME THAT THE CYCLO-PENTANO-PERHYDRO-PHENANTHRENE MOLECULE LIES FLAT IN THE PLANE OF THE PAPER. THE HYDROGENS ATTACHED TO THE CARBONS OF THE RINGS WILL PROJECT BELOW AND ABOVE THE PLANE OF THE PAPER. THOSE HYDROGENS LYING BELOW THE PLANE OF THE PAPER ARE BONDED BY A DASHED LINE (---H) AND ARE CALLED ALPHA (α) LINKAGE WHILE THOSE PROJECTING ABOVE THE PAPER ARE SHOWN BY A SOLID LINE (—H), A BETA (β) LINKAGE.

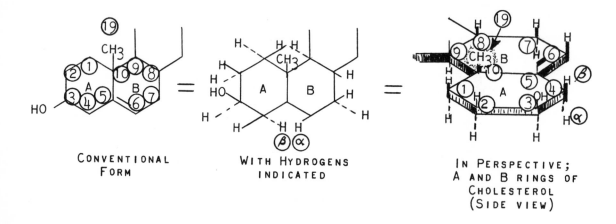

CONVENTIONAL FORM

WITH HYDROGENS INDICATED

IN PERSPECTIVE; A AND B RINGS OF CHOLESTEROL (SIDE VIEW)

MAP 171. CONFORMATION AND CONFIGURATION OF STEROIDS

3. IN THE CASE OF CHOLESTEROL THE ANGULAR METHYL GROUPS, CARBONS 18 AND 19, ALWAYS LIE IN THE PLANE ABOVE THE PAPER, I.E. THEY HAVE BETA LINKAGES. THE SPATIAL POSITIONS OF THE HYDROGENS (OR OTHER GROUPS) ON THE ASYMMETRIC CARBONS OF THE MOLECULE ARE RELATIVE TO THE POSITIONS OF THE ANGULAR METHYLS.

CHOLESTEROL

(• = CENTERS OF ASYMMETRY)
ASYMMETRIC CARBONS:
3, 5, 8, 9, 10,
13, 14, 17, 20.

CHOLESTANOL
A/B TRANS, B/C TRANS, C/D TRANS

COPROSTANOL
A/B CIS, B/C TRANS, C/D TRANS

MAP 171.   CONFORMATION AND CONFIGURATION OF STEROIDS

4. THE REDUCTION OF CHOLESTEROL YIELDS DIHYDROCHOLESTEROL WHICH MAY
    BE RESOLVED INTO TWO COMPONENTS, CHOLESTANOL AND COPROSTANOL,
    DIFFERING ONLY IN THE CONFIGURATION OF THE H ON CARBON 5.

    FOR CHOLESTANOL THE H ON CARBON 5 HAS AN ALPHA LINKAGE RELATIVE
    TO THE METHYL GROUP ON CARBON 10 WHICH BY DEFINITION HAS A BETA
    LINKAGE. THE H AND METHYL THEN LIE ON OPPOSITE SIDES OF THE
    CHOLESTANOL MOLECULE AND ARE TRANS (SOMETIMES CALLED ALLO) WITH
    RESPECT TO EACH OTHER. SINCE RINGS A AND B SHARE THE ASYMMETRIC
    CARBONS 5 AND 10, THE SPATIAL RELATIONSHIP BETWEEN THE SUBSTITUENTS
    ON THESE CARBONS IS DESCRIBED BY THE EXPRESSION A/B TRANS OR A:B
    TRANS. SIMILARLY THE RELATIONSHIP OF SUBSTITUENTS ON CARBONS 8
    AND 9 AND ON CARBONS 13 AND 14 ARE INDICATED BY B/C TRANS AND C/D
    TRANS RESPECTIVELY. THE HYDROXYL GROUP IS ATTACHED BY A BETA
    LINKAGE TO CARBON 3. THE STERIO ISOMERISM OF COPROSTANOL MAY BE
    DESCRIBED IN A SIMILAR MANNER.

5. BY CONFINING THE NUCLEUS OF THE STEROIDS TO THE SINGLE PLANE OF
    THE PAPER THE CONFIGURATION IN SPACE OF SIX-MEMBERED RINGS, EITHER
    FUSED OR FREE, IN THREE DIMENSIONAL CONFORMATION HAS BEEN IGNORED.
    PERSPECTIVE FORMULAE IN WHICH THE CARBONS OF THE NUCLEUS AS WELL
    AS THEIR SUBSTITUENTS ARE SHOWN IN THREE DIMENSIONS GIVE A MORE
    ACCURATE PICTURE OF THE STEROID MOLECULE.

CHOLESTANOL

MAP 171. CONFORMATION AND CONFIGURATION OF STEROIDS

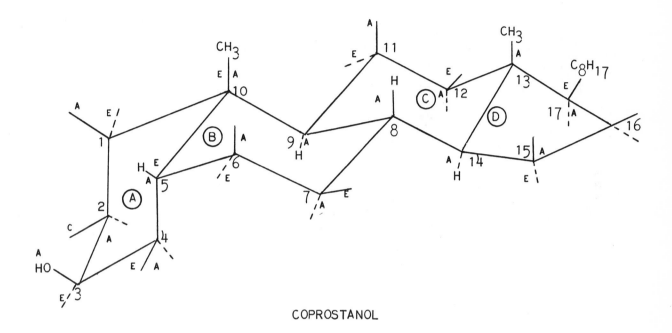

COPROSTANOL

FOR A DISCUSSION OF PERSPECTIVE FORMULAE AND STEROIDS IN GENERAL,
SEE L. F. FIESER AND M. FIESER'S STEROIDS; NEW YORK, REINHOLD
PUBLISHING CORPORATION (1959).

MAP 172. NOMENCLATURE OF STEROIDS

1. KETO GROUPS -- POSITION DESIGNATED -- ENDING "-ONE"

   AS: 17-KETO-ANDROSTANE   OR
   ANDROSTAN-17-ONE

   TWO KETO GROUPS -- ENDING "DIONE"; THREE, "TRIONE" ETC.

   AS: 3,17-KETO-ANDROSTANE   OR
   ANDROSTAN-3,17-DIONE

   DOUBLE BONDS INDICATED BY $\triangle$ -- SUPERSCRIPT SHOWS POSITION, THUS

   $\triangle^4$ = DOUBLE BOND BETWEEN CARBONS 4 AND 5

   THE BASIC HYDROCARBON DESIGNATED AS UNSATURATED BY ENDING "ENE"

   IF THERE IS A POSSIBILITY OF CONFUSION, SPECIFY THE BOND AS:

   $\triangle^{8:9}$, $\triangle^{8:14}$ OR $\triangle^{8(9)}$, $\triangle^{8(14)}$

   AS: $\triangle^4$-ANDROSTEN-17-ONE

   $\triangle^{3,5}$-ANDROSTENDIEN-17-ONE

   HYDROXY GROUPS -- USE HYDROXY OR ENDING "OL"

   AS: ANDROSTAN-3-OL
   ANDROSTAN-3-OL-17-ONE

2. THE STEROIDS MAY BE DIVIDED ON THE BASIS OF SUBSTITUENTS ON CARBON 17

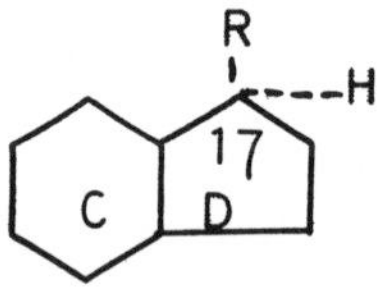

R	SUBSTANCE
-H	ANDROGENS
-H	ESTROGENS
2 CARBON CHAIN	PROGESTERONE AND ADRENAL CORTICAL STEROIDS
5 CARBON CHAIN	BILE ACIDS
8, 9, OR 10 CARBON CHAIN	STEROLS

MAP 172. NOMENCLATURE OF STEROIDS

3. THE BASIC HYDROCARBONS FROM WHICH THE STEROID MAY BE CONSIDERED TO BE DERIVED:

A. THE BASIC NUCLEUS OF THE STEROLS IS USUALLY REFERRED TO AS THE HYDROGENATED NUCLEUS OF THE PARENT SUBSTANCE. HENCE, CHOLESTEROL IS $\triangle$5-CHOLESTENE-3β-OL. (FOR FORMULA SEE MAP 171.) LANOSTEROL WOULD BE 4-DIMETHYL-14-α-METHYL-$\triangle$8(9)CHOLESTRIENE. MOST FREQUENTLY THE TRIVIAL NAMES OF THE STEROLS ARE USED AND MODIFICATIONS OF THE STEROL ARE INDICATED BY PREFIXES OR SUFFIXES ON THE TRIVIAL NAME, E.G. AN ADDITIONAL DOUBLE BOND IN THE CHOLESTEROL MOLECULE BETWEEN CARBONS 7 AND 8 WOULD BE CALLED 7-DEHYDROCHOLESTEROL OR $\triangle$7-CHOLESTEROL.

B. BILE ACIDS:

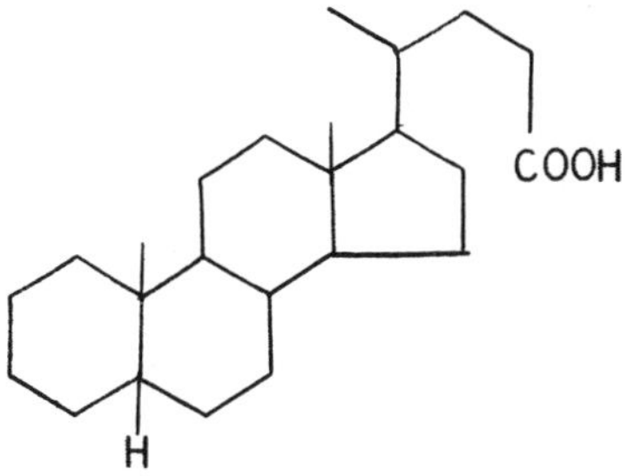

CHOLANIC ACID
A:B = CIS

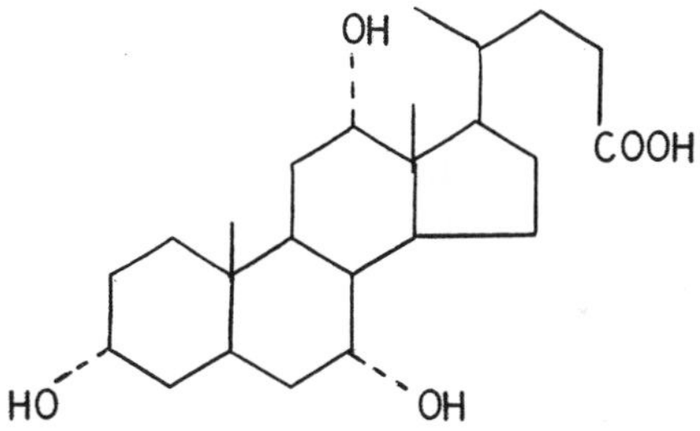

CHOLIC ACID
(3α-, 7α-, 12α-TRIHYDROXY-CHOLANIC ACID)

240

MAP 172. NOMENCLATURE OF STEROIDS

C. ANDROGENS AND ESTROGENS:

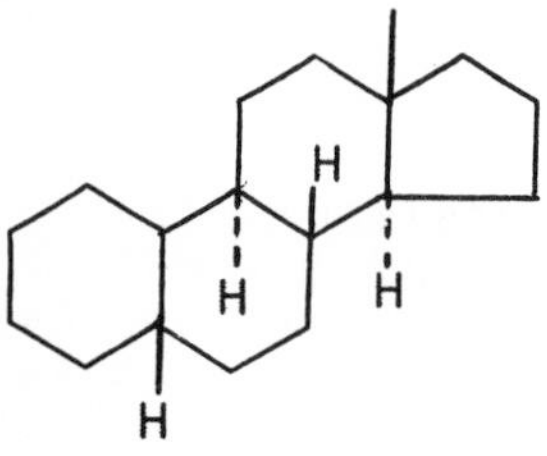

ESTRANE

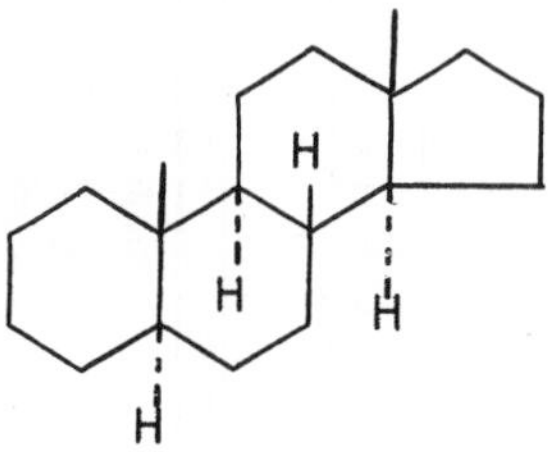

ANDROSTANE

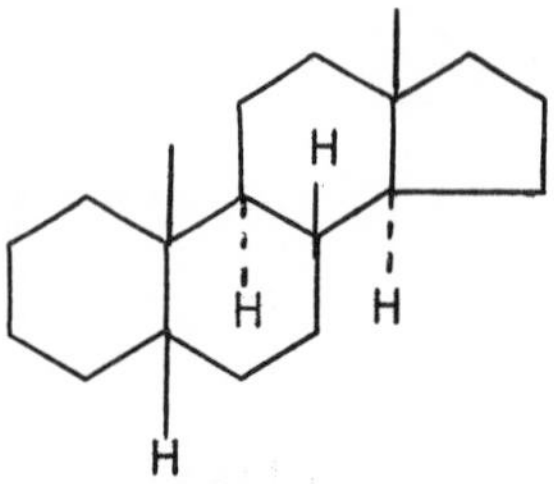

5β-ANDROSTANE
(ETIOCHOLANE)

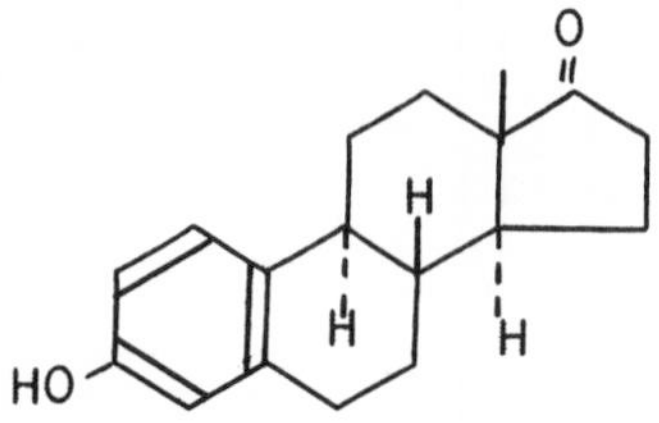

ESTRONE
(Δ¹,Δ³,Δ⁵-ESTRATRIENE-
3β-OL-17-ONE)

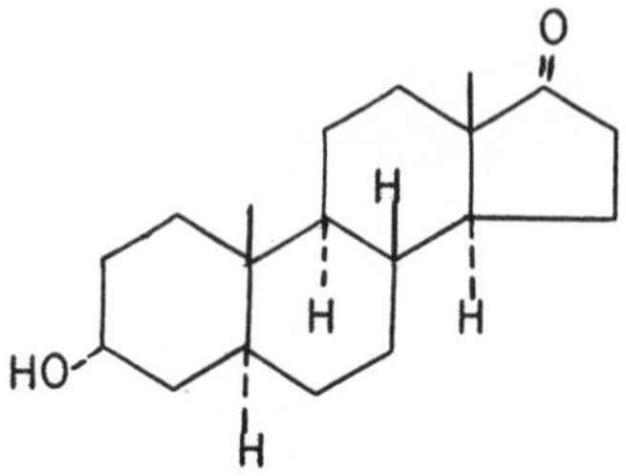

ANDROSTERONE
(ANDROSTANE-3α-
OL-17-ONE)

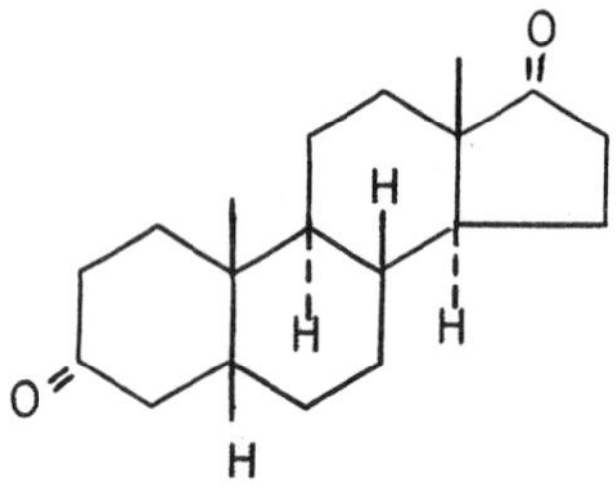

5β-ANDROSTANE-3,
17-DIONE

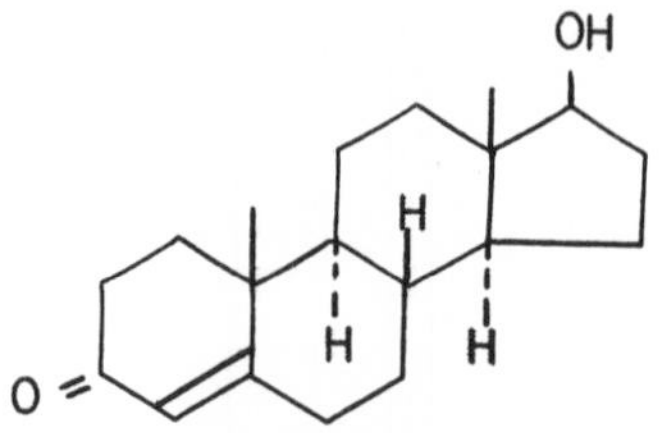

TESTOSTERONE
(Δ⁴-ANDROSTENE-3-ONE-17-OL)

MAP 172. NOMENCLATURE OF STEROIDS

D. PROGESTERONE AND ADRENAL CORTICAL STEROIDS:

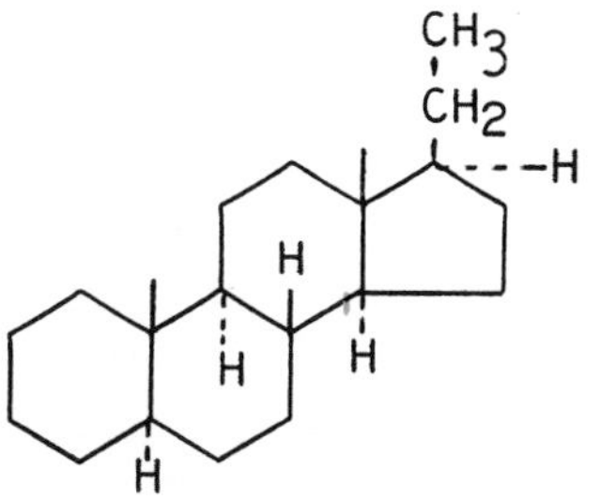

5α-PREGNANE
(ALLOPREGNANE)

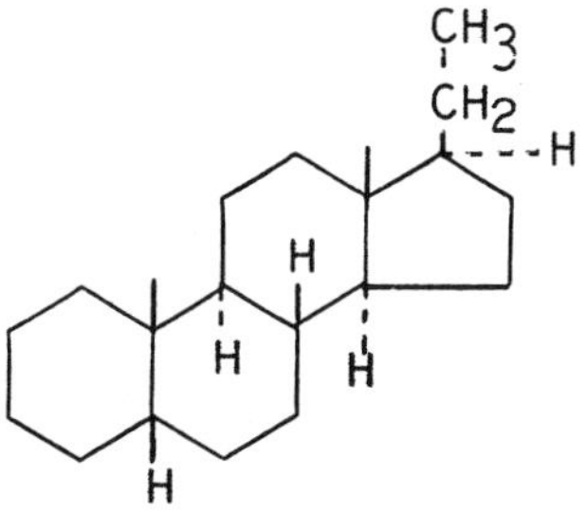

PREGNANE
(5β-PREGNANE)

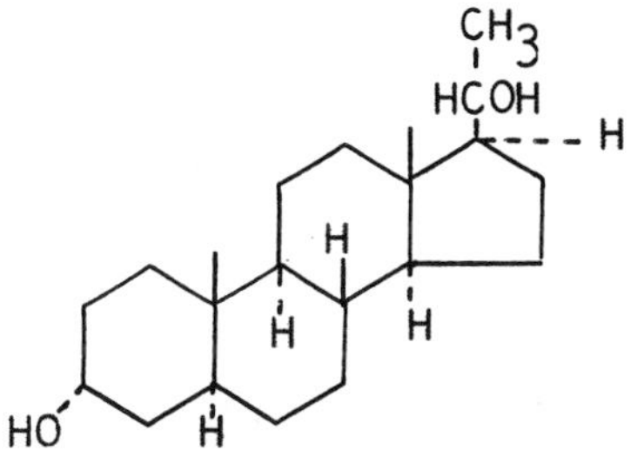

5α-PREGNANE-3α,20α-DIOL

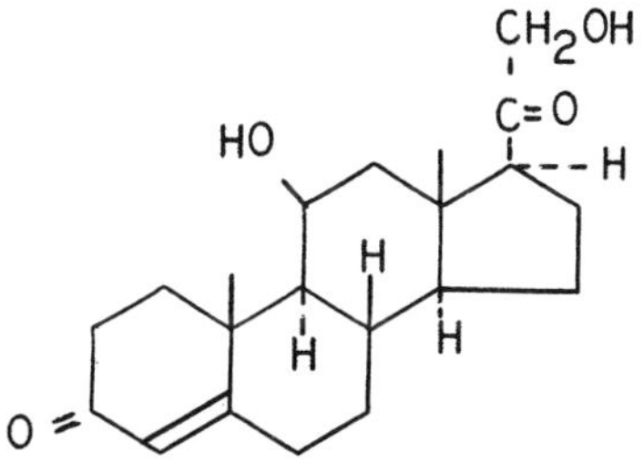

CORTICOSTERONE
(Δ^4-PREGNENE-11β,21-DIOL-3,20-DIONE)

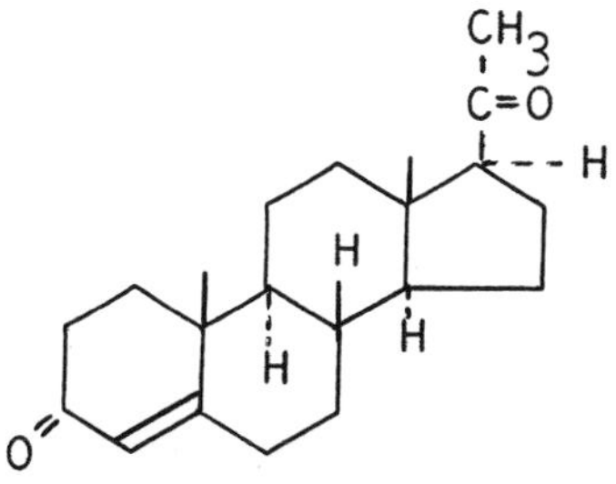

PROGESTERONE
(Δ^4-PREGNENE-3,20-DIONE)

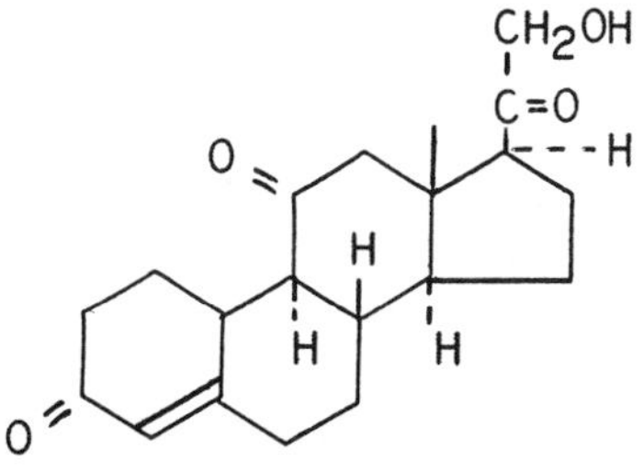

11-DEHYDROCORTICOSTERONE
(Δ^4-PREGNENE-21-OL-3,11,20-TRIONE)

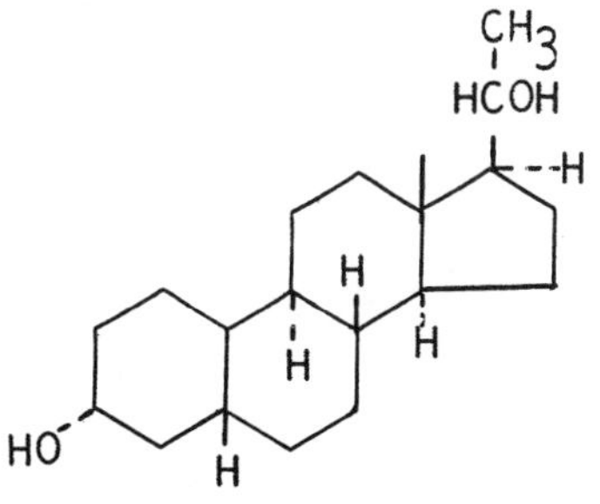

PREGNANEDIOL
(5β-PREGNANE-3α,20α-DIOL)

NOTES

MAP 173. CAROTENOIDS

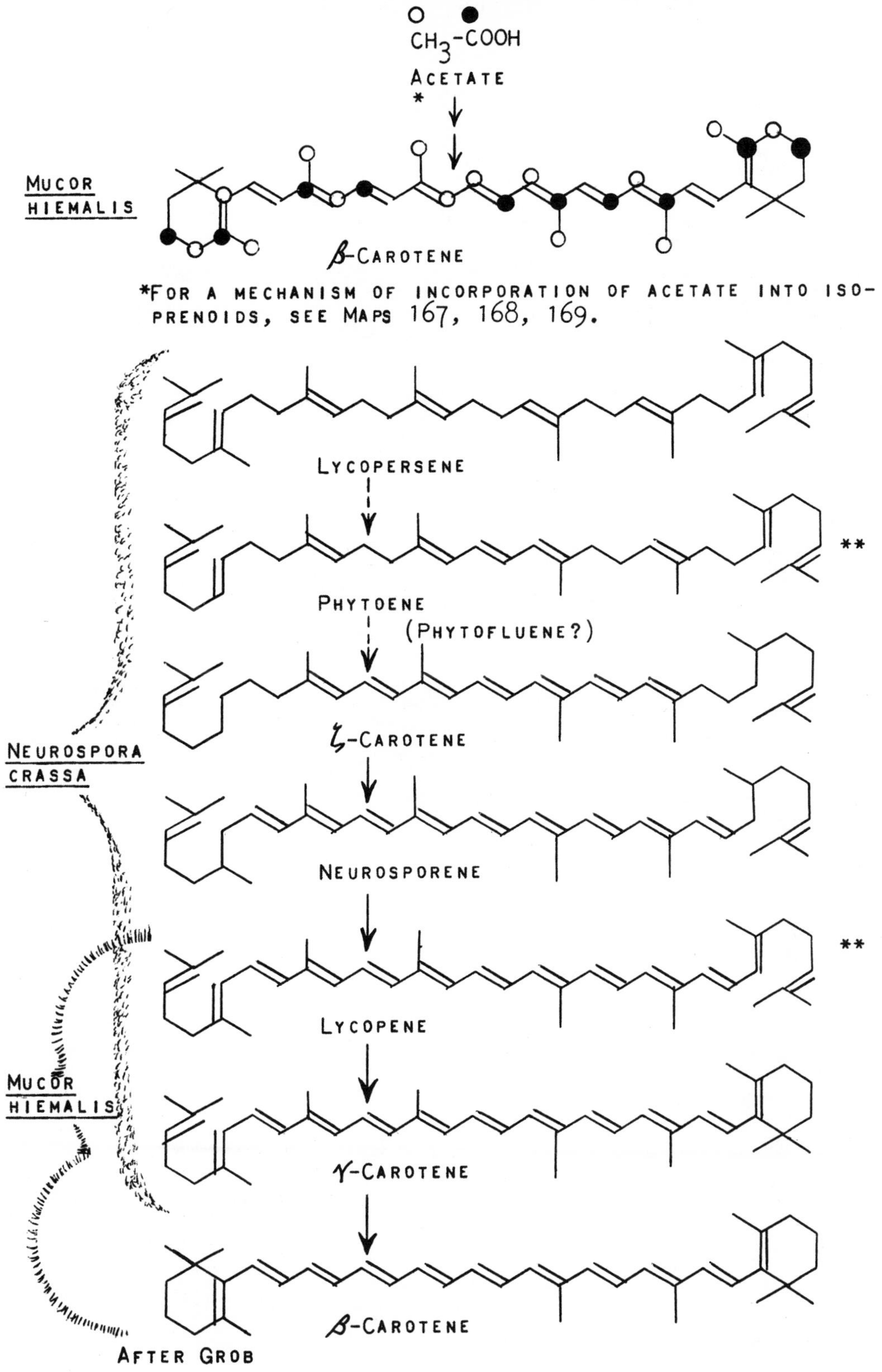

$$\underset{O}{\overset{\circ}{}}\quad \underset{}{\overset{\bullet}{}}$$
$$CH_3-COOH$$
ACETATE
*

MUCOR HIEMALIS

β-CAROTENE

*FOR A MECHANISM OF INCORPORATION OF ACETATE INTO ISO-
PRENOIDS, SEE MAPS 167, 168, 169.

LYCOPERSENE

PHYTOENE
(PHYTOFLUENE?)

ζ-CAROTENE

NEUROSPORA
CRASSA

NEUROSPORENE

LYCOPENE **

MUCOR
HIEMALIS

γ-CAROTENE

β-CAROTENE

AFTER GROB

** Purcell, Thompson and Bonner, J. Biol. Chem., 234, 1081, 1959, show that Phytoene and Lycopene cannot serve as precursors of β, γ, and ζ-Carotenes in Tomato Fruit.

244

MAP 174. SYNTHESIS OF TRIGLYCERIDES AND PHOSPHATIDES

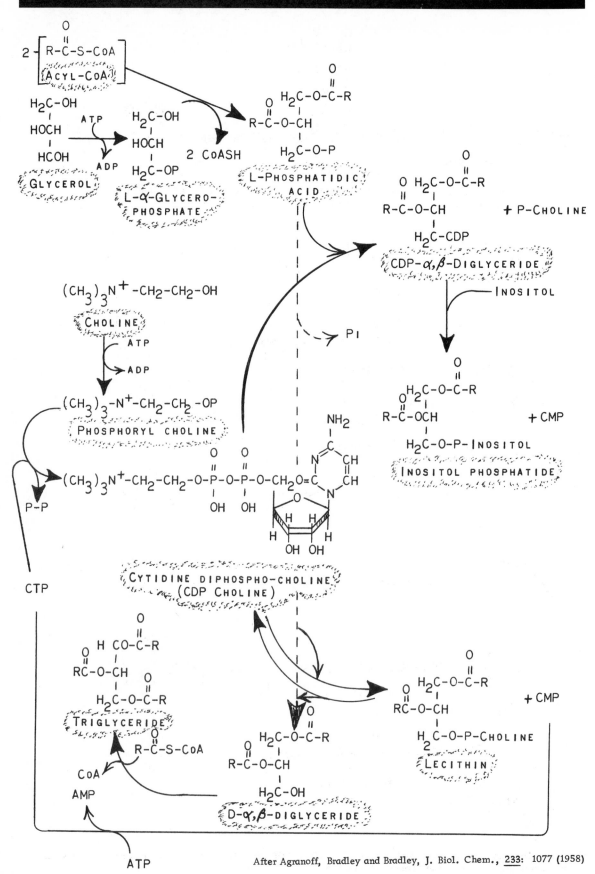

After Agranoff, Bradley and Bradley, J. Biol. Chem., 233: 1077 (1958)

MAP 175. SYNTHESIS OF COMPLEX LIPIDS

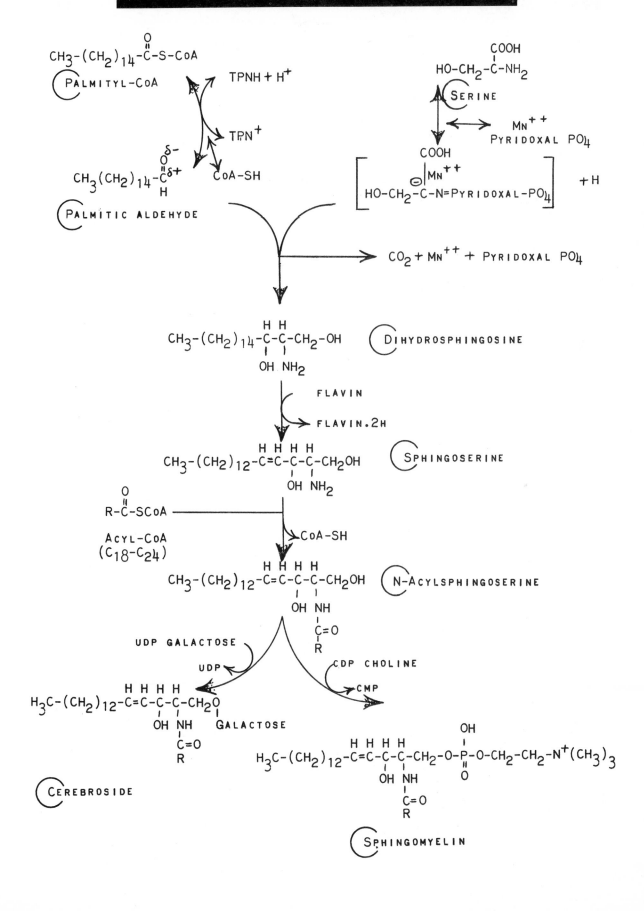

NOTES

Chapter 16
OTHER REACTIONS

TABLE OF CONTENTS

Map No.	Title	Page No.
176	The Choline Cycle	249
177	Creatine Synthesis	250
178	"Active" Methionine and Methyl Transfer	251
179	Formic Acid Metabolism	253
180	Formaldehyde Metabolism	255
181	Folic Acid Metabolism	256
182	Folic Acid Coenzymes	257
183	Riboflavin Metabolism	259
184	Biotin	261
185	Vitamin B_{12}	262
186	Porphyrin Synthesis	263
187	Synthesis of Penicillin	264
188	Action of Penicillin	265

MAP 176. THE CHOLINE CYCLE

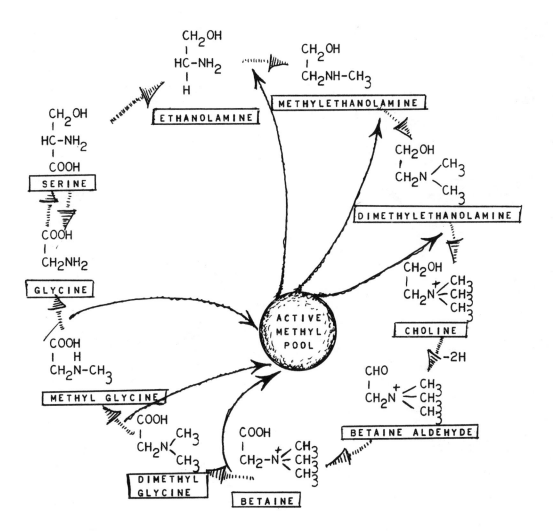

MAP 177. CREATINE SYNTHESIS

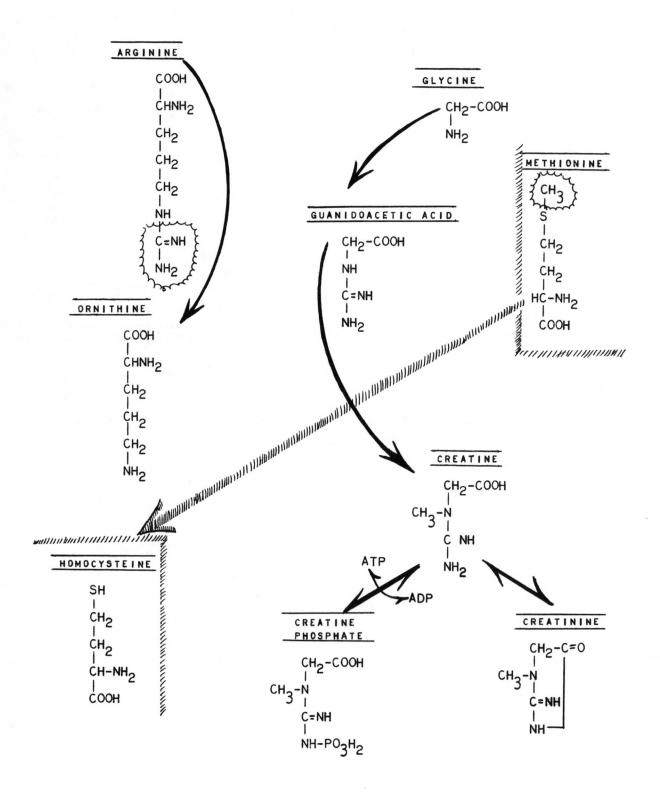

MAP 178.   "ACTIVE" METHIONINE AND METHYL TRANSFER

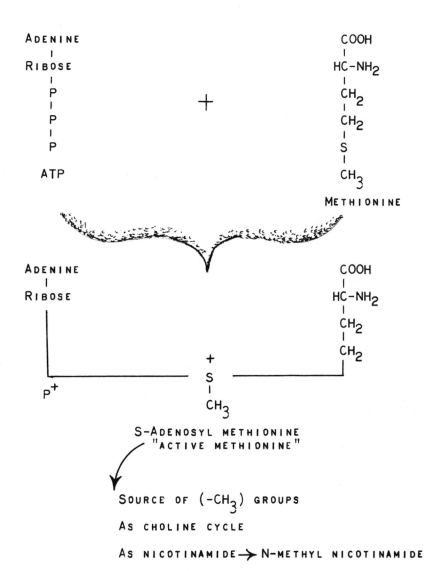

ADENINE
|
RIBOSE
|
P
|
P
|
P
|
P

ATP

\+

COOH
|
HC–NH$_2$
|
CH$_2$
|
CH$_2$
|
S
|
CH$_3$

METHIONINE

ADENINE
|
RIBOSE

COOH
|
HC–NH$_2$
|
CH$_2$
|
CH$_2$

P$^+$

\+
S
|
CH$_3$

S-ADENOSYL METHIONINE
"ACTIVE METHIONINE"

SOURCE OF (–CH$_3$) GROUPS

AS CHOLINE CYCLE

AS NICOTINAMIDE → N-METHYL NICOTINAMIDE

NOTES

MAP 179. FORMIC ACID METABOLISM

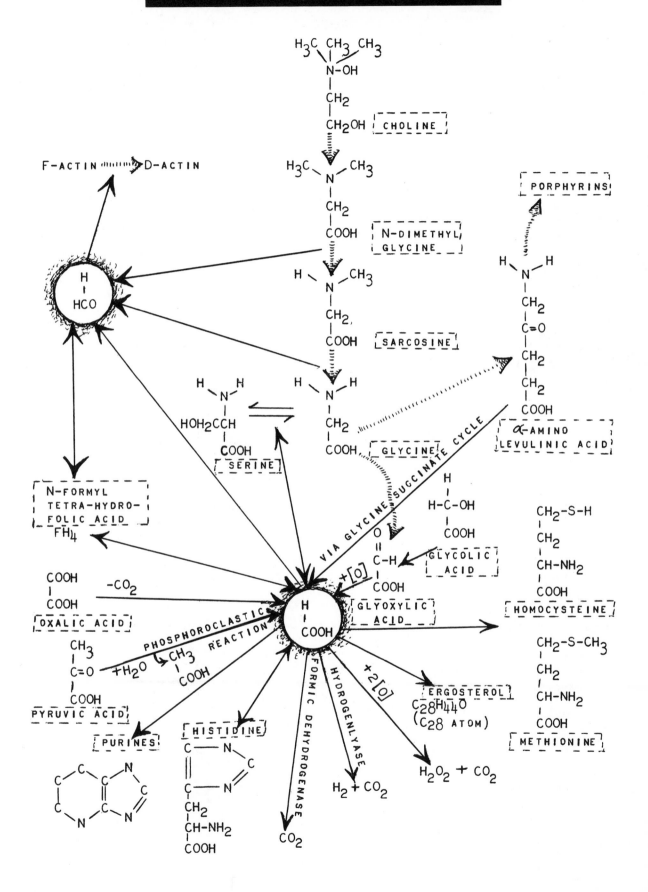

NOTES

MAP 180. FORMALDEHYDE METABOLISM

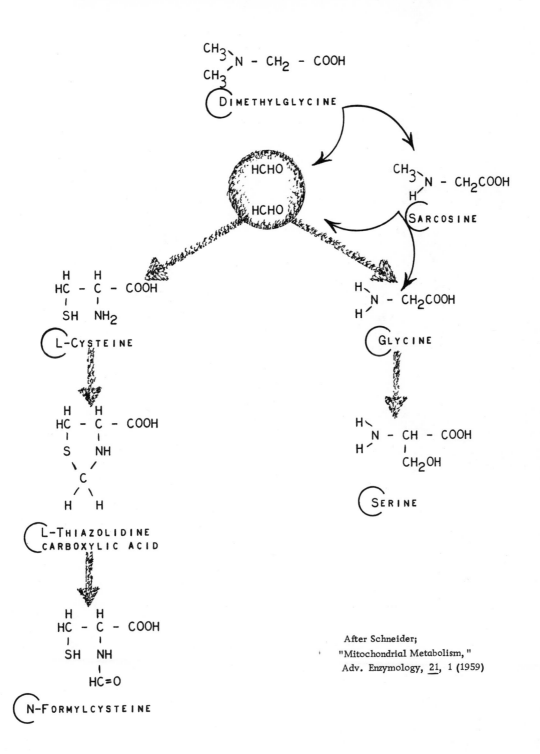

After Schneider;
"Mitochondrial Metabolism,"
Adv. Enzymology, 21, 1 (1959)

MAP 181. FOLIC ACID METABOLISM

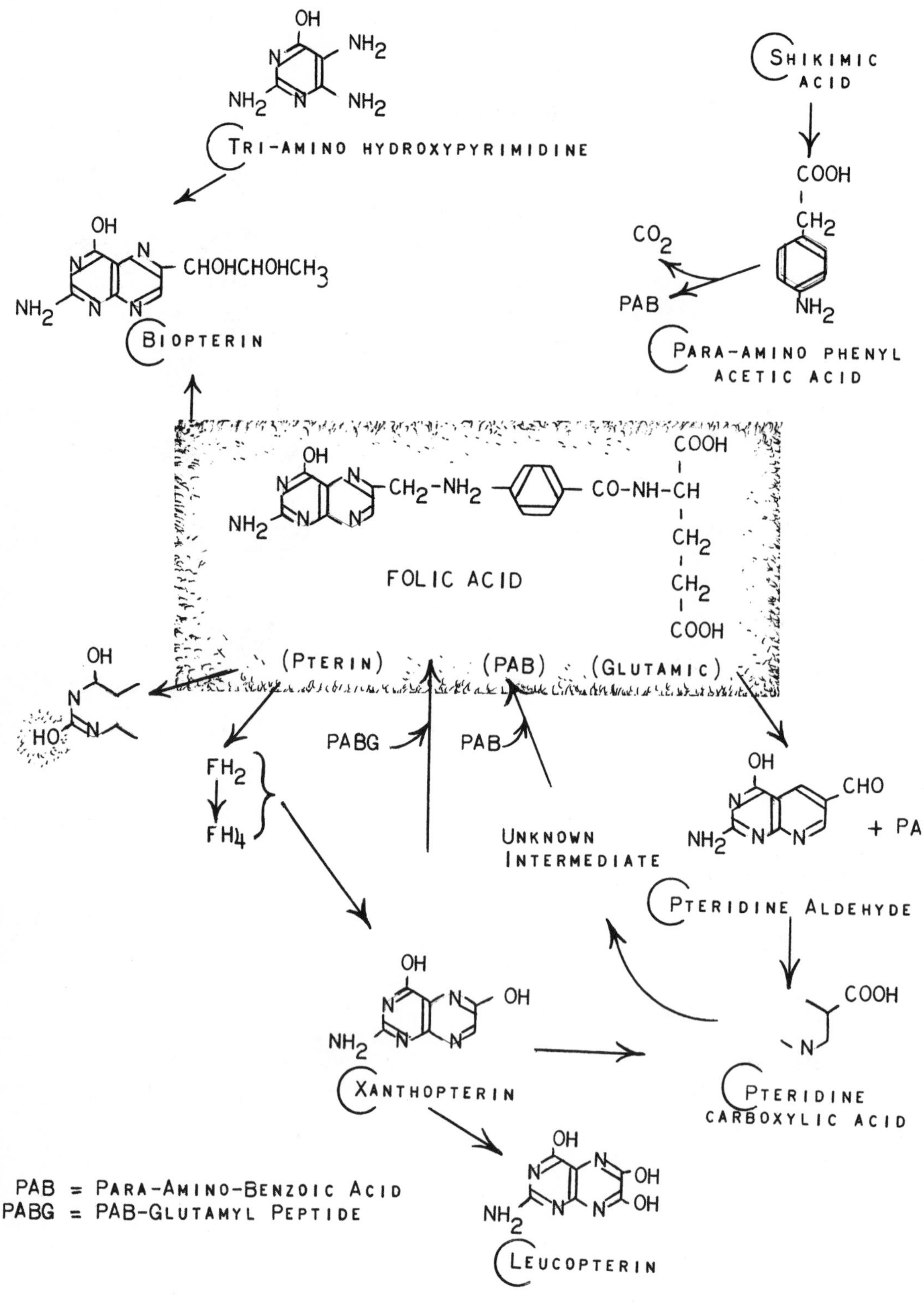

PAB = PARA-AMINO-BENZOIC ACID
PABG = PAB-GLUTAMYL PEPTIDE

MAP 182. FOLIC ACID COENZYMES

(GLUTAMYL) - (PARA-AMINOBENZOYL) - (PTERIDINE)

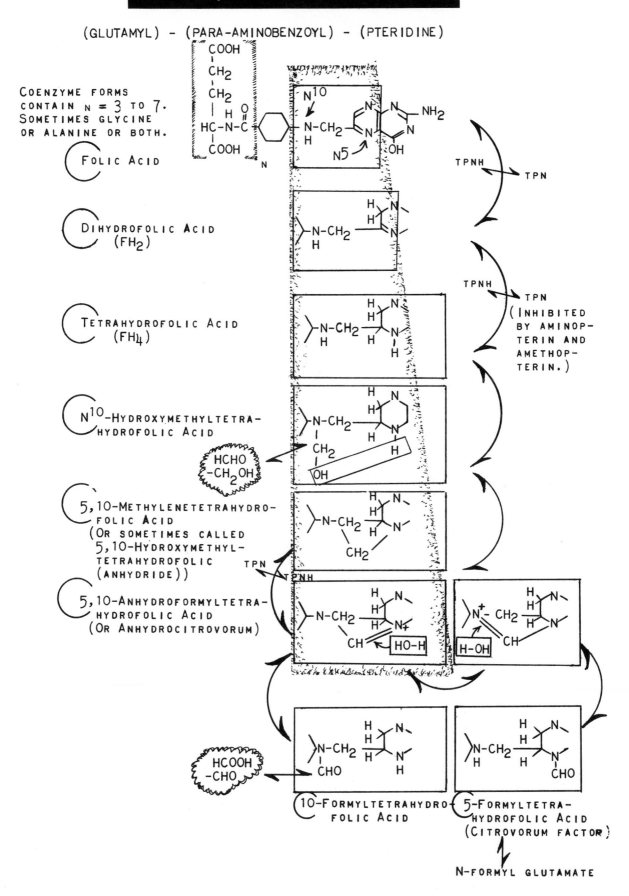

COENZYME FORMS
CONTAIN N = 3 TO 7.
SOMETIMES GLYCINE
OR ALANINE OR BOTH.

FOLIC ACID

DIHYDROFOLIC ACID
(FH$_2$)

TETRAHYDROFOLIC ACID
(FH$_4$)

N^{10}-HYDROXYMETHYLTETRA-
HYDROFOLIC ACID

5,10-METHYLENETETRAHYDRO-
FOLIC ACID
(OR SOMETIMES CALLED
5,10-HYDROXYMETHYL-
TETRAHYDROFOLIC
(ANHYDRIDE))

5,10-ANHYDROFORMYLTETRA-
HYDROFOLIC ACID
(OR ANHYDROCITROVORUM)

TPNH — TPN

TPNH — TPN
(INHIBITED
BY AMINOP-
TERIN AND
AMETHOP-
TERIN.)

TPN
TPNH

HCHO
-CH$_2$OH

HCOOH
-CHO

10-FORMYLTETRAHYDRO-
FOLIC ACID

5-FORMYLTETRA-
HYDROFOLIC ACID
(CITROVORUM FACTOR)

N-FORMYL GLUTAMATE

NOTES

MAP 183.   RIBOFLAVIN METABOLISM

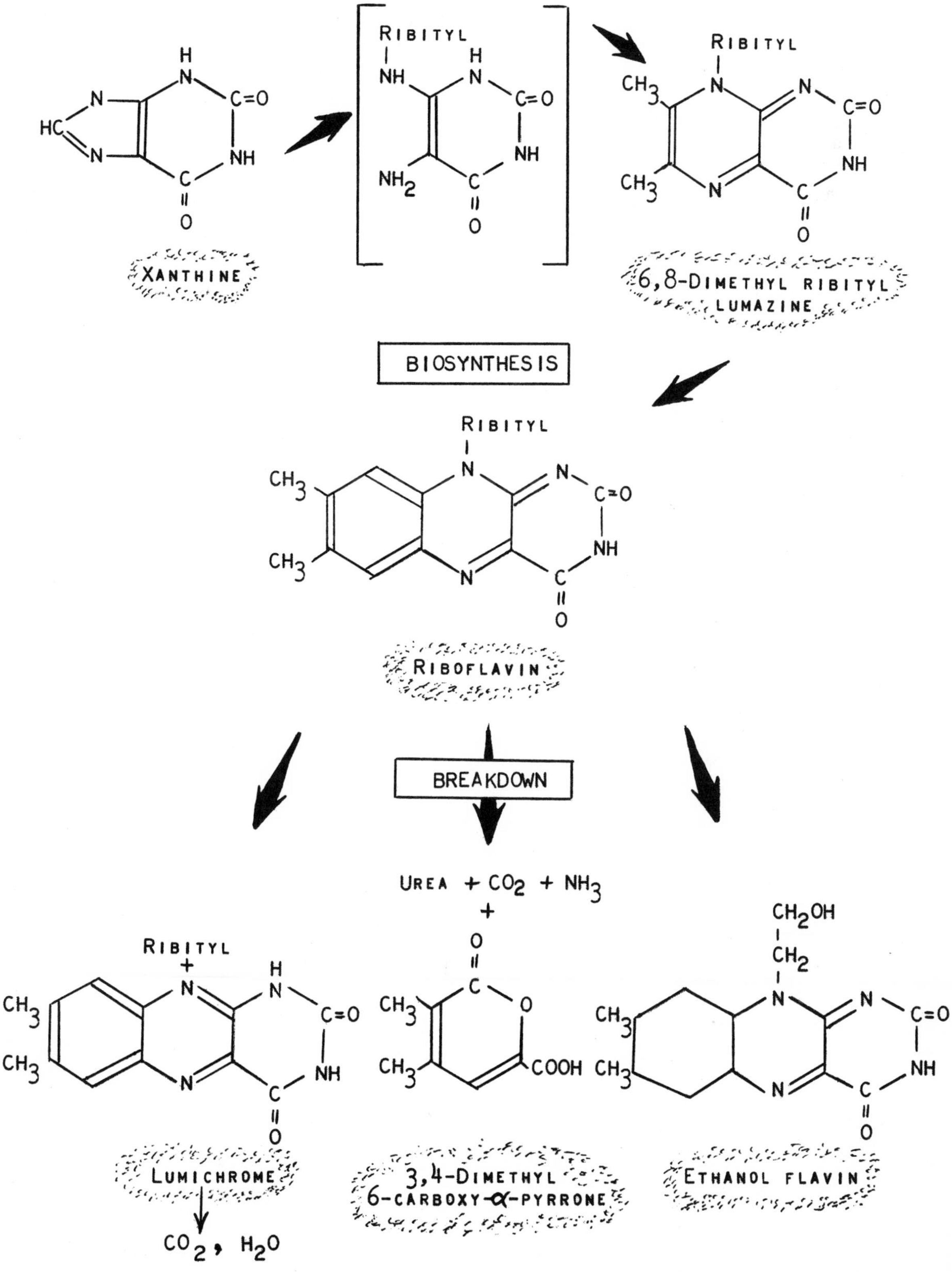

XANTHINE

RIBITYL

6,8-DIMETHYL RIBITYL LUMAZINE

BIOSYNTHESIS

RIBOFLAVIN

BREAKDOWN

$UREA + CO_2 + NH_3$
+

LUMICHROME

CO_2, H_2O

3,4-DIMETHYL 6-CARBOXY-α-PYRRONE

CH_2OH

ETHANOL FLAVIN

NOTES

MAP 184. BIOTIN

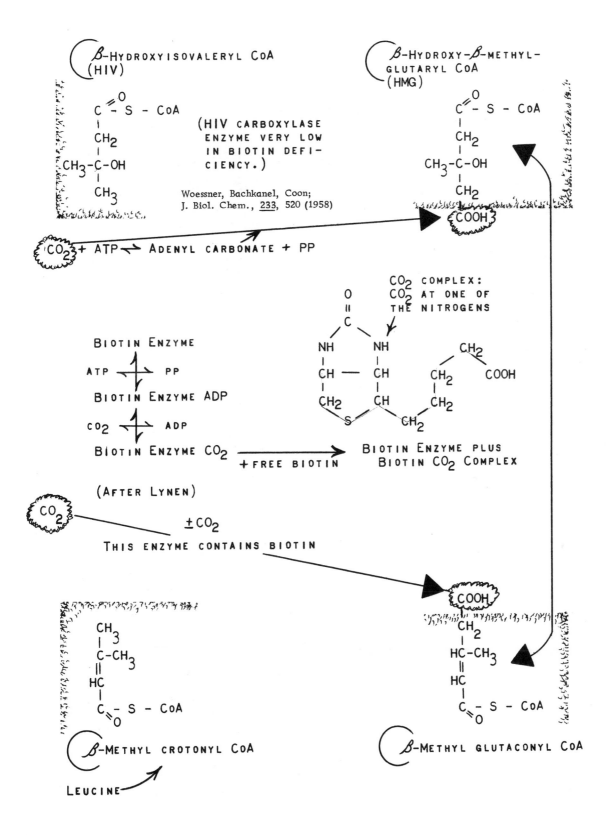

β-HYDROXYISOVALERYL CoA
(HIV)

(HIV CARBOXYLASE
ENZYME VERY LOW
IN BIOTIN DEFI-
CIENCY.)

Woessner, Bachkanel, Coon;
J. Biol. Chem., 233, 520 (1958)

CO_2 + ATP ⇌ ADENYL CARBONATE + PP

β-HYDROXY-β-METHYL-
GLUTARYL CoA
(HMG)

CO_2 COMPLEX:
CO_2 AT ONE OF
THE NITROGENS

BIOTIN ENZYME

ATP ⇌ PP

BIOTIN ENZYME ADP

CO_2 ⇌ ADP

BIOTIN ENZYME CO_2 ——→ BIOTIN ENZYME PLUS
+ FREE BIOTIN   BIOTIN CO_2 COMPLEX

(AFTER LYNEN)

CO_2 ——— ± CO_2

THIS ENZYME CONTAINS BIOTIN

β-METHYL CROTONYL CoA

LEUCINE

β-METHYL GLUTACONYL CoA

MAP 185. VITAMIN B$_{12}$

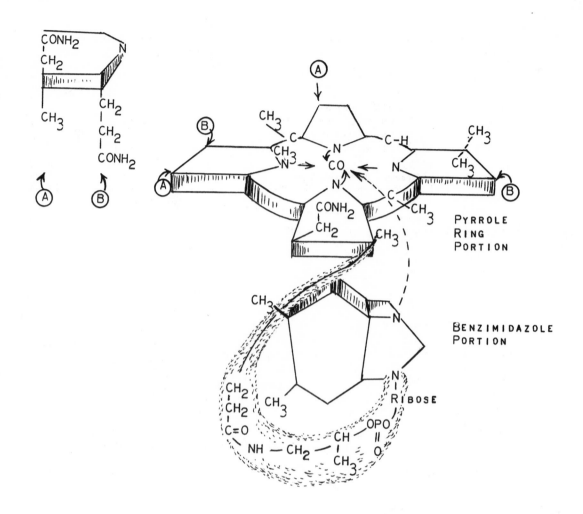

VITAMIN B$_{12}$ FUNCTION

GENERAL:

1. METHYL GROUP SYNTHESIS
2. DEOXYRIBOSIDE SYNTHESIS
3. -S-S- TO 2-SH
4. PROTEIN SYNTHESIS

SPECIFIC:

GLUTAMIC ACID

β-METHYL ASPARTIC ACID

...REQUIRES A COENZYME IN WHICH THE VITAMIN B$_{12}$ IS COMBINED WITH ADENYLIC ACID IN AN UNKNOWN FASHION.

MAP 186. PORPHYRIN SYNTHESIS

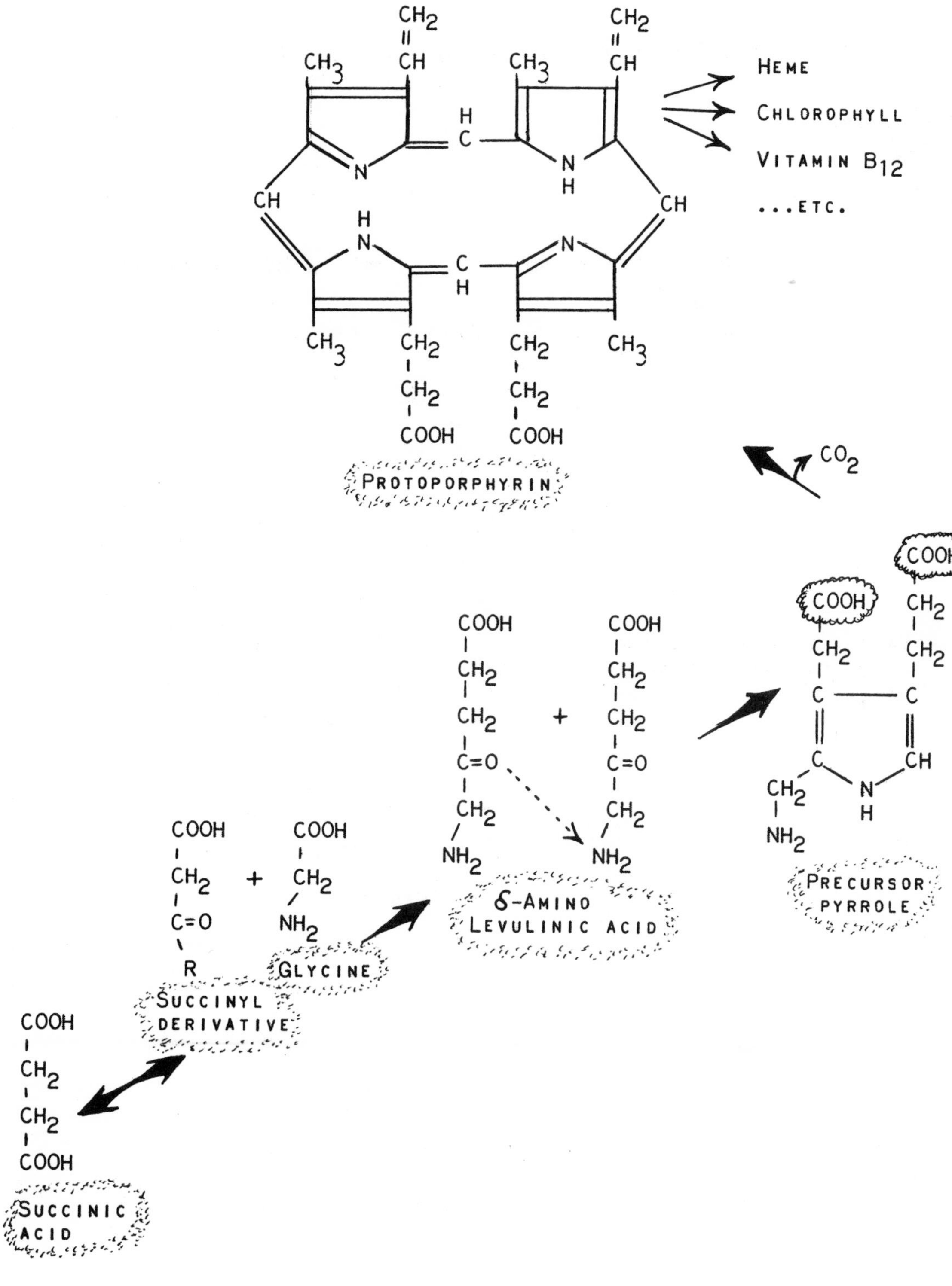

264

MAP 187.   SYNTHESIS OF PENICILLIN

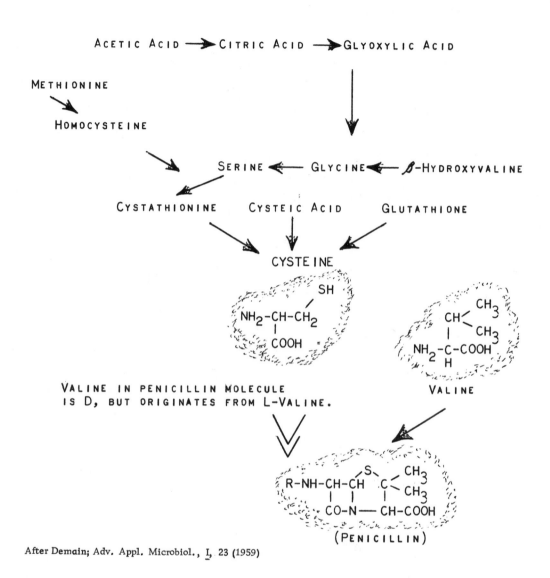

VALINE IN PENICILLIN MOLECULE
IS D, BUT ORIGINATES FROM L-VALINE.

After Demain; Adv. Appl. Microbiol., I, 23 (1959)

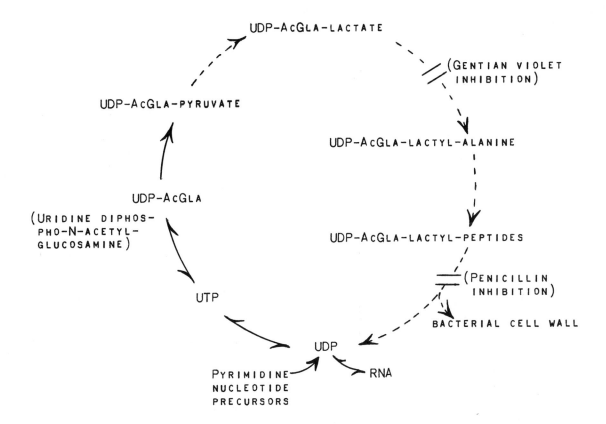

MAP 188.   ACTION OF PENICILLIN

UDP-AcGla-lactate

(Gentian violet inhibition)

UDP-AcGla-pyruvate

UDP-AcGla-lactyl-alanine

UDP-AcGla

(Uridine diphos-pho-N-acetyl-glucosamine)

UDP-AcGla-lactyl-peptides

(Penicillin inhibition)

UTP

Bacterial cell wall

UDP

Pyrimidine nucleotide precursors

RNA

After Strominger, J. Biol. Chem., 234, 1520 (1959)

NOTES

INDEX

A

Acetaldehyde, 9, 87, 89, 91, 131
Acetic acid, 61, 74, 79, 81, 82, 89, 90, 92, 99, 115, 243, 253, 264
Acetoacetic acid, 87, 93, 125, 171, 180, 229
Acetoacetyl CoA, 227, 229
Acetoin, 87, 91
Acetol, 93
Acetolactic acid, 87, 91
Acetone, 87, 93, 229
Acetyl, 142
Acetylations, 87
Acetylbutane diol, 90
Acetylcoenzyme A (acetyl-CoA), 27, 74, 79, 80, 87, 92, 93, 94, 97, 99, 125, 126, 127, 148, 170, 227, 229
Acetylglucoseamine and phosphates, 25, 27
Acetylglutamic acid, 148, 210
Acetylglutamic acid semialdehyde, 148
Acetylkinase, 92
Acetylmethylcarbinol - see Acetoin.
Acetylornithine, 148
Acetylphosphate, 67, 74, 87, 92
Acetylsphingoserine, 245
Aconitic acid, 79, 81
Acrylyl-CoA, 227
Actin, 253
"Active" - in general, see compound
"Active" dihydroxyacetone, 32, 39
"Active" glycolaldehyde, 32, 35, 36, 39, 123
"Active" methionine, 251
Acyl-CoA, 227, 244, 245
Acylmalonyl-CoA, 227
Acyloins, 60, 90, 91
Adenine, 207, 208, 219, 221, 222, 223
Adenosine, 207
Adenosine-5-monophosphate (adenylic acid), 72, 74, 95, 119, 150, 190, 203, 205, 207
Adenosine-5-phosphosulfate (APS), 134
Adenosine-3'-phospho-5'-phosphosulfate (PAPS), 134
Adenosine diphosphate (ADP), 5, 6, 7, 11, 17, 21, 22, 27, 33, 41, 67, 72, 74, 92, 95, 103, 151, 204, 205, 207, 212, 216, 219, 250, 261
Adenosine triphosphate (ATP), 5, 6, 7, 11, 17, 21, 22, 27, 32, 33, 41, 61, 67, 68, 69, 70, 72, 73, 74, 92, 95, 103, 119, 131, 134, 142, 149, 150, 151, 190, 191, 203, 204, 205, 207, 211, 212, 227, 230, 244, 250, 251, 261
Adenyl acetate, 73
Adenyl methionine (adenosyl methionine), 73, 251
Adenylo-amino acids, 119
Adenylo-succinic acid ribotide, 207
Adenyl sulfate, 73
ADP - see Adenosine diphosphate
Adrenal cortical steroids, 238
Adrenalin, 182
Agmatine, 151
AIR, AIR-2, AIR-3, AICR - see under Amino-imidazole
Alanine, 87, 88, 99, 114, 116, 123, 144, 196, 197
Alcohol (see also Ethanol), 72
Alcohol dehydrogenase, 89
Aldehyde mutase, 89
Aldehyde oxidase, 53, 89
Aldolase, 8, 9
Allantoic acid, 99, 208, 209
Allantoin, 208, 209
Allopregnane, 241
Allose-6-phosphate, 37
Alpha-glycerol phosphate, 14, 15, 17
Alpha-glycerol phosphate dehydrogenase, 17
Alpha-methyl-beta-alanine - see Beta-amino isobutyric acid
Amanitine, 195
Amethopterin, 257
Amides, 107
Amine, 147
Amine oxidase (see also Monamine oxidase), 53, 163
Amino acid, 111, 119, 142, 208
Amino acid activation, 119
Amino acid nucleotide complex, 119
Amino acid oxidase, 53, 116, 144
Amino groups, 107, 108
Aminoadipic acid, 157
p-Aminobenzoic acid (PAB, PABA), 112, 256, 257
p-Aminobenzoyl glutamyl peptide (PABG), 256
Aminobenzoyl pyruvic acid, 196
Aminobutyric acid, 115, 126, 151
Aminodicarboxy acid, 108

Aminoethanol, see Ethanolamine
Aminohydroxy benzoyl pyruvic acid, 196
5-Amino-4-imidazole carboxamide acid
    ribotide (AICR), 205
5-Amino-4-imidazole carboxylic acid
    ribotide (AIR-2), 205
5-Amino-4-imidazole ribotide (AIR), 204,
    205
5-Amino-4-imidazole-N-succinyl carbox-
    amide ribotide (AIR-3), 205
Aminoisobutyric acid, 215
Aminoketoadipic acid, 123
Aminoketovaleric acid, 145
Aminolevulinic acid, 82, 123, 253, 263
Aminomethyl trans-cis-muconic acid, 197
Aminophenol glucuronide, 26
p-Aminophenyl acetic acid, 256
Aminopropanol group of vitamin B_{12}, 131
Aminopterin, 257
Ammonia, 27, 74, 99, 107, 108, 109, 112,
    113, 114, 115, 123, 125, 135, 143, 147,
    149, 153, 158, 192, 208, 210, 212, 259
Ammonification, 107
AMP, see Adenosine-5-monophosphate
Amylopectin, 21
Amylose, 21
Androgens, 238
Androstane, 240
5-Beta-Androstane-3,17-dione, 240
Androstane-3-one-17-ol, 240
Androsterone, 240
Anhydrocitrovorum factor - see Anhydro-
    formyl tetrahydrofolic acid
Anhydroformyl tetrahydrofolic acid, 257
Aniline, 26
Aniline glucuronide, 26
Anthranilic acid, 73, 167, 168, 190, 191,
    192, 196
APPP - see Deoxyadenosyl triphosphate
APS, 134
Arabino-γ-lactone, 45
Arabinose, 25, 45, 72
Arabinose oxidase, 53
Arabonic acid, 45, 79, 82, 96
Arginine and phosphates, 67, 73, 116,
    142, 143, 145, 147, 150, 151, 250
Arginino-succinic acid, 142, 150
Aromatic rings, 32, 39
Arterenol - see Nor-adrenaline
Ascorbic acid, 45, 47
Ascorbic oxidase, 53
Asparagine, 113, 114
Aspartic acid, 74, 99, 102, 108, 113, 114,
    116, 137, 142, 144, 149, 150, 157,
    162, 163, 207, 210, 211
Aspartic oxidase, 114

Aspartyl phosphate, 137, 144, 157
Aspartyl semialdehyde, 137, 157
ATP, see Adenosine triphosphate
Auxin, 193
Azaserine, 203

B

Barbituric, 214
Benzaldehyde, 168, 188
Benzimidazole, 262
Benzoic acid, 168, 188
Benzoquinone, 187
Benzoyl formic acid - see Phenylglyoxalic
    acid
Benzyl alcohol, 168, 188
Beta - see compound
Beta-alanine, and ribotide, 102, 114, 214,
    227
Beta-glycerol phosphate, 14
Beta-hydroxybutyric acid, 87, 93, 229
Beta-hydroxybutyryl CoA, 93
Betaine, 249
Betaine aldehyde, 249
Bile acids, 238
Biopterin, 256
Biotin, 94, 149, 205, 261
"Bridge oxygen", 70
Bufotenin, 195
Butyl alcohol, 93
Butylene glycol, 87, 90
Butyric acid, 87, 93
Butyric aldehyde, 93
Butyryl CoA, 93

C

Caffeic acid, 167, 175
Camphor, 230
Canaline, 153
Canavanine, 153
Canavano-succinic acid, 153
Carbamyl aspartic acid, 149, 210, 211,
    214
Carbamyl-beta-alanine, 214
Carbamyl glutamic acid, 115, 149
Carbamyl isobutyric acid, 215

Carbamyl phosphate, 74, 142, 143, 147, 149, 210, 211
Carbon dioxide, 32, 34, 41, 61, 79, 83, 89, 92, 93, 94, 99, 101, 103, 129, 147, 149, 151, 192, 193, 205, 210, 227, 229, 230, 245, 253, 259, 261
Carboxylase, 89
Carboxymethyl butenolide, 170
Carboxymuconic acid, 172, 179
Carboxy uracil, 215
Carotenoids, 125, 230
Carotine, 243
Carriers, 71
Catalase, 53
Catechol, 168, 170, 172, 187, 192
Catecholase, 53
CDP - see Cytidine diphosphate
CDP-choline - see Cytidine diphospho-choline
Cerebrosides, 134, 245
Chlorogenic acid, 167, 175
Chlorophyll, 263
Cholanic acid, 239
Cholestanol, 235, 236
Cholesterol, 233, 234, 235, 236, 239
Cholic acid, 239
Choline, 17, 87, 123, 137, 139, 244, 249, 253
Choline cycle, 137, 139, 249, 251
Choline phosphates, 244
Chondroitin, 134
Cis-Aconitic acid - see Aconitic acid
Cis-Muconic acid - see Muconic acid
Citramalic acid, 115
Citratase, 81
Citric acid, 79, 80, 81, 87, 95, 123, 142, 143, 264
Citric acid cycle, 142, 143
Citrovorum factor, 257
Citrulline, 74, 116, 142, 143, 147, 149, 150, 210
CMP - see Cytidylic acid
CO$_2$ - see Carbon dioxide
Cocarboxylase - see Thiamine pyrophosphate
Coenzyme A (CoA), 27, 61, 73, 74, 92, 93, 95, 97, 103, 127, 129, 148, 227, 229, 244, 245
Coenzyme Q, 62, 63
Collagens, 145
Coniferyl alcohol, 175
Conjugation reactions, 26
Copper, 112
Coprostanol, 235, 236, 237
Corticosterone, 241

Coumaric acid, 175
CPPP - see Deoxycytidine triphosphate
Creatine, 151, 250
Creatine phosphate, 67, 250
Creatinine, 151, 250
Cresol, 169
Crotonyl CoA, 93
CTP - see Cytidine triphosphate
Cyclo-pentano-perhydro-phenanthrene, 234
Cystathionine, 135, 136, 137, 139, 264
Cysteic acid, 116, 135, 264
Cysteine, 74, 103, 116, 135, 136, 137, 139, 219, 255
Cysteine sulfenic acid, 135
Cysteine sulfinic acid, 135
Cystine, 116, 135, 173
Cystine disulfoxide, 135
Cytidine diphosphate (CDP), 74, 212, 219
Cytidine diphospho-alpha, beta-diglyceride, 49, 244
Cytidine diphospho-choline, 73, 244, 245
Cytidine triphosphate, 73, 74, 212, 244
Cytidylic acid (CMP), 212, 217, 244, 245
Cytochrone(s), 54, 55, 59, 63, 68, 69, 110
Cytochrome oxidase, 53, 68, 69
Cytosine, 212, 221, 222, 223
Cytosine monophosphate - see Cytidylic acid
Cytosine riboside, 212

D

D-actin, 253
DAMC - see Diacetylmethylcarbinol
Dehydrocholesterol, 233, 239
Dehydrocorticosterone, 241
Dehydroquinic acid, 167
Dehydroshikimic acid, 167
Deoxyadenosyltriphosphate, 73, 220
Deoxycytidine triphosphate, 73, 220
Deoxyguanosine, 74
Deoxyguanosine triphosphate, 73, 220
Deoxynucleic acid, 73, 213, 217, 220, 221, 222, 223
Deoxyribose aldolase, 9, 262
Deoxyribose-1-phosphate, 74, 213
Deoxyribose-5-phosphate, 221, 222, 223
Deoxyuridine-5-phosphate, 213

270

Dephospho-CoA, 103
Desamino-DPN, 199
Desamino-nicotinylmononucleotide
     (d-NMN), 199
Desmasterol, 233
Desmethyl-lanasterol, 233
Dextrin, 21
Diacetyl, 87, 90
Diacetylmethylcarbinol, 90
Diacetylphosphatidic acid, 17
Diacetylreductase, 90
Diamine oxidase, 53, 163
Diaminopimelic acid, 116, 157
Diglyceride, 244
Dihydrocholesterol, 236
Dihydrofolic acid, 256, 257
Dihydronaphthalene-diol, 173
Dihydroorotic acid, 211
Dihydrosphingosine, 245
Dihydrothymine, 215
Dihydrouracil, 214
Dihydrouridylic acid, 214
Dihydroxyacetic acid, 177
Dihydroxyacetone, 5, 17, 32, 39
Dihydroxyacetone phosphate, 3, 4, 8, 9,
     15, 17
Dihydroxychalcone, 175
Dihydroxyfumaric acid, 53, 101
Dihydroxyisovaleric acid, 128
Dihydroxyphenols, 187
Dihydroxyphenylacetaldehyde, 174, 183
Dihydroxyphenylacetic acid, 174, 183
Dihydroxyphenylalanine - see DOPA
Dihydroxyphenylethylamine, - see DOPA-
     mine
Dihydroxyphenylglycollic acid, 171
Dihydroxyphenylglyoxylic acid, 171
Dihydroxyphenylpyruvic acid, 174, 183,
     186
Diiodotyrosine, 185
2,5-Diketogluconic acid, 82, 96
2,5-Diketoglutaric acid, 79
Diketosuccinic acid, 101
Dimethylacrylyl-CoA (see Methylcrotonyl-
     CoA), 125
3,4-Dimethyl-6-carboxy-alpha-pyrrone, 259
Dimethylcholestadiene, 233
Dimethylethanolamine, 249
Dimethylglycine, 249, 253, 255
Dimethyl-14-alpha-methyl-cholestriene,
     239
6,8-Dimethyl-ribityl-lumazine, 259
Dimethyltryptamine, 193
Dinicotinoyl ornithine, 199
1,3-Diphosphoglyceric acid, 3, 4, 10, 11,

13, 67
2,3-Diphosphoglyceric acid, 13
Diphosphopyridine nucleotide, 10, 17, 26,
     45, 48, 54, 55, 56, 57, 60, 61, 63,
     68, 69, 73, 81, 88, 89, 90, 97, 101,
     110, 112, 113, 127, 162, 167, 181, 207,
     211, 227, 229, 231
Dipicolinic acid, 157
DNA - see Deoxynucleic acid
DOPA, 116, 182, 183, 187
DOPAmine, 174, 183
DOPAchrome, 183
DOPAquinone, 183
DPN - see Diphosphopyridine nucleotide
DPN-cytochrome c reductase, 55
DPNH - see Diphosphopyridine nucleotide
DPNH oxidase, 53

E

Electron transfer, 53
Enol-phosphopyruvic acid - see Phospho-
     pyruvic acid
Enolase, 11
Enoyl-CoA, 227
Ergosterol, 253
Erythrose-4-phosphate, 5, 9, 36, 37, 39,
     40, 167
Erythrulose, 36, 48
Erythrulose-1-phosphate, 9
Estrane, 240
Estrogens, 238
Estrone, 240
Ethanol, 87, 89
Ethanolamine, 123, 249
Ethanolflavin, 259
Etiocholane, 240
Excretion products, 208

F

F-Actin, 253
FAD - see Flavin adenine dinucleotide
FAICR, 205
Farnesyl pyrophosphate, 230-231
Fat, 4, 17
Fatty acids, 87, 93, 128, 227

Ferulic acid, 175
FGAM, 204
FGAR, 204
FH$_2$ (Dihydrofolic acid), 256, 257
FH$_4$ (Tetrahydrofolic acid), 253, 256, 257
Flavin adenine dinucleotide, 58, 59, 73, 110, 112, 227
Flavin mononucleotide, 110, 112, 245
Flavoprotein, 54, 63, 68
Fluorokinase, 95
FMN - see Flavin mononucleotide
Folic acid, 204, 213, 256, 257
Formaldehyde, 9, 158, 255, 257
Formamide, 161
5-Formamido-4-imidazole carboxamide ribotide (FAICR), 205
Formic acid, 24, 87, 92, 99, 110, 161, 162, 163, 253, 257
Formic dehydrogenase, 92
Formimino aspartic acid, 162
Formimino-L-glutamic acid, 161
Formylacetic acid, 102
Formylanthranilic acid, 192
Formylaspartic acid, 162
Formyl CoA, 99
Formylcysteine, 255
Formyl glutamic acid, 161, 257
Formylglycine amide ribotide (FGAR), 204
Formylglycine amidine ribotide (FGAM), 204
Formylkynurenine, 194
Formyltetrahydrofolic acid (citrovorum factor), 253, 257
"Free radicals," 59
Fructose, 5, 21, 48, 72, 177
Fructose-1-phosphate, 9
Fructose-6-phosphate, 3, 4, 5, 6, 7, 9, 21, 32, 36, 37, 39, 40, 177
Fructose-1,6-diphosphate, 3, 4, 5, 6, 7, 8, 9, 15
Fumaric acid, 55, 74, 79, 83, 113, 114, 142, 150, 153, 171, 180, 205, 207
Fumaryl acetoacetic acid, 93, 171, 186

G

Galactose, 25, 45
Galactose-1-phosphate, 24
Galactonic acid, 45, 47
Galactono-gamma-lactone, 45, 47

Galactono-gamma-lactone dehydrogenase, 47
Galacturonic acid, 45, 47
GAR (Glycine amide ribotide), 204
GDP (etc.) - see Guanosine diphospho - ...
Gentisic acid, 171
Gentisic aldehyde, 171
Geranyl pyrophosphate, 230
Gluconic acid, 33
Gluconolactone and phosphates, 32, 33, 177
Glucose, 3, 5, 6, 7, 21, 25, 45, 49, 72
Glucose amine, 25, 27
Glucoseamine phosphates, 27
Glucose-1-arabinoside, 72
Glucose oxidase, 53
Glucose-1-phosphate, 19, 20, 21, 22, 24, 72, 73, 74
Glucose-6-phosphate (and dehydrogenase), 3, 4, 5, 6, 7, 19, 20, 21, 27, 32, 33, 72, 173
Glucose-1,6-diphosphate, 19, 20
Glucosone, 177
Glucuronic acid, 25, 45, 49
Glucuronic acid phosphates, 26
Glutamic acid, 74, 79, 82, 88, 99, 102, 113, 115, 116, 142, 143, 145, 147, 148, 149, 158, 161, 186, 196, 199, 203, 204, 262
Glutamine, 27, 74, 113, 115, 142, 199, 203, 204, 207
gamma-Glutamylcysteine, 74
Glutamyl-gamma-semialdehyde, 145
Glutathione, 12, 74, 264
Glyceraldehyde, 17
Glyceraldehyde-3-phosphate, 3, 4, 5, 8, 9, 10, 12, 15, 32, 35, 36, 37, 39, 40, 43, 67, 192
Glyceric acid, 123
Glycerokinase, 17
Glycerol, 4, 14, 17, 244
Glycerol dehydrogenase, 17
Glycerol phosphate, 14, 244
Glycerophosphoryl choline, 17
Glycine, 74, 99, 116, 131, 151, 204, 249, 250, 253, 255, 263, 264
Glycine amide ribotide (GAR), 204
Glycogen, 21, 72, 74
Glycol aldehyde, 5, 9, 32, 35, 36, 39, 123
Glycolic acid, 99, 123, 253
Glycolic acid oxidase, 53
Glyoxalase, 12
Glyoxalic acid, 79, 81, 99, 101, 123, 144, 208, 209, 253, 264

272

Glyoxylic acid - see Glyoxalic acid
GPPP - see Deoxyguanosine triphosphate
GTP - see Guanosine triphosphate
Guanidine, 153
Guanido acetic acid, 151, 250
Guanido butyraldehyde, 151
Guanido butyramide, 151
Guanido butyric acid, 151
Guanido-keto-isovaleric acid, 151
Guanine, 72, 74, 207, 208, 219, 221, 222, 223
Guanosine, 74, 207
Guanosine diphosphate (GDP), 74, 82, 207, 219
Guanosine diphospho-mannose, 73
Guanosine triphosphate, 73, 207
Guanylic acid, 207
Gulonic acid (gulonate), 45

H

Heme, 53, 263
Heptulose (and phosphates) - see also Sedoheptulose, 39
Hexokinase, 5
Hexose diphosphate - see Fructose-1,6-diphosphate
Hiochic acid - see Mevalonic acid
Histamine, 159, 163
Histidine, 116, 158, 159, 253
Histidinol (and derivatives), 158
HMG - see Hydroxymethylglutaric acid
Homocysteic acid, 135
Homocysteine, 135, 136, 137, 139, 151, 250, 253, 264
Homocystine, 135
Homogentisic acid, 53, 171, 172, 186
Homoserine, 126, 130, 131, 135, 136, 137, 139, 153, 157
Homoserine phosphate, 130, 131
Homovanillic acid, 174, 183
Homovanillin, 174, 183
Hydrogen, 87, 92, 253
Hydrogenase, 92
Hydrogenlyase, 92, 253
Hydroxyacetylene diurein carboxylic acid, 209
Hydroxyacyl CoA, 227
Hydroxyanthranilic acid, 53, 190, 194, 196, 197
Hydroxybenzaldehyde, 169

Hydroxybenzoic acid, 169
Hydroxybutyric acid, 87, 93, 229
Hydroxyglutamic acid, 144
Hydroxyhydroquinone, 187
Hydroxyimidazole acetic acid, 162
Hydroxyindole acetic acid, 195
Hydroxyindole pyruvic acid, 195
Hydroxyisovaleric acyl CoA (HIV-CoA), 229, 261
Hydroxykynurenine, 194, 196, 197
Hydroxylamine, 108, 109, 111, 112
Hydroxylation enzymes, 53
Hydroxymethyl cytosine, 215
Hydroxymethyl glutaric acid (HMG), 125, 261
Hydroxymethyl glutaryl CoA, 125, 229, 261
Hydroxymethyl tetrahydrofolic acid, 123, 257
Hydroxymethyl uracil, 215
Hydroxyphenyl acetaldehyde, 174, 186
Hydroxyphenyl acetic acid, 174, 186
Hydroxyphenyl lactic acid, 181
Hydroxyphenyl pyruvic acid, 3, 5, 123, 167, 174, 181, 182, 186
Hydroxyphenyl serine, 116
Hydroxyphosphopyruvic acid, 123
Hydroxyproline, 143, 144
Hydroxypropionic acid, 17, 227
Hydroxypyruvic acid, 36, 101
Hydroxyquinone, 187
Hydroxytryptamine - see Serotonin
Hydroxytryptophan, 116, 195
Hydroxyvaline, 264
Hypoxanthine, 207, 208

I

Iditol, 48
IDP - see Inosine diphosphate
Imidazole acetaldehyde, 163
Imidazole acetic acid, 53, 162, 163
Imidazole acetol, 158
Imidazole acrylic acid, 161
Imidazole glycerol phosphate, 158
Imidazole propionic acid, 161
Imidazole pyruvic acid, 159, 160
Imino-amino caproic acid, 145
Imino-fructose-6-phosphate, 27
Indican, 192
Indigo, 192

Indole, 53, 190, 191, 192
Indole acetaldehyde, 193
Indole acetic acid, 53, 190, 193
Indole glycerol phosphate, 191, 192
Indole pyruvic acid, 193
Indoxyl, 192
Inosine, 74, 207
Inosine diphosphate, 83, 207
Inosine triphosphate, 83, 207
Inosinic acid (Inosine monophosphate, IMP), 205, 207
Inositol, 49, 244
Inositol phosphatide, 49, 244
Iodogorgoic acid - see Diiodotyrosine, 185
Iodothyronamine, 185
Iodothyropyruvic acid, 185
Iodotyrosine, 185
Iron, 112
Isatin, 192
Isobarbituric acid, 214
Isobutyryl CoA, 128, 129
Isocinchomeronic acid, 197
Isocitric acid, 79, 81, 82, 99, 123, 142
Isodialuric acid, 214
Isoleucine, 93, 116, 126, 127, 130
Isopentenyl pyrophosphate, 236
Isoprenoid, 229
Isopropyl alcohol, 87, 93
Isosuccinyl CoA - see Methylmalonyl CoA
Isovaleryl CoA, 125
Itaconic acid, 79, 81, 115
ITP - see Inosinetriphosphate

J

K

Keto acids, 108, 111, 142
Keto-acyl CoA, 227
Keto-adipic acid, 168, 169, 170
Keto-butyric acid, 126, 130, 131, 135
Keto-3-deoxy-6-phosphogluconic acid, 9, 32, 43
Keto-deoxyphosphoglucoheptonic acid, 167
Keto-gluconic acid, 177
Keto-glucose, 177

Keto-glutaric acid, 45, 79, 82, 88, 96, 113, 115, 142, 143, 157, 158, 186, 196
Keto-hydroxybutyric acid, 126
Keto-isocaproic acid, 125
Keto-isovaleric acid, 128, 129
Keto-methylbutyride CoA, 127
Keto-methylvaleric acid, 126, 127
Keto-myoinositol, 49
Keto-pantoic acid, 102
Keto-phosphogluconic acid, 32, 34
Keto-valine, 102
Kinases, 72
Kojic acid, 177
Kynurenase, 196
Kynurenine, 190, 194, 196
Kynurenine-3-hydroxylase, 53
Kynurenic acid, 190, 196

L

Laccase, 53
Lactic acid, 12, 87, 88
Lactic acid dehydrogenase, 88
Lactic acid oxidase, 53
Lactose, 24
Lactose-1-phosphate, 24
Lanosterol, 233, 239
Lanthionine, 135
Lecithin, 17, 244
Leucine, 116, 124, 125, 261, 279
Leucopterin, 256
Levan, 72
Lignin, 167, 186
Lipase, 17
Lipoic acid, 60, 61
Lipoxidase, 53
Lipoyl AMP, 61
Lipoyl hydrolase, 61
Luciferase, 53
Luciferin, 73
Lumazine, 259
Lumichrome, 259
Lycopene, 243
Lycopersene, 243
Lysine, 114, 116, 157

M

Malate synthase, 99
Maleylacetoacetic acid, 171, 172, 186
Malic acid, 79, 83, 99, 142
Malic enzyme, 83
Malonic acid, 87, 94, 214
Malonyl CoA, 94, 227
Malonyl semialdehyde, 227
Mandelic acid, 168
Mannose phosphates, 5, 20
Melanin, 183, 187
Mesaconic acid, 115
Mesotartaric acid, 101
Methionine, 114, 116, 126, 135, 136, 157, 250, 251, 253, 264
Methionine sulfoxide, 135
Methyl acrylyl CoA, 129
Methyl amine, 99
Methyl aspartic acid, 115, 262
Methyl barbituric acid, 215
Methyl butyryl CoA, 127
Methyl crotonyl CoA, 125, 229, 261
Methyl cytosine, 215
Methyl ethanolamine, 249
Methyl glutaconyl CoA, 229, 261
Methyl glycine, 249
Methyl glyoxal, 12
Methyl histamine, 163
Methyl hydroxybutyryl CoA, 127
Methyl hydroxytryptophan, 195
Methyl imidazole acetic acid, 163
Methyl malonyl CoA, 74, 79, 95, 227
Methyl nicotinamide, 199, 251
Methyl nicotinamide pyrridone, 199
Methyl orotic acid, 215
Methyl transfer, 249, 251, 262
Methoxy tyramine, 174, 183
Mevaldic acid, 229
Mevalonic acid, 125, 229, 230
Mevalonic phosphates, 230
Mevalonolactone, 229
Mevalonyl CoA, 125
Mitoquinone, 62
Mixed function transferases, 53
Molybdenum, 110
Monamine oxidase, 53, 163
Monophenols, 187
Muconic acid, 170, 172
Mucopolysaccharides, 26
Myoinositol, 49
Myokinase, 72

N

N-acetylglucoseamine and phosphates, 27
Naphthalene, 173
Naphthol, 173
Naphthyl mercapturic acid, 173
Neurosporene, 243
N-10-formyltetrahydrofolic acid (see also Formyl tetrahydrofolic acid), 74
Niacin - see Nicotinic acid
Nicotinamide (and derivatives), 173, 199, 251
Nicotinic acid, 197, 199
Nicotinuric acid, 199
Nitrate assimilation, 111
Nitrate reduction, 107, 110
Nitric acid (nitrate), 107, 109, 110, 111, 112
Nitric oxide (NO), 112
Nitrification, 107, 109
Nitrogen, 107, 108, 112
Nitrogen fixation, 108, 111
Nitrous acid (Nitrite), 107, 109, 110, 111, 112
Nitrous oxide (N_2O), 112
Nor-adrenaline, 183
Nor-bufotenin, 195
N-10-tetrahydrofolic acid, 161
Nucleoside pyrophosphate (as ATP, ITP, etc.), 73
Nucleoside triphosphate (as ATP, ITP, etc.), 72

O

Octulose-8-phosphate, 37
O_2 - see Oxygen
Optical isomerism, 14
Ornithine, 74, 116, 142, 143, 145, 147, 148, 149, 151, 210, 250
Orotic acid, 73, 149, 211
Orotidine-5-phosphate, 73, 211
Oxalacetic acid, 79, 80, 81, 83, 101, 117, 142
Oxalic acid, 99, 214, 253
Oxaloglycolic acid, 99, 101
Oxalosuccinic acid, 79, 81, 82
Oxaluric acid, 219
Oxalyl CoA, 99

Oximes, 109
Oxygen, 63, 68, 69, 162
Oxygen transferases, 53

P

PAB (PABA) - see Aminobenzoic acid
PABG, 256
Palmitic aldehyde, 245
Palmityl-CoA, 245
Pantoic acid, 102
Pantoine, 102
Pantothenic acid, 102, 103
Pantothenlene, 103
Pantothenylcysteine, 103
PAPS, 134
Pectic acid, 26
Pectin, 26
Penicillin, 264, 265
Peroxidase, 53
Peroxide oxidases, 53
Phenanthrene, 168
Phenols, 53, 134, 168
Phenylacetaldehyde, 174
Phenylacetic acid, 174, 188
Phenylalanine, 53, 116, 167, 181, 188
Phenylglyoxalic acid, 168
Phenyllactic acid, 188
Phenylphosphate, 72
Phenylpyruvic acid, 167, 174, 175, 181, 188
Phosphatases, 72
Phosphatidic acid derivatives, 17, 244
Phosphoarginine, 151
Phosphocholine, 244
Phosphocreatine, 151
Phosphofructokinase, 5
Phosphogluconic acid, 6, 32, 33, 34, 43
2-Phosphoglyceric acid, 3, 4, 11, 32, 41, 67
3-Phosphoglyceric acid, 3, 4, 11, 13, 15, 32, 41, 123
Phosphohexoisomerase, 5
Phosphohexokinase, 5
Phosphohydroxypyruvic acid, 123
Phosphopantetheine, 103
Phosphopentose isomerase, 35
Phosphopyruvic acid, 3, 4, 67, 79, 83, 95, 167
Phosphoribityl pyrophosphate (PRPP), 72, 73, 191, 199, 203, 211, 212

Phosphoribosylamine (PRA), 203, 204
Phosphoribulose kinase, 41
Phosphoryl oxalacetic acid, 83
Phosphoserine, 123
Phosphoshikimic acid, 167
Phytic acid, 49
Phytin, 49
Phytoene, 243
Phytofluene, 243
Picolinic acid, 197
Pipecoliccacid, 157
Polynucleotides, 74
Polytryptophan, 190
Porphyrins, 87, 123, 253, 263
PP - see Pyrophosphate
PRA, 203, 204
Pregnane, and derivatives, 241
Premercapturic acid, 173
Prephenic acid, 167, 181, 188
Progesterone, 238, 241
Proline, 115, 116, 143, 145, 147
Propionic acid, 79, 95
Propionyl CoA, 74, 79, 95, 126, 127, 227,
Protein, 107, 119, 208, 262
Protocatechuic acid, 53, 167, 169, 170, 172
Protoporphyrin, 263
PRPP - see Phosphoribityl pyrophosphate
Psylocybin, 193
Pteridine derivatives, 256, 257
Pterine, 256
Purines, 123, 208, 253
Pyridoxal (and derivatives), 108, 111, 117, 131, 186, 245
Pyridoxamine (and derivatives), 108, 111, 117
Pyridoxic acid, 117
Pyridoxine (and derivatives), 117
Pyrimidines, 53, 149, 217, 265
Pyrocatechase, 53
Pyrophosphate, 22, 24, 25, 26, 73, 119, 150, 190, 199, 203, 212, 261
Pyrrole, 262, 263
Pyrrole - carboxylic acids, 144
Pyrroline - carboxylic acids, 145
Pyruvic acid, 3, 4, 9, 11, 43, 61, 67, 79, 80, 83, 87, 88, 89, 91, 92, 95, 115, 123, 124, 126, 128, 135, 192, 253
Pyruvic kinase, 95
Pyruvic oxidase, 53

Q

Quercetin, 175
Quinic acid, 167
Quinolinic acid, 197

R

Reductone, 177
Rhamnose, 177
Ribitol, 48, 259
Riboflavin, 58, 259
Riboflavin phosphate, 58, 73
Ribose-1,5-diphosphate, 20
Ribose nucleic acid (RNA), 207, 217, 219, 265
Ribose-1-phosphate, 20, 72, 74, 212
Ribose-5-phosphate, 32, 35, 36, 37, 72, 158, 203, 211
Ribose-5-phosphate pyrophosphate (PRPP), 203
Ribosyl-imidazole acetic acid, 163
Ribulose, 36, 48
Ribulose-diphosphate, 32, 41
Ribulose-5-phosphate, 32, 34, 35, 36, 40, 41, 45, 199
Ring structures (see also Aromatic rings), 32
RNA (Ribose nucleic acid), 207, 217, 219, 265
Rubber, 230

S

S-adenosyl methionine, 251
Salicylic acid, 168
Saligen, 168
Sarcosine, 99, 255
Sedoheptulose-7-phosphate, 32, 35, 36, 39, 40
Sedulose-7-phosphate - see Sedoheptulose-7-phosphate
Senecioic acid - see Methylcrotonyl CoA
Serine, 116, 123, 135, 136, 137, 139, 191, 195, 205, 245, 249, 253, 255, 264
Serotonin, 190, 195

Shikimic acid, 32, 167, 181, 256
Sodium fluoride, 11
Soluble polynucleotides (RNA), 119, 190
Sorbitol, 48
Sorbose, 48
Sphingomyelin, 245
Sphingoserine, 245
Squalene, 231, 233
Starch, 21, 72
Steroids, 87, 125, 134, 230, 234, 236, 237, 238
Steroid hydroxylases, 53
Succinic acid, 54, 55, 63, 74, 79, 81, 82, 83, 93, 97, 99, 123, 142, 160, 170, 229, 263
Succinic dehydrogenase, 55
Succinic monoureide, 160
N-Succinyl carboxamide, 205
Succinyl CoA, 74, 79, 82, 93, 95, 227, 229
Sucrose, 21, 72
Sucrose phosphate, 21, 25
Sulfate, 134, 135
Sulfopyruvic acid, 135
Sulfur, 137

T

Tartaric acid, 99, 101
Tartronic acid, 101
Taurine, 135
Testosterone, 240
Tetrahydrofolic acid (FH_4), 74, 161, 253, 256, 257
Tetrahydronicotinic acid, 197
Tetrose or tetrose phosphates (see also Erythrose) 32, 39
Thiamine, 72
Thiamine pyrophosphate, 60, 61, 72, 91, 99
Thiazolidine carboxylic acid, 255
Thioctic acid, 60
Thiolase, 93
Thiopyruvic acid, 135
Threitol, 48
Threonine, 116, 126, 130, 131, 137, 157
Thymidine triphosphate, 73, 220
Thymine and derivatives, 213, 215, 221, 222, 223
Thyroxine, 182, 185
Tiglyl-CoA, 127

Tocol, 62
Tocopherol, 62
TPN - see Triphosphopyridine nucleotide
TPN Cytochrome C reductase, 55
TPNH oxidase, 53
TPP - see Thiamine pyrophosphate
TPPP - see Thymidine triphosphate
Transacetylase, 92
Transaldolase, 39-40
Transamination, 88, 114, 115, 125, 126,
     127, 129, 159
Transketolase, 35, 39, 40
Triaminohydroxy pyrimidine, 256
Tricarboxylic cycle - see Citric acid cycle
Triglyceride, 244
Trigonelline, 199
Trihydroxy cholanic acid, 239
Triiodothyronine, 185
Trimethylene glycol, 17
Trimethylglycine, 249
Triose phosphate (see also Glyceralde-
     hyde-3-phosphate or Dihydroxyacetone
     phosphate), 79, 191
Triose phosphate isomerase, 8
Triphosphopyridine nucleotide, 10, 33,
     45, 48, 55, 56, 57, 81, 83, 112, 113,
     173, 181, 199, 205, 211, 227, 229,
     245, 257
Tryptamine, 193
Tryptophan, 116, 167, 168, 190, 191, 192,
     193, 194, 195
Tryptophanyl adenylate, 190
Tryptophanyl ATP, 190
Tyrosine, 93, 116, 167, 175, 181, 182,
     185, 186, 187
Tyrosine, 186
Tyrosol, 186

U

Ubiquinone, 62, 63
UDP - see Uridine diphosphate
UDP-acetylgalactoseamine, and deriva-
     tives, 27, 265
UDP-acetylglucoseamine, 27, 73
UDPG - see Uridine diphosphoglucose
UDP-galactose (UDP-gal), 24, 26, 73,
     245
UDP-galacturonic acid, 26
UDP-glucoseamine, 27
UDP-glucuronic acid, 26
UDP-sugar, 25

UMP - see Uridine-5-phosphate
Uracil, 74, 102, 212, 214, 215, 219
Urea, 142, 143, 147, 151, 153, 208, 209,
     212, 214, 259
Ureido isobutyric acid (carbamyl isobu-
     tyric), 215
beta-Ureidopropionic acid (carbamyl-beta-
     alanine), 102, 214
Ureidosuccinic acid (Carbamyl aspartic
     acid), 74, 211
Uric acid, 208, 209
Uricase, 53
Uridine, 74, 212
Uridine diphosphate (UDP), 21, 22, 26,
     27, 74, 212, 219, 245, 265
Uridine diphosphoglucose (UDPG), 21,
     22, 24, 26, 73
Uridine-5-phosphate, 211, 212, 213, 214,
     215, 217
Uridine triphosphate (UTP), 22, 24, 25,
     26, 27, 73, 74, 265
Urocanic, 159, 160, 161
UTP - see Uridine triphosphate
UTP-pyrophosphate, 21

V

Valine, 102, 116, 124, 128, 129, 264
Violacein, 195
Vitamin B$_1$ - see Thiamin
Vitamin B$_2$ - see Riboflavin
Vitamin B$_6$ - see Pyridoxine, pyridoxal,
     117
Vitamin B$_{12}$, 115, 262, 263
Vitamin C - see Ascorbic acid
Vitamin K$_1$, 62

W

X

Xanthanylic acid, 207
Xanthine and derivatives, 207, 208, 259

Xanthine oxidase, 53, 89
Xanthopterin, 256
Xanthurenic acid, 190, 196
Xylitol, 45, 48
Xylose, 25, 45
Xylose-5-phosphate, 74
Xylulose, 45, 48
Xylulose-5-phosphate, 36, 37, 40

Y

Z

Zwischenferment, 33
Zymohexase, 8
Zymosterol, 233